Marriages of
Convenience

The honour of your presence is requested
at not one but *two* weddings!

Two unusually *convenient* weddings.

However, even the brides and grooms
don't know it yet, but these
marriages that start as simple
contracts—end with
happy ever afters!

Two novels on this perenially popular theme
by two favourite authors.

Lindsay Armstrong was born in South Africa but now lives in Australia with her New Zealand-born husband and their five children. They have lived in nearly every state of Australia and tried their hand at some unusual, for them, occupations, such as farming and horse training—all grist to the mill for a writer! Lindsay started writing romances when their youngest child began school and she was left feeling at a loose end. She is still doing it and loving it.

Sara Craven was born in South Devon and grew up, surrounded by books, in a house by the sea. After leaving grammar school she worked as a local journalist, covering everything from flower shows to murders. She started writing for Mills & Boon in 1975. Apart from writing, her passions include films, music, cooking and eating in good restaurants. She lives in Somerset.

*M*arriage of *C*onvenience

THE MARRYING GAME

BY

Lindsay Armstrong

THE MARRIAGE DEAL

BY

Sara Craven

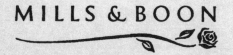

MILLS & BOON

MILLS & BOON and MILLS & BOON with the Rose Device are registered trademarks of the publisher.
Harlequin Mills & Boon Limited,
Eton House, 18-24 Paradise Road, Richmond, Surrey, TW9 1SR

THE MARRYING GAME and THE MARRIAGE DEAL were first published in separate single volumes by Mills & Boon Limited.
THE MARRYING GAME in 1989 and THE MARRIAGE DEAL in 1986.

This edition printed 1997

THE MARRYING GAME © Lindsay Armstrong 1989
THE MARRIAGE DEAL © Sara Craven 1986

ISBN 0 263 79411 3

Set in Times Roman 11 on 12 pt
05-9608-97668 C

Printed and bound in Great Britain by
Mackays of Chatham PLC, Chatham, Kent

THE MARRYING GAME

For Jacqui Bianchi—in grateful memory

CHAPTER ONE

LOVER'S POINT jutted into the sea from between two beaches. One was long and white and stretched southward into the distance, while the other curved about a perfect little bay with a steep green cliff behind it, rising to the road. Across the road were a variety of residences, but for the most part they were shuttered holiday homes that saw their owners infrequently.

It was from a renovated building of four flats opposite the Point that Kirra Munro stepped into the bright morning. She was twenty-two, had shining dark hair that touched her shoulders, blue-grey eyes and a classically beautiful face that was rescued from being haughty by a lovely mobile mouth and a wide smile.

She was wearing a one-piece emerald-green swimming-costume beneath an open filmy-white blouse, and the costume emphasised the lines and curves of her slender figure without being unduly revealing. She carried a fluffy navy blue beach-towel in one hand, and she stood for a long moment with the other hand raised to shade her eyes as she gazed about. There was not a soul in sight, and she breathed deeply, almost as if relaxing. This lack of people was no doubt due to the fact that it wasn't school holidays—a time when the sleepy little seaside town of Yamba on the Clarence River suffered a population explosion.

And it caused Kirra to smile faintly in

5

appreciation as she crossed the road, took the steep, winding steps down to the bay, dropped her things on to the beach and waded into the surf.

The water was beautiful, fresh and invigorating, and the only company she had was a school of dolphin frolicking further out.

She came out regretfully after about half an hour, smoothing the wet hair off her forehead, and looked back out to sea—it stretched away towards the horizon like a swathe of pale blue rippled silk, so beautiful it hurt her heart. But then, she reflected, her heart was in a peculiar state of flux, once again. And that was why she was here, to try to read it . . .

That was when Lover's Point claimed her notice once more, and she decided to explore it.

It was a steep climb up a sand dune, but once up she could see Lover's, as the locals called it, with a bird's-eye view: a smooth grassy dome surrounded by a shelf of flat rock and broadening from the narrower ridge of sand and bush where she stood.

For several minutes she pondered whether to walk round the rocky, plate-like shelf that was alive with seagulls enjoying the outgoing tide, or straight down the middle, but the fact that she had no shoes settled the matter and she opted for the middle course, setting off with a long stride and a sense of anticipation that brought a wry look to her eyes as she wondered if this was how Cortés had felt.

But the sand and the spindly casuarinas gave way to rougher ground and thicker bush, and she faltered suddenly and sank down with a sharp exclamation of pain. Her eyes widened as she awkwardly inspected her heel and saw the jagged sliver of wood in it, for it was obvious that this was going to be no easily-dealt-with splinter. But she gritted her teeth and tried to pull it out, only to have it break between her nails just above the skin. She sighed exasperatedly and decided there was nothing for it but to limp home where she had a pair of tweezers.

But even putting the weight on the ball of her foot was painful, she found, as she limped a few steps, then sat down, biting her lip. 'Oh, damn,' she muttered, 'this is ridiculous!' And got up again determinedly—only to collapse once more, but this time more from fright than pain as the bushes parted and a tall man appeared in front of her.

'Oh!' she gasped, as the stranger stopped in surprise and lowered a basket and fishing-rod to the ground. 'You gave me such a fright!'

'So it would appear,' the man agreed, with the corners of his mouth twitching. 'Let me help you up. I'm quite harmless, you know.'

Kirra found herself smiling weakly. 'It wasn't only that—I've got a splinter in my foot that's killing me. I don't suppose you'd have a pair of tweezers on you?' she asked with an attempt at humour, since, as he was only wearing a pair of faded canvas shorts, it was highly unlikely. He was also, she noted, well built with wide shoulders and, she realised a second or so later, standing over her and looking down at her with a faint but unmistakable glint of appreciation in his eyes as he took in her long, slender legs and the green swimsuit that was moulded to her body beneath her flimsy and damp blouse.

Something in his gaze held her captive briefly, then just as she'd decided she'd had enough of it, appreciative or otherwise, and started to tilt her chin defiantly at him, he smiled at her and the corners of his eyes crinkled so attractively that she took an unexpected breath.

He said, 'Not on me, I'm afraid. But I think I might have a pair in my first-aid kit. Let's have a look.'

He knelt down beside her and picked up her foot, and Kirra felt her flesh prickle with a strange awareness as she studied the long, strong lines of his tanned back which was turned towards her. She licked her lips. 'Can you see it?'

'Mm. Can you walk or should I carry you?' He put her foot down gently.

She grimaced. 'I'm not exactly a lightweight. Perhaps if I could use you as a crutch . . . Would you mind?'

'Not at all,' he said easily, and just as easily slid his arms beneath her and stood up in a fluid, unhurried movement.

Kirra opened her mouth to protest, but he looked down at her with so much laughter in his hazel eyes that she found herself quite unexpectedly smiling back at him like a trusting child. But she did say, 'What about your things?'

'I'll come back for them.' He shouldered the bushes aside and she turned her face towards his body to escape the leafy twigs—and experienced a peculiar desire to rub her cheek against his smooth brown skin. Really, Kirra! she thought with an inward grin, and lifted her head immediately, only to tense visibly.

'What is it?'

'You're going the wrong way—the road's back there.'

'If,' he said, glancing down into her wary blue-grey eyes, 'you're worried that I'm about to kidnap you or anything else unpleasant, you needn't be.'

Kirra felt her face flame. 'I . . . what I mean is . . .' She trailed off lamely.

'I know what you mean,' he said, and she could tell that he was laughing at her again inwardly, but just as she stiffened resentfully he added, 'I'm camped on the Point, you see. And,' he lowered her to the ground but kept his arm around her, 'here we are.'

Kirra stood on one foot and looked around. They were in a small hollow with thick turf beneath their feet, and in front of them was a khaki tent with a blue awning, pitched beneath a clump of ti-trees. Behind them, she saw as she turned awkwardly, the ground fell away sharply so that from the tent there would be a fabulous view of sea and surf and the coastline stretching into the distance.

'Oh!' she exclaimed, then, 'What a marvellous idea! Have you been here long?'

'A few days. Why don't you sit down?' He helped her to a canvas chair beneath the awning. Then he searched through a knapsack and produced a tin with a red cross on it. 'I've never had to use this before, so I'm not sure . . . ah, yes, tweezers, some antiseptic and Band-Aids.' He looked up at her and said with a lurking grin, 'All we need is a bullet for you to bite.'

She giggled. 'How about a slug of bourbon without the branchwater?'

'Uh . . . Scotch? For medicinal purposes, of course,' he offered gravely.

'No, thanks,' she laughed. 'I'll just rely on my

stiff upper lip. I'm quite good at that, I'm told.'

But a few minutes later she wasn't so sure of it. The splinter was out and revealed as a good inch long with a wickedly sharp point, and her eyes were shimmering with tears.

She swallowed and sniffed as she looked at it lying in the palm of his hand, and then wiped her nose with the back of her hand. 'Sorry. I'm not usually such a baby.'

'I thought you were rather brave,' he said quietly as he poured antiseptic on to her heel and then stuck on a Band Aid. 'There. How about that Scotch now?'

She nodded, and he produced a bottle and poured a couple of stiffish tots into two tin mugs and handed her one. She took a sip and felt the warmth of it course through her body and sighed. Then she looked up at him with a grin and raised her mug. 'Here's to a Good Samaritan. I'm sorry I cherished some unkind thoughts about you.'

He raised his eyebrows quizzically. 'You weren't to know. Would you like to stay for lunch—as we've sorted that out?'

She looked at him questioningly.

'I've got four freshly caught bream in my basket and some damper I made this morning. How does that sound?'

'It sounds—magical,' she said slowly.

'Right! Stay where you are, ma'am. Lunch will be ready in a tick.'

Kirra sat in the filtered sunlight, nursing her mug and grappling with a feeling of mingled delight and unreality as she watched her rescuer prepare the meal. He had retrieved his fishing gear and her towel and lit a small primus, and in no time at all the bream were sizzling aromatically in a pan.

'I hope I bump into you the next time I get a splinter in my foot,' she said teasingly as she watched him take some cheese from a cool-box and grate it with a sharp knife.

He shrugged. 'I hope you never get another one like that one.'

'Are you a . . . professional wanderer?' she asked with her head to one side.

He turned the bream before answering, and sprinkled the cheese over them. Then he glinted her a green-flecked glance as he said, 'Often. Why do you ask?'

'Well, you seem so competent! As if it's home from home.'

'Have you never been camping?'

'Once.' She pulled a face. 'My mother managed to turn it into a cross between a luxury safari gone wrong and an exercise in refined torture. I had no idea it could be so simple.' She looked around. Inside the tent there was the minimum of equipment: a sleeping-bag and mattress, a pillow and a pile of books, and one small bag of clothes. Under the awning, apart from the camp table and the chair she sat in, there was only a bowl with some cooking-utensils, the cool-box and a hurricane lamp. She shook her head. 'We were so bogged down with equipment, it was unbelievable.'

He looked amused and she fell silent, wondering about his face. Not the face of a professional wanderer, she thought, or at least her conception of one, which was bearded and shaggy. This face was anything but, she decided; in fact it was rather . . . how to describe it? It gave you the impression that its owner was a sophisticated, self-contained

and very adult man. The kind of face you normally
saw above a sober suit and bent on the pursuit of
wealth or its near neighbour, power. Or both. But
his body was another matter, a thing of smooth,
powerful, streamlined elegance, and for a crazy
moment she felt a surge of something like joy at a
man who looked as if he had proved himself to
himself and didn't need to go on proving it to the
rest of the world; he wasn't yet another sleek,
pampered, faintly over-fed denizen of the world
she normally occupied, but a man simply content
to wander . . .

'What is it?'

His words brought her out of her reverie with a
start, and a faint tinge of colour to her cheeks as
she realised he was looking at her curiously.

'Nothing,' she said hastily. 'We haven't even
introduced ourselves. My name is Kirra, which is a
contraction of Kirralee. My mother maintains it's
Aboriginal—the Kirra part—but she might be
guessing.'

'Kirra . . . It fits, somehow.'

'Does it? An odd name for an odd person?'

'I didn't say that.' He laid out two plates and slid
the fish on to them. 'Is that how you see it?'

She grinned. 'No. Although there might be some
who do. Actually, I'm rather proud of it. I just
wish my mother hadn't added to it. What's yours?'

'Matthew. Commonly known as Matt—nothing
as romantic as yours.'

'Very bibical,' she said as she took a mouthful of
fish. 'Mm! This is marvellous.'

'I'm glad you approve, Kirra.'

They ate in silence for a while. Then she said
between mouthfuls, 'Where will you go from

here? Or don't you have any preconceived plans—just where the whim takes you? Or maybe you follow the fishing,' she said dreamily.

'You sound as if you'd like to do that yourself.'

'I really think I would. You might have converted me. How beautifully simple,' she said a shade drily.

'Or might you be contemplating running away from something?' he queried.

Kirra removed a bone from her mouth and looked at him, but he was eating his fish tranquilly, sitting cross-legged on the ground.

'Why do you say that?'

'You sounded—disillusioned.'

She put her knife and fork down carefully, and said slowly, 'Perhaps I am. I also feel . . . sort of hemmed in. I came away to sort it all out, actually, but . . . when you don't seem to understand yourself, that's not terribly easy, is it? Do you ever get that feeling?'

It took him so long to reply, she began to feel slightly uncomfortable, and she pictured him wondering if she wasn't as odd as her name.

Then he laughed and his eyes crinkled in that heart-stoppingly attractive way as he said, 'Don't look so worried, it's a very human way to feel. Is it on account of some man?'

Kirra hesitated. 'It's on account of me,' she said quietly, then added, 'Why do men always assume they're so bothersome to women?'

He shrugged. 'I don't know. They say it makes the world go round.'

Not mine, it doesn't, she thought. That's the problem. Then she sighed and patted her stomach appreciatively as she pushed her empty plate away.

'Do you mind if we don't talk about me any more? It's a very boring subject and not worthy of a simply splendid meal.'

'All right. What would you like to talk about?'

'Let's see . . . If I hadn't gatecrashed your camp, how would you have spent the rest of this beautiful day? More fishing?'

'Later, yes. But now I'd spend a couple of hours quite lazily, maybe reading. Then I'd go down for a swim and perhaps a spot of snorkelling off the rocks in search of crabs for dinner. And then after dinner,' he shrugged, 'listen to some music by starlight, read some more, sleep.'

Kirra stared at him with her lips parted.

'Perhaps you'd care to join me,' he said.

'Would . . . would I spoil it?'

He looked at her thoughtfully. 'You might enhance it . . .'

'I mean,' she broke in, 'I know what it's like when you really want to be alone—strangely enough that's what I thought *I* needed today, but now . . .' She broke off, flinching.

But he said simply, 'Then don't be.'

'Tell me all the places you've been to,' said Kirra.

They were sitting in front of a fire with a canopy of stars above them and the sound of the ocean all around. Out to sea there were a myriad little lights pricking the darkness as the fishing fleet from Yamba and Iluka—its twin town across the mouth of the river—trawled.

Kirra wore an old jumper many sizes too big for her over her swimsuit, and her hair was a tangle as only a head of hair that hasn't seen a comb since two swims and a sea breeze can be. But in the firelight her face glowed, as if the memory of the day that stretched behind was something precious.

As indeed it was. They had swum together and talked about everything under the sun but themselves. Then he'd shown her the rudiments of snorkelling, and she'd been enchanted, and even interested in the cooking process of the three unfortunate crabs they had caught.

Dinner had been another delicious meal: crab, asparagus from a tin, potato salad from a tin, but fresh lettuce and tomatoes from the cool-box. damper again and some Camembert and biscuits to round it off. Then they had built up the fire and Matt had spread a ground-sheet out, and for a while they had played Mozart on a battery tape-recorder.

She looked across at him as he lay stretched out and propped up on one elbow, sipping his coffee, and waited for his answer. She had learnt during the day that he often took his time before speaking—in fact, she'd learnt quite a bit about him, but perhaps most importantly that, even on a much longer acquaintance, she still mightn't know him very well. For there was a quality of detachment about him that let you in so far and no further. And there was often a glimmer of amusement in his hazel eyes as they rested on her, which should have irritated her but oddly didn't. For the rest, she knew from his conversation and speech that he was well educated, he'd told her that he was thirty-seven, admittedly in response to her asking; then he had guessed her age accurately. He had also told her that he'd travelled overseas, and that he'd grown up in Victoria.

He said at last, 'Places like this, or cities?'

'Like this, perhaps even wilder,' she said. 'I can't imagine you enjoying cities.'

He looked across at her quizzically. 'You'd be bored stiff with the wilds before very long, Kirra.'

She sighed and swirled the coffee in her mug. 'I suppose so. It's a question of being able to do without people, isn't it? How do you manage it? Was it a long hard road before . . . this happened?'

'Why do you assume I can do without people?'

'I don't know,' she mused. 'Something about you. And you did say you were a wanderer. That doesn't sound like someone who needs people too much.'

He was silent, staring into the fire. Then he said, 'You're not quite right. I do need . . . people.'

'Do you mean women?'

His hazel eyes lifted to hers. 'From time to time.'

'But that . . that's a physical need, isn't it?' she said rather drily. 'Not a mental one.'

'It all depends,' he said, watching her. 'If it's a two-way thing, then it has to be more than a physical need. Hasn't it ever happened that way for you?'

'It . . .' She broke off and bit her lip then lifted her shoulders in a curiously wry gesture and smiled faintly. 'I'm probably a bit muddled up on the subject,' she murmured, and fell silent.

'But not . . . completely inexperienced?'

Kirra looked away, then back at him. 'No.'

He held her gaze steadily until she lowered her lashes over the blue-grey of her eyes, then all he said, finally, was, 'Would you like some more coffee?'

Something that could have been a sigh of relief caught at her throat, and she nodded mutely and handed him her mug. But she couldn't help watching him as he bent over the fire to get the coffee-pot. He too wore an old jumper over his shorts, and his thick, .

fairish hair was ruffled and streaked with salt. And, in a flash of awareness that took her breath away and made her flesh tingle right up to the roots of her hair, she realised that she was more physically aware of this man than she had ever been in her life, and that it had been growing all day like a secret longing—that it was totally inexplicable and incredibly embarrassing, particularly in the light of her earlier words.

Then she realised he was standing in front of her, offering her her mug back, and she took it with suddenly clumsy, shaking hands and set it on the ground, but not before she had spilt some and scalded her fingers.

'I . . . I . . . after this,' she said disjointedly and hurriedly, 'I really ought to be going. It must be quite late.' She didn't dare lift her eyes, she thought with a miserable bump of her heart, because he would quite possibly be amused again.

But his voice was quiet and sober as he said, 'Why don't you stay, Kirra?'

Shock held her rigid for a moment. Then she spoke hoarsely and without thinking, 'What . . . why?'

'I thought you knew. I thought I might be having the same effect on you . . . as you're having on me.'

Her lashes flew up. 'I am. Am I?' she said shakily. 'I didn't know . . .' She stopped and licked her lips.

'Yes, you are,' he said very quietly, and held down a hand.

She took it slowly and let him draw her to her feet.

'How did you know?' she whispered, then flushed brilliantly. 'I didn't . . . was I that transparent?' She looked away.

'Does it matter?' He linked his fingers about her

wrist and, with his other hand on her chin, turned her face back towards him. 'Do you have to hide it?'

Their eyes locked. 'You managed to hide it,' she murmured.

'Mainly because I didn't want to scare the living daylights out of you. If you recall, you did wonder about me.'

'I know,' she said dazedly.

'And now?' he queried, his hazel eyes direct and almost sombre.

'Now?' she repeated, her lashes fluttering in confusion. 'Can it happen like this? So . . . like this? I feel as if I'm dreaming.'

'It can happen any way you like, Kirra.' His fingers left her chin and traced the outline of her mouth, and his eyes were suddenly curiously intent.

'What,' she caught her breath, 'do you mean? I don't . . . I don't understand . . .'

'I mean you can tell me to stop and I will. Or you could—*we* could talk about it, and how it's been for you—not exactly a picnic, I gather. Or,' his hazel gaze roamed her face, 'we could dispense with words altogether. It's up to you.' He dropped his hand and just stood there, watching her.

Kirra trembled from head to toe, and her hands came up involuntarily; she clasped them together and started to say something, but stopped, and entirely of her own free will, she was to remember for ever after, moved into his arms.

It was a long, slow kiss like no other she had known. And a communion of two bodies that moulded them to each other and left her rejoicing in the unmistakable knowledge that he did indeed want her. It was the feel of his strong hands on her body, but also the feeling that no hands had been or could be wiser or know her so well. It was the taste of him, and the way she felt at the same time languorous, with skin so silken and soft, yet electrically alive, her pulses beating an erotic tattoo that brought a faint dew of sweat to her brow as their bodies entwined and they kissed. They broke off and breathed together, then kissed again with a mutual hunger and curious urgency.

When it ended, she clasped her hands around the back of his neck and stared gravely up into his eyes. And in an unconscious gesture she loosened her interlocked fingers so that she could fiddle with the ring that was normally on her left hand . . .

It was like being shot, she remembered later. She unwound her arms and whispered distractedly, with every vestige of colour draining from her face, 'What am I doing? I must be mad . . . oh, please let me go!'

He looked down at her steadily for what seemed like an age, his eyes narrowing sardonically.

'You don't under . . . understand,' she stammered. 'I'm engaged to be married. All the arrangements are being made.' She flinched as he smiled incredulously. 'Oh, I don't know what you must think of me!'

He released her and stepped backwards. 'I think perhaps we ought to have talked first, after all,' he said coolly. 'But you still can if you'd like to.'

She put a hand to her mouth and discovered tears on her cheeks. And the enormity of what she'd done, together with the enormity of trying to explain, washed over like a black tide of despair and she whirled about and started to run.

She wasn't sure when she first became aware that he was following her. Perhaps when the blackness in front became less dense and she stopped twisting and dodging to wonder why, and turned to see the bobbing light of a torch behind her. She swallowed and gasped for air, and realised she'd lost all sense of direction and had no idea which way to go.

Then it was too late. He called her name sharply and the torchlight played over her. She stood as still as a statue as he approached, wondering fearfully what he intended to do. He was entitled to be angry, if nothing else . . .

And it was certainly anger she saw darkening his eyes as he stopped right in front of her and said coldly, 'You're mad!'

'I kn-know,' she said huskily, 'but please don't . . .'

'Don't what?' he retorted contemptuously. 'Take by force what you were so eager to offer until you changed your mind? At the moment I couldn't think of anything I'd like to do less, sweetheart,' he said deliberately, 'so set your mind at rest.' And he looked her up and down so coolly and mockingly that she flushed and set her teeth.

'Then why follow me?'

'Because you're liable to break your neck, which I couldn't fix as easily as I did the splinter. And for some perverse reason,' he smiled derisively at her, 'it amuses me not to let that happen. I feel I owe it to your fiancé,' he said with soft, cutting mockery.

Kirra closed her eyes and swallowed several times. Then she said quietly, 'All right. If you could take me to the road . . . I am lost.'

It was a strange, silent journey, and she breathed exasperatedly when she realised that she hadn't in fact been that far from the road when he had caught up with her. She said abruptly, 'Thank you. I can manage from here.'

He shone the torch about and let it linger on a

battered Land Rover parked on the verge. 'That's mine,' he said equally abruptly. 'If you've much further to go, don't be herioc about it. You never know who you might encounter at this time of night—some man not as understanding as I am, perhaps.'

She stifled the sob that rose to her throat, and gestured across the road. 'It's just over there, honestly.'

He looked at her searchingly, then shrugged and turned away. 'Goodbye, then. It's been—interesting.'

She wilted miserably beneath the scorn and derision in his voice. 'I'm *sorry*,' She said desperately. 'I . . .' She broke off and shivered, wrapping her arms about her. 'I . . . oh!' she looked down at herself. 'I'm still wearing your jumper,' she said lamely. 'Here . . .'

He turned back briefly. 'Keep it.'

She hesitated, her lips framed to say his name pleadingly, but he walked away from her to be swallowed up in the darkness, so that all she could see was the light of the torch. She watched until she couldn't see even that. Then she turned wearily and walked home.

But she didn't fall asleep until the early hours of the morning, and then it was a restless, tormented slumber invaded by a peculiar sense of doom. When she finally dragged herself from it, it was to stumble straight out on to the balcony and immediately have that subconscious prediction of doom fulfilled. For the Land Rover was gone.

CHAPTER TWO

Six weeks later Kirra ran the last few steps to her front door, fumbling desperately for her key, and burst inside to the shrilling telephone.

'Hello?' she said breathlessly.

'Kirralee? Is that you, dear?'

'Yes, Mum,' Kirra replied with patient affection. 'I've just got home. I heard the phone ringing from the passageway, that's why I took so long to answer.'

'I'd probably have tried once again. Had a busy day?'

Kirra grimaced. 'A fiddly day. What are you and Dad doing this evening?'

'We're having a dinner party.'

Kirra eased her bag off her shoulder and removed her earrings. 'Oh?'

'Yes, a business associate of your father's,' her mother said brightly. 'Someone rather interesting. We'd love you to come—that's why I'm ringing,' she added.

Kirra glanced at her watch, 'Mum,' she said reluctantly, 'it's a bit late, and I don't really feel like socialising.'

'Darling,' Naomi Munro said with concern, 'since you came home from that mystery trip to New South Wales, you've been in a rather strange mood altogether. Is something wrong? Something you'd like to tell me? I won't press you but . . .' She broke off, then said in a rush, 'Postponing the wedding,

22

for example—not that I would want you to get married unless you were absolutely sure, but . . .' She paused again. 'Has Jeremy . . .'

'It's nothing to do with Jeremy,' Kirra broke in. 'It's . . . me. I just feel—I don't know how to describe it—*restless*,' she said on a curious note of bitterness.

'Has something happened to make you feel this way?' her mother queried.

Yes, Kirra thought. If only I could forget . . . She said wearily, 'Not really, and wondered why she couldn't confide in her mother. Probably something to do with having gone against her parents' advice once, and having reaped the consequences.

'Well, then, you've done the right thing,' Naomi said soothingly, although she added wryly, 'It's fortunate Jeremy is so patient.'

'When you're marrying the heir to the Munro fortune you can afford to be—or to put it another way, you can't afford not to be patient,' Kirra said with an unmistakable note of strain and cynicism in her voice.

Her mother was silent for an unusually long time. Then she said, more confusedly than reproachfully, Kirra thought absently, 'Darling, Jeremy isn't like that, is he?'

Kirra closed her eyes. 'No. No, he's not. I shouldn't have said that. Mum . . .'

'Kirra, why don't you come to dinner tonight? It will be a change from brooding, at least.'

'I . . . all right,' Kirra said with a sigh.

It was just before seven-thirty when she parked her little sports car beneath the portico of the fabulous house she had always thought of as home. Situated on a bend of the Nerang River, it was a minor mansion in large grounds, and she sat for a moment staring absently ahead, then stepped out of the car and shook out her skirt.

Her dress was lavender-blue, with a finely pleated, strapless bodice and a clinging skirt that nevertheless had yards of filmy material in it. From the bodice her shoulders rose smooth and gleaming and quite unadorned. In fact, the only jewellery she wore was her diamond engagement ring and a fine gold chain on her wrist. Her hair was parted in the middle, showing a perfect widow's peak and cascading to her shoulders, dark and gleaming. She'd taken a few extra minutes to make her face up with care, and the result was glamourous but understated.

Stanley greeted her at the front door as he greeted everyone, and her face softened. Stanley was a permanent fixture in the Munro household. Both he and her father had been career soldiers, and had known each other from not long after her father had graduated from the Royal Military College in Duntroon. But whereas Kenneth Munro had risen to the rank of Major-General and been knighted, Stanley had been content to be his batman.

When Sir Kenneth had retired from the army to concentrate his time on his family and his business, Stanley had moved into the household and assumed a variety of roles: butler and chauffeur to name a couple. It was impossible to imagine the family without Stanley now.

And he greeted Kirra warmly and told her her parents were waiting for her in the living-room.

It was a magnificent room with cream carpeting, cream damask settees, soft green occasional chairs with fine, carved frames and spindly legs, paintings and exquisite lamps, and on the settees, cushions of every hydrangea blue and pink. A room to make you catch your breath, which Kirra did, but for a different reason, as she paused on the threshold and caught sight of her parents standing on the terrace just beyond, with their arms linked and her mother resting her head on her father's shoulder.

And she felt her heart contract at the sight of the two people she loved most in the world, two people who, although rather older than average parents, had brought her up with such care and so much love. Her gentle, scholarly father who was possibly the least likely-looking Major-General, but certainly had a passion for translating Caesar's Gallic wars, her bright, sometimes irrepressible mother . . . How come I get so mixed up, she thought bleakly, make such mistakes after all they've done for me?

Then her mother turned and saw her, and her eyes lit up warmly as they always did, but Kirra noticed, as she went forward to kiss them, that her father looked tired.

'Dad,' she said anxiously, what have you been doing? You look . . .'

'Old?' her father queried with a grin. 'I am getting on, you know, pet. Like a sherry?'

'Thanks, but I didn't mean . . .' Kirra broke off and accepted a glass from her father. Then the doorbell chimed musically and she realised she had no idea who her parents were entertaining. 'By the way, who . . .'

But Stanley appeared in the doorway and murmured, 'Mr Remington, sir.' He moved aside and a tall, fair man walked into the room. At the same time, Kirra choked on her sherry . . .

It *can't* be, she thought incredulously as she

coughed and turned away, and her mother hovered anxiously, ready to bang her on the back. Oh, God!

'No, I'm all right,' she muttered to her mother and, with the greatest reluctance, turned back to see her father with his hand outstretched to greet his guest, but looking back at her. As for Matthew Remington, he was looking at her with the beginning of a faint smile on his lips, and a look of sardonic amusement creeping into his eyes.

Then it was wiped out as her father turned back to him and said in his old-fashioned, courteous manner, 'Welcome to our home, Matt. May I introduce you to my wife, Naomi . . . and our daughter, Kirra—she doesn't make a practice of greeting guests this way, I can assure you,' he added with a mischievous smile. 'All right now love?' he asked Kirra.

'I'm fine,' Kirra murmured, but she found that the muscles of her throat felt stiff. She extended her hand as her mother had done, but couldn't bring herself to look up as she said, 'How do you do?' Here it comes! she thought. He's going to say . . . we've already met, or, she fell down by way of greeting me last time or . . . I've had some experience of your daughter, Sir Kenneth.

Matt Remington echoed none of her fevered imaginings, but he did keep hold of her hand until she was forced to look up, and then he said, 'What an unusual name. How do you do, Kirra?'

And while part of her sighed with relief, another part of her found itself screwed up into a tangle of emotions that defied description, although bitter resentment was certainly one of them as those hazel eyes rested on her face with that hateful amusement back again.

'It is, isn't it?' her mother said brightly. 'Actually,

it's Kirralee, but I'm the only one who doesn't shorten it. For years I thought it was an Aboriginal word, but I've never been able to find out what it means.'

'Really?' Matt said, as if he'd not heard any of this before.

'Yes, really.' Naomi smiled ruefully and put her arm through his in her own peculiarly natural way. 'Come, let us get you a drink.'

Kirra watched as they walked away, his fair head bent attentively towards her mother, and closed her eyes.

'That was a truly delicious dinner, Lady Munro,' Matt Remington said. They were back in the living-room with their coffee, and Kirra's father was pouring liqueurs.

No, it wasn't, Kirra thought darkly as she fiddled absently with her engagement ring and listened with half an ear to the conversation. It tasted like sawdust to me, and I can't believe this isn't some ghastly nightmare. A professional wanderer, eh?

She glanced through her lashes towards the settee her mother shared with their guest. He looked so perfectly at home. As if his black dinner-suit had been made for him, which it probably had; and with his snowy-white shirt front perfectly laundered and his thick fair hair smooth and tamed . . . He looked as if he could be anything, a successful politician, a mining magnate, she pondered, anything but a professional wanderer content to roam far and wide away from the bright lights and the dollar signs. Oh, Kirra, what a fool you made of yourself and let him make of you! And to *think* that for the past six weeks you've been perfectly miserable and actually wondered if you shouldn't have thrown up everything and thrown your lot in with his for a week or a year or however long he wanted you . . .

She came out of her painful musings with a start, to see her mother looking at her strangely.

'I'm sorry, I was dreaming,' she said quietly.

'I was just telling Matt about Jeremy.'

Kirra squirmed inwardly, but managed to meet that cool hazel gaze calmly.

'You have my best wishes,' he murmured, and if there was a hint of derision in his voice, only Kirra seemed to notice it.

'Thank you.'

'When is the big day?'

Her mother rushed in before Kirra could speak, 'She hasn't quite made up her mind.'

'Oh?' he smiled at Kirra with his eyebrows raised quizzically and his head turned away from Naomi Munro; and there was so much insolence in his smile, Kirra bit her lip and curbed a desire to rise swiftly and slap his face. Then he added, 'Well, that is the lady's prerogative, I believe.'

'Don't you encourage her!' Naomi said playfully. 'Tell me, are you married?'

'No.'

'Now that surprises me,' Kirra's mother said with the forthrightness for which she was famed. 'That you've managed to elude it, I mean,' she added with a twinkle in her eyes. 'I would have thought the girls would have been queuing for the honour—and I'm renowned for my judgement in these matters, aren't I, Kenneth?'

'I suppose that's why you chose me,' Sir Kenneth teased.

'Of course! Nothing but the best.'

Kirra moved restlessly in her chair, but Matt Remington laughed and the conversation proceeded easily, although to those who knew her she herself was unusually quiet. He kept up the game of pretending not to know her superbly, however, apart from the odd glance which spoke volumes to her, and he showed no sign of being put out by her silences, which for the life of her she couldn't help. In fact he was the perfect guest, interested in her father's military background, knowledgeable about Renaissance art which was her mother's ruling passion.

· It did strike Kirra a little odd once that, for business associates, there was no business discussed except in the most general terms, but then her father held to the old-fashioned view that one did not discuss such things in front of ladies—often to his wife and daughter's exasperation.

But the *coup de grâce*, to Kirra's mind, came when Matt Remington finally took his leave. He took her hand and for a bare moment let his gaze wander over her from head to toe, as if he was mentally stripping her naked, and rejecting what he saw.

'I don't understand,' Kirra said tautly to her mother while her father saw Matt Remington to his car. 'Who is he?'

'A very wealthy man,' Naomi Munro replied thoughtfully, and sighed uncharacteristically.

'So?' Kirra hoped the sardonic note with which the word came out was lost on her mother, but it was a vain hope.

Naomi sank down into a chair. 'You didn't like him. I find that rather strange.'

'Does it matter? I . . .' Kirra moved abruptly.

'I think I should have stayed home,' she said regretfully then. 'I didn't mean to be rude to your guest. Perhaps if I'd known more about him . . .' she added ruefully as she sat down herself.

'About Matt Remington?' her father queried, coming back into the room. 'What would you like to know?'

'Well,' Kirra said helplessly, 'what kind of a business associate, how long you've known him, why . . .' She stopped.

'He heads quite a large group of companies, at least one of which is closely related to our business. I haven't known him for long, although of course most people have heard of him, not only for his meteoric rise to fame but because of his father, but I must say I liked him', her father said with a strained smile.

Kirra opened her mouth to say that *she* had never heard the name before, but something in the way her father turned away from her gave her the impression he didn't want to talk about it any more, and she hesitated, then said instead, 'Dad, I'm sorry . . .'

'That's all right, my dear; We all have our off nights.' He turned back and looked at her rather penetratingly though, then added, with a deliberate effort at brightness she thought, 'How about a nightcap, girls? You drank very sparingly tonight, Kirra. I think you could afford a small one before you go, and you look as if you could do with it.'

Kirra drove home feeling guilty and totally at odds with herself, not to mention angry and confused.

Angry not only with Matt Remington and his insolent looks, but with fate, which had seen fit to cast up her monumental indiscretion at her like this, and fate again for allowing her to be one of the few people who had never heard of Matthew Remington—or his father, for that matter.

She nosed her car into the underground parking-garage of her apartment block which was across the road from Main Beach, switched off and leant her head wearily against the back of the seat. I suppose, she mused, the best thing to do is forget about it—what's been done can't be undone. Forget? she said to herself mockingly then. Aren't you forgetting the fact that you've thought of him pretty constantly for these past six weeks, or do you think that because you've discovered he also deceived you, it will make a difference?

'Why shouldn't it?' she murmured aloud. 'I didn't *deliberately* set out to deceive him either.' She broke off and felt the familiar colour rise to her cheeks as she thought yet again of her incredible lapse on Lover's Point. Then she set her teeth and tried to conjure up a picture of Jeremy in her mind's eye.

Jeremy, who was as tall as Matt Remington but with a ganglier frame; Jeremy, with his bespectacled grey eyes that glowed so engagingly when he talked about his life's work—he was a research chemist—and who loved her steadily, if undramatically, something she found so reasurring after Bret.

But all she could come up with was a pair of cool, mocking, hazel eyes and, to her horror, a quicker pulse-rate and a peculiar sensation at the pit of her stomach—signs she recognised all too well, and she flinched and got out of the car swiftly and slammed the door.

The next day she had lunch with her friend Philippa West, commonly know as Pippa. They had been to school together and Philippa was now married to an architect who sometimes worked in close association with the interior decorating firm Kirra worked for.

And after the usual chitchat and making enquiries about the house Pippa and Marcus were building, Kirra heard herself say, 'Pip, have you ever heard of Matthew Remington?'

Pippa narrowed her eyes thoughtfully. 'Who hasn't?'

Kirra grimaced. 'Me. I believe he has a famous father, too.'

'Yes—Jack Remington. He was a racing driver and playboy *par excellence*. He also ran through the family fortune several times over and was jolly lucky he had a son able to recoup them—particularly after he ran away with and married his girlfriend.'

Kirra blinked several times. 'Come again?'

Pippa smiled. 'Where've you been all these years?'

'I can't imagine,' Kirra said honestly. 'I loathe and detest motor-racing, so perhaps that's why I missed it all.'

'Well,' Pippa settled herself more comfortably, 'as the wife of a car fanatic, you've come to the right person. Apparently Jack Remington looked with scorn on his family's solid business background, and set out upon inheriting it, he was the only child, to blow it on fast cars and fast women, despite the fact he had a wife. The—er—product of that union is said son Matthew, and it was after his mother died that his father became enamoured of Matt's girlfriend. Fortunately, Jack didn't quite inherit all that the Remingtons over the years had so industriously achieved. He had a maiden aunt who had the foresight to bypass him and leave her share of it to his son. Word hath it that Matt Remington has increased that small inheritance tenfold by ten, is now a wealthier man than his father ever was and is able to cock his snoot at him . . . and his ex-girlfriend, who is now his stepmother—darling, you'll catch a fly in a minute,' Pippa said gently. And as Kirra shut her mouth with a click, she asked, 'Tell me why all this should be so riveting.'

'I . . . I met him recently,' Kirra said uncomfortably. 'That's all.'

Pippa smiled slightly. 'I believe—despite their differences in other respects, father and son have one thing in common—a devastating effect on women.'

'I wouldn't know about that,' Kirra said, with a total disregard for the truth but an overriding instinct for self-preservation, she later realised. 'So . . . he's a lover and a leaver, is he?'

Pippa shrugged. 'There've been a lot of women, by all accounts. No one's trapped him as yet, though. How did you come to meet him?'

'Through my parents,' Kirra said slowly.

Pippa finished her coffee and dabbled her mouth. 'How's Jeremy?' she asked, shooting Kirra a rather keen look.

'Fine!'

'Good,' Pippa murmured, and looked as if she had been going to say something but changed her mind at the last minute. 'You will both come to the house-warming, won't you? I can't give an exact date yet, but it should only be about six weeks away—that's if Marcus doesn't change his mind and decide to pull it all down and start again.'

Kirra laughed. 'He wouldn't!'

'Honestly, my dear,' Pippa said ruefully, 'he's *obsessed* with getting this house *perfect*!'

'I bet it will be, too,' Kirra said warmly, and

glanced at her watch. 'Time I was getting back to work. I'm afraid.' She pulled a face.

Pippa raised an eyebrow. 'Thought you loved your job?'

'I do,' Kirra said hastily. 'I do.'

But when she was back doing her beloved job, she had to acknowledge she was feeling restless even at work which really alarmed her because she did love her job. 'Damn him,' she muttered, but stopped to think of what she'd just learnt about Matthew Remington, which altered the picture yet again and undeniably in her favour, she thought. At least I didn't join a long line of discarded lovers, and they certainly sound like a family to stay away from—I wonder if it's all true. Pippa's not given to passing on idle gossip, but it sounds . . . it just sounds too bizarre to be true. Anyway, it's none of my business now, thank God, and perhaps knowing about all the women in his past will help me to forget.

The days passed with not a great deal of change to her state of mind, however—and there was Jeremy in the flesh, not just a mental picture so oddly hard to conjure up.

She cooked him dinner one evening and arranged to spend the following Sunday with him. Their evening was spent quietly together and he made no mention of the postponed wedding plans. But he kissed her goodnight with unusual fervour, and she found herself incredibly touched and almost prepared to think of a wedding date again. She also found herself trying to analyse their relationship.

She felt safe with Jeremy, she realised, which was important to her. He knew about the hectic times with Bret and how much she had been hurt. He

understood, although this sometimes niggled her
curiously, why she mistrusted a physical relationship,
and he was content to wait until they were married
for that. Perhaps, she thought with a sudden flash of
acuteness, she imagined this was how her father
would have conducted his courtship of her mother,
and their marriage had certainly endured.
Actually—her flash of perception continued—there
were some things about Jeremy that reminded her
very much of her father: his temperament, a quality
of uprightness that had been notably lacking in Bret
and those mad halcyon days of *their* engagement.

So why did she sometimes get this niggle of doubt?
That it might be a grave risk marrying a man you
hadn't slept with? This was the way it was supposed
to be done, and if anyone should know how one's
body could betray one, she should.

And then there was Jeremy's quiet conviction that
he loved her.

I must have been mad, she mused. What did get
into me? Perhaps all prospective brides suffered
moments of panic, and Matt Remington represented
something free and unrestrained, unsigned and
unsealed. Yes . . . that was part of the attraction.

She shivered suddenly and deliberately turned her
thoughts back to Jeremy.

Sunday was hot and sultry, and they teamed up with
some friends in the afternoon to go to a charity rodeo
at Nerang. Then, when Jeremy was going to drop her
home and go on to have a game of squash, she said
impulsively, 'Drop me off at Mum and Dad's
instead. I think a swim in their pool is the only sane
thing to do in this heat. The beach will be too windy.'

Jeremy changed direction cheerfully.

'Sure you wouldn't like to do that yourself?' she asked. 'I can guarantee they'll give us something long and cool to drink and they'll probably feed us.'

Jeremy grinned. 'That sounds awfully tempting, but I promised this bloke a game and I've had to put it off a couple of times already. Besides I need the exercise.'

Kirra laughed. 'Anyone would think you were fat!'

'Prevention is the key word. It's been known to happen even to beanstalks like myself.' He looked at her gravely, but his eyes were twinkling behind his glasses.

Kirra was assailed by a sudden rush of affection. 'You're my favourite beanstalk, you know,' she said huskily.

His eyes changed and she thought he was going to say something but instead he looked back at the road and concentrated rather intently on his driving.

There was an unfamiliar blue Rolls-Royce in her parents' driveway and Kirra grimaced.

Jeremy pulled up. 'Anyone you know?'

'No. But if they're here on a Sunday, they must be fun. Mum maintains a strict rule about Sunday entertaining—it's got to be people whose company they really enjoy. Will we go to that movie on Tuesday night?' She gathered her belongings and looked at him enquiringly.

'Why not? It sounds good. I'll pick you up.' He leant over and kissed her cheek, then added quietly, 'Love you, Kirra.'

Sunday was Stanley's day off, so Kirra let herself in with her key, guessing that her parents and their guests would be at the poolside on the other side of the house. She hesitated briefly, then decided she was dusty and windblown and she might as well change into her costume first.

She still had her own bedroom and kept some spare clothes there. The costume she slipped into was a rose-pink lycra, and she brushed her hair vigorously, shaped her eyebrows absently and, armed with a fluffy white towel, sallied forth.

She was half-way down the lushly carpeted passageway that led to the pool patio and the murmur of voices beyond, when the outer screen door opened and a tall figure filled the doorway, dark and almost unrecognisable because of the glow of sunset behind.

Almost, but not quite . . .

CHAPTER THREE

'WHAT the hell are you doing here?'

The words slipped out before Kirra could stop herself, although she stopped walking as if she had been shot.

Matt Remington, however, displayed no such surprise, he too stopped, but to raise his eyebrows at her quizzically and to lounge against the door-frame comfortably. Nor did he say anything, but crossed his arms—all he wore, she noted, was a pair of navy-blue trunks—and he continued to observe her as the silence lengthened.

Kirra licked her lips, slipping from shock and spontaneous anger to a feeling of foolish embarrassment.

'I beg your pardon,' she said stiffly. 'That was—rude of me. I just didn't expect . . . you were the last person I expected to see . . .' She trailed off, hating herself for sounding so inarticulate and placating.

A slight smile twisted his lips, as if he could read her thoughts perfectly. 'Expected to see—or hoped never to see again?' he asked softly.

'Yes, well, there is that,' she conceded with a return of some spirit. But then her shoulders slumped, because it was all so impossibly awkward. She knew that within minutes her parents would discover her presence, and there was no way she would be able to get out of staying.

Matt Remington straightened then and came

38

towards her, right up to her so that she had to tilt
her head to look up into those hazel eyes, her own
eyes wide and wary.

'I guess we'll just have to make the the best of
it,' he murmured, and added, 'Your . . . our secret
is safe with me, by the way.'

'What secret?' That slipped out too, and she
could have cried with frustration as his eyes
mocked her and he drawled, 'Why your lost day
with me, Kirra. The day you forgot all about—
Jeremy, isn't it? Yes,' he continued barely audibly,
'and such a *nice* young man, your mother assures
me. Does he know how vulnerable you are to the
fleeting attractions of passing strangers?'

What Kirra would have replied was, perhaps
fortunately, lost, because just as she had predicted
her mother came through the screen door, stopped,
blinked, then rushed into disjointed speech.

'I *thought* I heard voices—darling, I didn't know
you were here—what a surprise! How . . . nice,
we're going to have a cold supper round the pool
and now we'll be a foursome.' She stopped, rather
like a clock running down, and Kirra frowned
faintly because it was unlike her mother to sound
. . . *lame*, yes, that was it. Or to have a . . . pleading
look in her eyes? Oh God, I must have been worse
than I realised the other night, she thought, and
Mum's afraid I'm going to put on another display
of surliness, which in her book is unforgivable,
especially on Sunday.

She took a deep breath, ignored the speculative
look in her tormentor's eye—well, that was what
he was—and managed to say brightly, 'I'd love to
have supper with you, I'm dying for a swim and,'
she paused briefly but forced herself to go on,

'perhaps I should show Mr Remington a better side of me. I must apologise for the other night.' She looked at him directly. 'I was rather—out of sorts.' Make of that what you will she thought defiantly, while somehow managing to smile at him.

He smiled right back. 'Call me Matt, Kirra.'

Her mother's sigh of relief was audible.

The pool was heavenly as the sun sank below the horizon and the first faint stars pricked the velvety blue sky.

'This is the life, eh, Matt?' her father said.

Kirra, alone in the pool, sighed regretfully and decided it was time to get out and be sociable, or at least help her mother. But it was not easy to climb out unselfconsciously beneath Matt Remington's gaze, at least what she had felt to be his gaze on her ever since she'd dived into the crystal-clear water. Yet when she had looked at him obliquely he'd been lying back in a cane lounger, studying either his glass or her father.

Why *is* he here again? she wondered. For someone I'd never heard of before, he's achieved the status of an honoured guest.

But it was true, she acknowledged, that because her father's office, and the head office of the flourishing fine condiment business which her grandfather had started and which had made Munro's a household name in Australia, was forty miles away in Brisbane it was not uncommon for him to deal with local business matters and contracts from his study at home. Quite possibly they'd been closeted there during the afternoon, and it would have been only natural for her mother to offer a refreshing swim and supper afterwards.

On a Sunday, though? But then they obviously liked Matt Remington rather a lot . . .

She bit her lip perplexedly, then shrugged. It was nothing to do with her really, just supremely inconvenient and embarrassing! But she climbed out of the pool saying brightly. 'That was marvellous! Just what I needed. I'll give Mum a hand.'

'Stay where you are, Kirralee.' Her mother's disembodied voice floated out from the direction of the kitchen window. 'It's all ready—just needs assembling.'

Kirra hesitated, then sank down into a chair and accepted a drink from her father. She brushed her sleek, wet hair back. 'So,' she said, and thought it sounded rather desperate but pressed on, 'you're . . . do you live here on the coast . . . Matt?'

A flicker of a smile crept into his eyes. 'Actually, I'm something of a nomad,' he replied politely. 'The one place I call home, I see all too infrequently, unfortunately.'

'And where is that?' Kirra asked equally politely, although thinking—you have an incredible nerve even to mention the word nomad!

'On the Tweed,' he said briefly. 'But I do have a base in Surfers' now.'

'Here we are . . .' It was her mother bearing a tray to Kirra's relief and the next two hours passed fairly pleasantly as they ate delicious cold chicken and salad followed by a cheesecake, and drank a superb Riesling.

In fact, once or twice Kirra was moved to amazement at how natural she was able to be, and was forced to conclude that Matt Remington was

making it easy for her. Since their encounter in the
passage and his remark about nomads there had
been no further looks of veiled mockery, and it was
easy to see why her parents were so taken with their
new friend. Just as I was, she thought, and caught
her breath as for a moment she was transported
back to Lover's Point and another starlit night.

She closed her eyes briefly, unable to forget the
sequel to that marvellous evening and how she'd
fallen prey to . . . whatever it was she had fallen
prey to. He's an . . . enigma, she mused, lifting her
lashes and glancing at Matt through them. What
was he doing *there*, anyway? And how could he
now have her feeling almost comfortable—well,
slightly less consumed by a crazy mixture of
embarrassment at her behaviour and outrage that
he should have duped her so?

Which he had, she reminded herself, and paused
confusedly to wonder what she would have felt if
she'd met him again and he'd been exactly what she
had thought he was. For that matter—the old puzzle
rose up to taunt her—why had it been so appealing?
How much had been the man, and how much . . .

She sighed and realised everyone was looking at
her with varying degrees of amusement.

'That sounded as if you have the weight of the
world on your shoulders, pet,' her father said.

'No—just tired,' she answered, and added
ruefully, because it had obviously made her parents
happy to see her behaving so much better, 'I hope
you don't think I'm being rude again, Matt, but
it's work tomorrow and I think I might head off
home now.' She stood up. 'Oh!'

'What?' asked Naomi.

'I forgot—Jeremy dropped me off. But no

matter, I'll ring for a taxi.'

'No need for that,' Matt Remington said, also standing up. 'I've got an early start tomorrow, so if your parents will excuse me, I could drop you off on my way home.'

Kirra opened her mouth, but her father said, 'How kind of you, Matt!'

'You didn't have to do this.'

The big blue car even smelt expensive—there seemed to be acres of cream leather in it, and it had a cabriolet top; but the top was up, so that despite the acres of leather Matt Remington was uncomfortably close.

'No,' he agreed. 'I thought it was—practical, though.'

There was silence for about a quarter of a mile, then he glanced at her and said with a lazy grin, 'I take it—from the dark looks I was on the receiving end of the other night—that you feel I . . . er . . . misled you back at Yamba.'

Kirra flushed, not only with annoyance at having her thoughts read so accurately, but because, as she'd been reflecting earlier, it might be a dubious standpoint to hold.

She said coolly, however, 'You did.'

'Do you think if you'd known who I was you'd have been more—circumspect?' he asked meditatively.

Kirra compressed her lips, then retorted, 'What I do know is that it was obviously more than practicality that prompted you to offer me this lift. A golden opportunity to pin me down and torment the life out of me, more like,' she finished bitterly.

He laughed quietly and said wryly, 'Not an easy

thing to do—pin you down, I mean. I gather Jeremy is having a similar problem.'

'Leave Jeremy out of this,' said Kirra tautly.

'So there is a "this",' he drawled.

'There isn't . . .' Kirra whispered.

He said softly, 'Strange you should say that when I can still remember the taste of your mouth and the feel of your body—so well.'

They had stopped at a set of lights and Kirra stared straight ahead, but the tell-tale colour had mounted in her cheeks again and a pulse at the base of her throat throbbed betrayingly.

'You tasted——' he began, but Kirra had heard enough.

'Don't!' she cried, and turned anguished blue-grey eyes on him. 'It could only have been a . . . an encounter for you, a few days perhaps, then we'd have gone our separate ways. I . . . I can understand how you feel, I *know* I behaved abominably, I admit that—but what else can I do?'

He lifted an eyebrow at her and put the car in gear as the lights changed and they moved off. 'You could explain why you behaved so badly,' he smiled, 'and explain at the same time why you're so sure it could have only been a passing encounter for me. A rather curious assumption,' he said drily.

'You appear to have eluded anything more permanent for quite some time.' The words were out, but no sooner had she said them than she regretted them and wondered what demon of malice or subconscious annoyance had prompted them.

'That could be merely a matter of not having found the right person—perhaps a subject you should give some thought to,' he said sardonically.

'It . . . I . . . oh, *hell*!' Kirra looked out of window rather blindly.

'Hell being a woman, you mean?'

'Yes,' she flashed at him because he was laughing at her again. 'What's more, I don't intend to say another word on the subject. Turn left here,' she commented haughtily. 'It's that building up the road, the first tall one.'

There was silence until he pulled the Rolls up and Kirra made to get out, but he put a hand out and grasped her wrist, saying, 'Oh, no, you don't. Not yet, sweetheart. If you refuse to explain, I don't see why I shouldn't have a go.'

'Let me go,' Kirra said through her teeth, her eyes flashing magnificently.

But it only seemed to amuse him, and he switched the interior light on and let his gaze wander over her insolently as he drawled, 'Yes, it seems to me it must be one of two things. Either you're one of those witless birds who go about chasing up a storm then retreating in a panic or, and personally this is my preference, dear Jeremy is so unsatisfactory in certain respects, you just can't help yourself from time to time.'

Kirra gasped, but he ignored her and went on thoughtfully, 'Which leads me to wonder if something once happened to you to make you decide on a marriage of *minds* to a chinless wonder who leaves you feeling like a bitch on heat.'

For a moment Kirra was so stunned that she could only stare at him with her mouth open. Then a red film of fury swam before her eyes, and she actually attempted to punch Matthew Remington in the mouth.

'You . . . you disgusting . . .' she sobbed, finding her other wrist now in his keeping. 'You . . .'

'Let me finish,' he said mildly. 'There are plenty of imperfect marriages, I'm sure, but for a hot-blooded girl like yourself, if you can't find the perfect bloke,' he smiled slightly, 'I'd go for the other thing.'

'I'm not.' Kirra wept tears of rage and revulsion. 'If only you knew . . .'

'But I do,' he pointed out, releasing her wrists aburptly.

Kirra put her hands to her face and was dimly astonished at the state she was in—sweating, crying, shaking.

'I hate you,' she whispered, suddenly galvanised into collecting all her belongings. 'Not only that, but I'm glad I did what I did, because in fact all I did was dent your pride, which must be a puny affair at the best of times. And if you must know, it nauseates me to think of you having *anything* to do with my parents. I also hope to God I never lay eyes on you again, but don't imagine I'll be leaving it entirely up to God!'

She opened the car door and risked one last blazing look at him, which was a mistake, because there was something in those hazel eyes that seemed to say—we'll see about that . . .

She was tempted to say—oh, no, we won't. But the look was gone and she contented herself with slamming the door on his grave, polite wish that she sleep well.

Nor was God or any of her own efforts any help to her as she stood in the foyer pressing the lift button imperatively, her eyes still blazing and her breasts heaving with anger. In fact, she might just as well have wasted her breath rather than make futile threats, as a tap on her shoulder revealed.

She swung round and it was Matt Remington holding her door keys, which must have fallen out of her bag during her furious scrabbling for her possessions.

'Don't say it,' he warned, as intense but conflicting expressions chased across her face— looks of rage and foolishness, hatred and a sinking sense of having made herself ridiculous. All of which combined to leave her speechless, without the benefit of his warning, but she did try to snatch the keys from him—a mistake.

He closed his fist around them and said softly, his eyes gleaming wickedly, 'Temper, temper, my dear Kirra. Do you always allow your emotions such free rein?'

For an instant Kirra had the greatest difficulty in not bursting into tears. But the effort was so great that it left her drained; her shoulders slumped wearily and she closed her eyes—all of which, she told herself time and time again afterwards, was a tactical error of huge proportions, because it allowed Matt Remington to have his way with her, without her even putting up a fight.

She did, at the first feel of his arms sliding around her, open her eyes disbelievingly, and she certainly parted her lips, but it was a faint, husky sound of protest that came forth. Even that died as she stared up into his half-closed eyes and saw the flickering smile that played on his lips before his mouth covered hers.

But when the kiss ended she was curiously shaky on her legs, and had to bear the indignity of his keeping an arm around her shoulders while he summoned the lift—it had come and gone again during the interim. Then he handed her in, handed her the keys and stepped back with a mocking little salute as the doors started to close, a wordless gesture that somehow shouted its meaning loud and clear.

'No,' Kirra breathed, staring at the closed doors, realising that somone must have summoned the lift from above, and that for a distraught moment she couldn't even remember her floor. 'No . . . I didn't kiss you back, it wasn't anything like that. You were just too clever, and I was quite unprepared —which I'll never be again.'

She woke in the middle of the night, however, shaking and sweating again because in her dreams she'd relived the feel of his arms around her, of his tall, strong body against hers, of that almost insolently slow kiss.

By the morning she knew, though, that she hated Matt Reminghton more than ever, if that were possible—hated him because he probably could, and probably did at will, arouse many women with his expertise. But of all the things he'd done to her and said to her, what she hated him for most were his comments about Jeremy. I could kill him for that, she thought coldly.

She spent the week almost comfortably cocooned by her sense of outrage, so much so that, when the blow fell, she didn't recognise it immediately. In fact, it was only by chance that she was paging through the business section of the paper at all, trying to locate the advertisement for an estate auction said to be offering some interesting antique porcelain, when a smallish headline caught her eye . . . 'Condiment Conundrum'.

She almost didn't read it, and even when she did the veiled speculation of the article concerning the future of a carefully unnamed condiment company merely caused her to grimace and think ruefully that it would mean one less competitor for Munro's.

But half a minute later, still leafing through the paper, her heart suddenly started to pound and her mouth went dry; she visualised her father who was looking oddly tired these days, and the way her parents were almost—courting?—yes, courting Matthew Remington, who was such a rich man and in a related business . . .

'No,' she whispered, her eyes suddenly horrified. 'Oh God, no. Please tell me it's not so!'

'But why didn't you *tell* me?' she said almost frantically to her parents, standing before them as they sat side by side in their beautiful living-room that evening, holding hands.

'Darling, I did want to,' Naomi said gently. 'But your father felt it would be . . . well he didn't want to burden you with this when you rather obviously were . . .' She hesitated.

'So wrapped up in myself—I must have been blind,' Kirra said bitterly. 'Oh, forgive me—oh, Dad . . . Mum . . .'

After an emotional few minutes, Kirra recovered a bit and her father endeavoured to explain what had happened.

'It was mostly my fault.'

'Dad . . .'

'But it was, Kirra. I got out of step with things

—I thought it was enough for Munro's to rest on its name and reputation. But now a large part of the market has been captured by opposition companies, more innovative, advertising-orientated ones, and for some time now I've been pouring capital into the company which I might just as well have poured down the drain.'

'There's the house,' Kirra said quickly, 'and my apartment, anything . . .'

'Kirra, that's what we're down to now. It's all we have left to pay off our creditors, and it's just not enough to emerge from this débâcle honourably, I'm afraid.'

Kirra sprang up. 'But . . .'

Her mother spoke soothingly. 'We've tried everything, darling, but the financial climate is against us, as well as everything else. But we do have one last hope—Matt Remington. All is not lost yet, love. If your father can persuade him to sink enough money into the company for Munro's to make a comeback we still have the name.'

'How?' Kirra's voice trembled. 'I mean . . . how did you get on to him?'

'One of his companies manufactures glass bottles and is our largest creditor,' her father said. 'He's also a rather brilliant business entrepreneur, and if anyone can save Munro's, he can. Hopefully, as a creditor, it will appeal to him from the point of view of minimising his company's losses as well.'

Kirra groaned.

'Pet,' her father said anxiously.

'I just wish you'd told me,' she whispered. 'That night he came to dinner . . .'

'That was your mother's idea. She thought it

would help to present us as a family.'

'I've always believed in the power of personalities over cold, hard figures,' Naomi said wryly. 'And I did want to tell Kirra then, Kenneth, but you wouldn't let me,' she added with for her an unusual touch of asperity. 'I just hope that one day you'll realise your womenfolk are capable of bearing burdens, too!'

'I do now,' Sir Kenneth said, his eyes softening as they rested on his wife. 'You've been wonderful! As for you, my dear,' he turned to Kirra, 'you more than compensated last Sunday for any deficiencies at the dinner party. But let's not kid ourselves,' he sobered, 'in this kind of deal, it is going to be cold, hard facts and figures that count.'

Kirra flinched inwardly and thought, I wonder? She said quickly, 'So he hasn't made a decision yet?'

'No, but I've given him *carte blanche* with the books and the plant, and he's promised me one within a week.'

'I see.'

'Kirra,' her mother looked at her anxiously, 'won't you stay the night? You look so pale, darling, but whatever, we'll survive somehow. Perhaps we could become romantic nomads and live in a tent.'

Kirra stayed with them for the evening, but declined to stay the night. And once again, as she drove home, her mind was in a turmoil. So many thoughts, such as how it had never occured to her that her father might not have inherited *his* father's business acumen—after all, he was an acknowledged master strategist in a military sense. Yet now she wondered—and wondered with a pang why she'd never thought of it before—whether his heart and soul had ever been in the world of business, or hot sauces, French dressings and chutneys. But worst of all was the thought of her own blithe acceptance of all her parents had bestowed upon her, and the way she'd been so selfishly wrapped up in her own problems that she had not even sensed something was wrong.

Then she put her knuckles to her mouth and forced herself to think of Matt Remington, and to wonder how cold, hard figures would really stand up against the insults she had offered him, the things she'd said . . . more than enough to ensure that her beloved father went to the wall.

And she completed the drive home with tears streaming down her cheeks and the most painful question mark she'd ever endured printed on her mind.

CHAPTER FOUR

THE reception-room Kirra sat in the next morning was quietly but luxuriously furnished, and the door through which she'd come was marked with his name—in gold lettering, just the sight of which had been enough to make her heart beat with fright—and an impressive list of companies below.

Then it had taken her some time to persuade the pretty young receptionist that Mr Remington would see Miss Munro even without an appointment if only she would pass on the name. Not that Kirra had been at all as sure of this as she had sounded, but finally the girl had lifted the phone and spoken hesitantly into it.

Nor had Kirra missed the spark of speculation in her eyes, as she had replaced the phone and said, 'Mr Remington will see you, Miss Munro, if you don't mind waiting.'

Which was what she doing now, flipping unseeingly through trade journals, growing more tense and nervous by the minute, more convinced she was doing the wrong thing and equally convinced that he was deliberately keeping her waiting.

Now he knows you're here, it can only look ridiculous if you back out, she told herself fretfully, but how lucky—trying for a lighter note—you had the forethought to ask for the whole day off.

Nothing lightened her sense of doom though,

and she restlessly smoothed the straight skirt of the grey linen summer suit she wore with navy-blue accessories.

She had chosen the outfit deliberately because it was the most businesslike one she possessed, and would, she hoped, banish some of the other impressions Matthew Remington no doubt had of her. But she knew there were shadows beneath her eyes, testimony to a sleepless night, although she didn't know that they added considerably to the pretty young receptionist's pleasurable curiosity as to the nature of Kirra's call on her boss. Or that she had just decided Kirra must be in love with him—something she had been unable to avoid herself from afar—and was losing him. Then a bleeper sounded beside her and she rose and told Kirra, with infinite sympathy, that Mr Remington would see her now.

Kirra followed her with a faint frown of surprise, but forgot all else as the girl opened a door and stood aside, 'Miss Munro, Mr Remington.'

Matt Remington didn't rise. Instead, he took off a pair of gold-rimmed glasses and sat back in his chair as Kirra stepped into the room and stopped, pressing her suddenly sweating palms to her sides.

Then he said drily, 'This is a surprise, Kirra. Sit down.'

She sat as she'd been trained to do, with a straight back, her hands clasped loosely and her ankles crossed, and glanced across the wide, paper-laden desk between them to see that he was waiting expressionlessly. She swallowed and, with a queer little sigh, said, 'I don't know where to begin.'

'Do you ever?' he asked with irony.

She coloured and bit her lip, wondering with

some irony herself where all her fire had gone. But
this was something quite different and totally
intimidating—this was like confronting a different
man, a man to whom the kisses he had accepted or
stolen meant nothing. But then, I almost knew
that, she thought shakily. I just didn't know the
kind of power he could wield. Now I do . . .

She licked her lips as he waited with an eyebrow
raised coolly. Then he said, 'Perhaps I can assist
you. You know, don't you? Did your parents
finally decide to tell you?'

'No,' she said huskily. 'I read something in the
paper and . . . confronted them.'

'Bravo, Kirra! And you've even gone one step
further—you've come here to ask me to save
Munro's. How brave. Do they know you're here?'

Kirra took a breath and flinched at the
detachment in his eyes and voice despite his words.
'No,' she said very quietly, 'and I've actually come
only to ask . . . to ask you not to let what . . .
happened between us, influence you. It would
be . . .'

'You thought I might?' he broke in.

'I don't know what to think,' she said unevenly,
feeling, with a cold, sinking sense of certainty, that
it had been a terrible mistake to come.

'Oh, I think you do,' he said softly. 'Wouldn't it
give you great pleasure to point out how heartless
I'd be if I discontinued my nauseating contact with
your parents in the light of what you now know?
Do you know,' he looked at her dispassionately
and continued thoughtfully, 'if you'd come here
today and offered to . . . er . . . take up with me
where you once left off, anything to save your
parents from bankruptcy, I might have

preferred it. Not that I'd have accepted . . . But you've played the wrong tune, again, sweetheart.'

'I didn't mean it to sound the way you made it . . .'

'Of course you did,' he said indifferently.

'All right, what if I did?' she retorted bitterly. 'As for the other tune,' her eyes flashed scathingly, 'I can just imagine how you would have gloated. And while we're on the subject, do you come out of all this smelling like a rose, Mr Matthew Remington, professional wanderer turned business magnate? Just how long, I wonder, would you have enjoyed taking me in, the way you did——' She broke off and put a hand to her mouth.

'So we're back to that,' he said with a grin. 'Has it occurred to you that perhaps we *both* were somewhat evasive? Also, that it suited your poor-little-rich-girl frame of mind to build a romantic daydream about a man you found camping somewhere?'

'I'm not a poor . . .'

'You did say you felt . . . hemmed in. I know now it wasn't anything to with Munro's. As for being a poor little rich girl—in the mixed-up sense of the phrase—why else would your parents be afraid to tell you about this disaster that's befallen them?' His hazel eyes flicked her contemptuously.

Kirra flinched and reddened.

'Then there's Jeremy still dangling on his string.'

Kirra straightened and gritted her teeth. 'If . . . if you've quite finished, I'll go. But you're wrong about one thing. The only reason I came to see you *was* for my parents, and I didn't . . .' She groped for words, swallowed, then looked straight at him and said very quietly, 'Is it too late to . . . *beg* you to change your mind for their sake?'

He didn't answer immediately, but studied her expressionlessly. Then he swung his chair round to stare out of the window briefly. 'There is one way we could bargain about this, Kirra.' He swung back and looked at her with narrowed eyes.

Kirra was seized with an insane premonition, then she thought, no, he said he wouldn't . . . but what?

She rushed into speech. 'I'd sell everything I possess,' she offered eagerly. 'My apartment, my car, my jewellery . . .'

His lips quirked. 'Do you think that much would save Munro's? And how would you live?'

She shrugged. 'It might help. And I'm not quite as hopeless as you appear to imagine. I do have a career to support me,' she added with dignity.

'What do you do?'

'I work for a firm of interior decorators.'

'Are you an interior decorator?'

'I did a course,' she said stiffly. 'What's wrong with that?' she asked at his wry look.

'Nothing! Very . . . proper,' he commented, making her feel as if she couldn't have chosen a more idle, frivolous career. 'But what do you actually do?'

'I collect *objets d'art* for the firm. I have a fair reputation for a keen eye and a sense of values,' she said defiantly, uncaring if she'd allowed a prickle of hostility to break through her defences again. Because . . . oh hell, she thought, with a sudden bleak look which didn't escape him.

He smiled gently. 'Very commendable, Kirra. But the money in itself would be like a drop in the ocean, and anyway, it wasn't what I had in mind.'

She moved abruptly. 'I have nothing else to offer.'

'Not entirely. You have yourself.'

She froze, then said through stiff lips, 'I don't think I heard you right.'

He raised an eyebrow. 'Yes, you did, Kirra.'

'But you said,' she burst out, 'just now you said . . .' She couldn't go on.

He sat back. 'That was something different.'

'What do you mean? Forgive me, but I got the distinct impression we were discussing the exchange of my body for your intervention to save Munro's,' she said, her voice rising.

His lips twitched and the old amusement was back in his eyes. 'Plain speaking, Kirra,' he said quizzically.

She jumped up. 'No, it is not, damn it! What do you mean if you don't . . .' She stopped because she was quivering in every nerve, and it was like a nightmare, this, and at any moment she would start screaming like a fishwife at him. 'What do you mean?' she asked through her teeth.

'I was talking about taking possession of your . . . beautiful body, honourably, dear Kirra,' he said almost lazily, 'in exchange for my intervention to save Munro's. I was talking about marrying you.' He smiled faintly as her mouth dropped open and her eyes almost fell out on stalks. 'It's a very old idea, you know,' he added conversationally. 'Daughters, especially beautiful ones, have been a form of barter for centuries. And the more beautiful, the more valuable.'

Kirra stared at him, dumbfounded, then groped her way back to her chair. 'I don't believe this,' she said weakly. 'I . . . we're not living in the Dark Ages. And if you imagine my father would *dream* . . . I told you, he has no idea I'm here!'

'The thought never entered my head. I'm sure your father would be horrified, although,' he shrugged, 'he could even feel relieved to know you're . . . safe. But I thought you might like to make the gesture yourself if it does mean so much to you not to see your father go to the wall.'

'Safe?' Kirra said faintly, feeling suddenly dizzy and ill. 'Safe,' she repeated, 'with a man who has blackmailed me into marrying him, who doesn't even *like* me, who thinks I'm a mixed-up freak?'

'Actually, Kirra,' he interrupted, sitting up and looking amused again, 'perhaps I should remind you that here are some things we like very much about each other.' His hazel gaze lingered on her mouth, then dropped to the curve of her breasts beneath the linen jacket.

'Oh,' she said despairingly, her cheeks burning, and she dropped her head into her hands. 'I don't believe this. Anyway, I'm *engaged*.'

'So you keep telling me,' he said derisively. 'However, without even having met Jeremy, I don't think he's the right one for you, Kirra—but then I've mentioned that before. And don't ask me why I have this conviction, because I should have thought it was obvious.'

Kirra raised suddenly tearful eyes to Matt Remington across the desk. 'I hate you for . . . what you've implied about Jeremy,' she said huskily. 'He's worth ten of you. He . . . he's the nicest man I know, and I love him.'

Their gazes caught and held, and when Matt spoke it was on a different note altogether. 'Perhaps you've confused warmth and friendship—which I'm not knocking, but it's a different thing from a true, total commitment between a man and a woman.'

Kirra caught her breath and felt as if her heart had been pierced by an arrow . . . of truth? She whispered, 'How can you say that? How can you talk about a true, total commitment, when you're trying to force me to marry you for . . . revenge?'

'Kirra,' he said, reverting to that lazy, conversational tone, 'I can guarantee that within six weeks of marrying me, you'll have forgotten all about things like revenge and barter.'

'Oh! Of all the . . . *oh*!' was all she could manage to say.

'As for true and total,' he went on, seemingly unperturbed by her furious, frustrated agitation, 'we have a lot to build on. We're physically,' he said softly, 'rather . . . spontaneously attracted to each other, wouldn't you say? When we don't let other things intrude, we've even been known to enjoy each other's company.'

'For one day!'

'A lot can happen in a day.' His eyes glinted.

Kirra put a hand to her head helplessly. 'But *marriage* . . .'

'You did point out to me recently that I'd eluded it for too long.'

'I didn't say *that* . . .'

He raised a quizzical eyebrow at her. 'I quite got the impression you felt rather bitter about it, though.'

'I . . .' Kirra closed her mouth, then she tried again. 'You're not . . . you can't really be serious.'

'I am,' he assured her blandly.

'But there's nothing I could bring you.' She trailed off and coloured brightly at the mocking little smile twisting his lips. 'All right,' she said stiffly then, 'but when that *palls*, what then?'

'If it palls,' he murmured, 'we'll do what most couple do—who have a vested interest in each other.'

'But don't you see?' she cried. 'What possible vested interest could you have in me once you're not interested in sleeping with me?'

'Oh,' he drawled, 'by that time we'll probably have started a family. I shall certainly accord you the . . . respect due the mother of my children.'

Kirra stared at him, speechless.

'Incidentally, that's where some of the things you could bring me will come in. Despite your rather pathetic confusion on the subject of men, dear Kirra, you have a certain kind of class—and a very famous name to go with it. My background,' he paused, 'has become a little tarnished. So I can assure you that if you play your part, our . . . arrangement will be . . .'

'I don't believe I'm hearing this,' she broke in faintly.

He shrugged and flicked her with a dispassionate glance that said all too clearly, take it or leave it.

'When,' she licked her lips, 'do I have to make up my mind?'

'The sooner the better. I'd hate to get the feeling I was doing all this work,' he gestured at the papers on the desk, 'for nothing,' he said softly.

'But . . . if I hadn't come here today,' she stared at him in anguish, 'what would you have done then?'

'My dear Kirra, I always knew you would come, if not today . . .'

'But say I hadn't found out until you *had* made a decision one way or the other!'

'You wouldn't have remained in ignorance much longer.'

'You disgust me,' she whispered.

He grinned. 'I can foresee some lively times between us, Kirra,' he said.

Her nostrils flared and she pinched her lips into a thin line. 'How soon is the sooner the better?' she asked through her teeth.

'Let's see,' he glanced at the diary on his desk, 'despite so much being at stake, you should have a little time to consider, it, I guess. Why don't you invite me to dinner tomorrow night? We could, if you are so minded, hammer out the details.'

Kirra closed her eyes again, this time because she felt she was in danger of fainting from sheer rage and disbelief. But somehow or other she found the composure to stand up and say crisply, 'Very well, shall we say—seven-thirty?'

'Seven-thirty will be fine.' He stood up himself and came round the desk to her. 'There is one other thing. It would be wiser if you'd . . . disengaged yourself from Jeremy before you consent to marry me.'

'*Consent*?' she hissed.

'Or whichever way you care to look at it,' he replied mildly. 'And if you don't agree with me that it's long overdue in its own right, if you know what I mean, why don't you try thinking back to Lover's Point? In fact,' he lifted a hand and trailed his fingertips down the side of her face, 'thinking back might just help you make the right decisions all round. For once.'

'Oh, do you think so?' she retorted, moving out of his reach. 'I prefer to think forward.'

He leant back against the desk and folded his

arms thoughtfully. 'Tell me about him.'

'Who?'

'The first man in your life—I assume there was at least one other apart from Jeremy—and now me.'

'He's dead.' Kirra stopped and bit her lip. 'I don't have the slightest intention of telling you about him—it's none of your business, for one thing,' she added with a rising tide of frustration in her voice.

'It could be that everything about you will soon be my business,' he said with a mocking little smile.

'I . . . I . . . oh hell!' she whispered. 'Just let me get out of here!'

He straightened. 'There's nothing stopping you. Until tomorrow night, then.' And he strolled across the room and opened the door for her.

She stood where she was, rooted to the spot and staring at him helplessly, a gaze he returned enigmatically, then with a glint of amusement in his hazel eyes. And finally he said with a glance at his watch, 'I'm afraid I have another appointment in about ten minutes, Kirra. Sorry, but . . .'

'Oh!' she breathed and glared at him, then swept past him without another word, her head held high. Not high enough to miss his wry grin, however.

The next evening was breathless and humid, although great banks of cloud had built up out to sea, promising reviving showers, but tantalisingly staying out at sea.

At twenty past seven, Kirra stood in the middle of her lounge, confident that everything was ready—that was all she was confident of. That her apartment looked its best, polished and gleaming, that dinner was taken care of and that she looked her best. Why it was so important to her to present this image, she wasn't sure.

She wore a slim, ivory, waistless dress with padded shoulders, very short sleeves and a V-neckline; at her neck was a two-strand pearl choker set with a square topaz that had a tinge of blue fire in its depths. She had been to the hairdresser that afternoon, and her dark hair gleamed beneath the light like a well-mannered fall of heavy silk, framing her face and just brushing her shoulders. She'd even had a manicure, something she normally did herself; but it wasn't her perfectly painted oval nails that caused her to look at her hands frequently, it was the lack of Jeremy's ring. And, each time she did, a feeling of pain pierced her heart.

Coming home from work, she'd invested a small fortune in a new perfume, new for her but a very famous one; and for considerably less, she had bought a bunch of pink chrysanthemums.

What she had not done, despite laying down these battle-lines—and it had struck her at the last minute that this poised, groomed and perfumed version of herself was a bit incongruous, but then consoled herself that she desperately needed poise at least—what she had not done, was come up with an actual plan of battle. In fact, she was all too acutely aware that she couldn't really bring herself to believe Matthew Remington intended to force the issue. She was living in the hope that she would discover tonight that it had been a hoax—surely it had to be! He could have virtually any woman he chose, so why her—and why like this?

She sighed and her hall clock chimed seven-thirty just as the doorbell rang. She took a deep breath and attempted to wipe all emotion from her expression 'as she went to answer it.

For a moment they just gazed at each other, Kirra unaware that she'd not been totally successful about removing a last glint of hostility from her blue-grey gaze; Matt Remington looking austere and inscrutable in a dark suit and a plain white shirt.

Then she realised he was carrying a gold foil-topped bottle in one hand and a bunch of creamy rosebuds in the other. 'Roses! And champagne,' she murmured. 'How kind! Do come in. You're the first man I know to do that.'

He raised a sceptical eyebrow. 'I should have thought I'd joined a long queue.'

'I meant—brought flowers by hand, not sent them,' she said defensively.

'Then I'm glad I did,' he replied. 'In years to come, we can treasure it as one of the first "firsts" of our relationship.'

Kirra tightened her lips, but took the flowers and champagne from him. 'Make yourself at home while I deal with these,' she said tautly.

When she brought the roses back in a vase, he was standing in the middle of her lounge with his back to her, his hands in his pockets, staring at the darkened view through the open sliding doors. He turned as she put the vase down, and as she straightened he said, 'You're looking stunning, Kirra.'

'Thank you. Would you like a drink? And can I take your jacket?'

'Yes, thanks, on both counts,' he replied

politely, and for a few minutes, while Kirra busied herself with these formalities, he looked around her lounge and dining alcove.

She'd decorated them herself in a blend of styles, that worked surprisingly well. The walls were a pale, smoky grey, and the dining-table and occasional tables were lacquered a slightly bluer grey, had smoked glass tops and were all of a sleek, spare design. The spareness stopped there, however. Two deep, comfortable couches upholstered in wistaria-blue linen faced each other across a big, low glass table that stood on a dusky pink and soft blue close-textured rug. The pink was repeated in cushions on the couches and lampshades, and the table bore a lot of her favourite things: her beaten silver statue of a Chinese coolie, her plaited straw horse, a glazed pottery dish. There were also books, magazines and the chrysanthemums she had bought that afternoon in a stubby crystal vase.

Matt Remington came out of his contemplation of her room as she handed him his drink, and said, 'Very nice, Kirra.'

'I'm glad you approve,' she said with some irony, prompted not only by a desire to show him she didn't need his approval, but because he looked disturbingly tall and oddly at home in his shirt sleeves and with his tie loosened. If I'd known he was going to look so at ease, I'd have let him stifle in his jacket, she thought darkly.

'Were these sent?' he asked idly, touching the fluffy pink heads of the chrysanthemums with his long fingers, and curiously transmitting the feel of those soft, cool, tightly packed petals to her fingertips.

'No. I bought those to ch——' She stopped

'To cheer yourself up?'

'Yes,' she said baldly.

He studied her taut expression silently, then his gaze slid to her left hand and he lifted an eyebrow and said softly, 'So you did it.'

'*Yes* . . . I mean . . .'

He waited.

Kirra clenched her teeth. 'I didn't do it because of you—other than in the sense that I might be in no position to be engaged to another man.'

'Why *did* you do it, then?' he asked, a slight smile twisting his lips.

She took a sip of her drink, then shrugged and sighed. 'In the end, I didn't—he did,' she said bleakly. 'He came to see me last night, and when I started to say something he . . .' She stopped and blinked.

'Go on,' Matt said quietly.

'He said he'd known for a while I was unhappy and . . . confused, and it had to be because I wasn't ready to marry him. He . . .' her voice shook, 'said he was releasing me from our engagement because he'd come to understand I wasn't for him. If you've any idea how bad that made me feel . . .'

'Perhaps,' Matt said absently. 'All the same, I'm glad it happened that way, because it means Jeremy understood you. If you weren't in this predicament, you'd probably be feeling relieved.'

Kirra stared at him, desperately wanting to contradict him.

Why don't we sit down?' he murmured, and his hazel eyes glinted at the way she tossed her head in sudden fury, but she sat all the same.

He sat down opposite her and stretched his arm along the back of the settee, while Kirra, battling

once more for composure, found herself staring at
him again, incredulously this time and also
wondering a little helplessly how she could restore
him to the quiet stranger who had taken out her
splinter on Lover's Point. I should have known he
could be like this, she thought. It's all there if you
know what to look for: the self-assurance, the
plain dynamic arrogance of that superb body,
which his beautifully tailored clothes, if anything,
enhance, the intelligence in his eyes and sometimes
the wry cynicism in the twist of those well-cut lips
. . . the way you just *know* he's expert at pleasing
women and . . . and despising them . . .

She took a jolting little breath as he looked up
suddenly and his hazel gaze clashed with hers. But
not me, please don't let me . . . how could I
possibly be attracted *now*? her thoughts continued
feverishly.

'You were thinking?' he drawled.

'I . . . yes, I was.' She forced herself to sound
cool and dispassionate. 'I was wondering when you
were going to end this farce, as a matter of fact.'

'Which farce?' he queried.

Kirra smoothed her skirt, then hoped he hadn't
noticed how her hand had trembled. 'The one you
referred to earlier as the *predicament* I find myself
in now,' she said, and couldn't resist adding, 'Don't
you think you've got enough mileage out of it?'

'Mileage?' he repeated. 'No—because it's no
farce, Kirra. Either you marry me or your parents
go bankrupt. In my terminology, that's what you
call a deal, not a . . .'

'A deal?' she interrupted scathingly. 'I hesitate
to disagree with you, but in anyone's terminology
it's nothing but a plan to avenge yourself and

humiliate me!'

'Kirra, you've said all that,' he reminded her lazily. 'Let's not repeat ourselves. Is there no . . . new ground you'd like to cover?'

Kirra closed her eyes and put a hand to her mouth. Then she said abruptly, 'All right. I can't understand why it has to be marriage. Wouldn't . . . blackmailing me into being your . . . mistress,' she swallowed suddenly and looked away, 'be even more satisfactory, if anything?'

Matt sat forward with his glass cradled in his hands, contemplating it, then he looked up and across at her with a devilish glint of mockery in his eyes. 'Are you offering yourself for that position?'

She said hastily, 'No . . . well . . .'

He waited, then smiled faintly. 'Let's see if I can read your mind. Did it occur to you as a viable alternative? Did you picture yourself as a martyr to the cause?'

'Stop it,' she whispered.

He sat back. 'Then you weren't, as a last-ditch effort, planning to offer me a less permanent and purely sexual proposition—I'm glad of that, Kirra. You would have found it impossible to carry through, you know.'

'*You* . . .' her cheeks were flushed hectically and her blue-grey eyes dark with first, naked embarrassment because he had read her mind, then a raging desire to demolish him, 'you *really* think you're God's gift to women, don't you? How was I ever so taken in?'

He grimaced. 'You didn't seem to mind my . . . talent at lovemaking once, and I'm sorry if it bothers you now, but I think you'll appreciate it in the end, Kirra.'

'Oh——' It was more a groan of disbelief and despair and she stood up convulsively. 'I . . . let's have dinner before I'm sick! I suppose it's no good appealing to your gentlemanly instincts.'

'I'm afraid not,' he said softly, looking up at her, his eyes gleaming now with something she couldn't decipher—unless it was laughter. 'Can I give you a hand?'

'No.' She frowned suddenly and started to say something, but changed her mind and walked away into the kitchen. But, as she started to dish up the first course, there was a question mark in her mind. *Was* he serious?

She fed him plump little oysters in their shells, rare roast beef with baked potatoes and fresh green beans, and a fruit salad spiked with Marsala and served with whipped cream.

And all through the meal she followed his lead obediently, which was to converse easily and impersonally. Not, she thought once, that she achieved anything like that famous—or was it infamous?—ease of Lover's Point, but she did her best—she couldn't think what else to do, and it had struck her, anyway, that if she could be normal she might have a better chance of unravelling some of the things she simply didn't understand about him. It wasn't until his remarks at the conclusion of the meal that she also realised she was still hoping it was all a bad dream.

He said, 'That was great. You have the makings of a first-class hostess—did I mention that once we're married I intend to set up a more . . . prolific social life than I've lived until now? More respectably prolific, at least,' he added with umistakable irony.

Kirra stared at him over the fruit salad.

'With a big house to match—I suppose you'd rather be based here than Melbourne or Sydney?'

She licked her lips. 'I think . . . I hear the coffee perking. Will you excuse me for a moment? We . . . we'll have it in the lounge.'

'Of course.'

She did more than make the coffee. She went into her bedroom and freshened her lipstick, brushed her hair and sprayed on some more perfume. Then she leant her forehead against the mirror and whispered, 'Please God, don't let this be happening to me.'

He was sitting in the lounge when she returned with the coffee-tray. She poured two cups from an elegant silver pot, asked him if he'd like a liqueur, which he declined, and finally there was nothing to do but sit down opposite him again and try to put her thoughts into words.

'C-could I ask you a favour?' she said haltingly.

'Go ahead.' He ran a hand through his thick, fair hair and stirred his coffee.

'If I ask you some questions, will you answer them honestly?'

He looked up. 'Yes.'

'Is . . .' Kirra hesitated, then took the plunge, 'is there some reason I'm not aware of for all this?'

'What do you mean?'

'Some reason why you're marrying a woman you basically despise, instead of . . . a woman you love, someone you could share a true and total commitment with? I mean,' she said huskily. 'those were your own words, so you must be aware that it's possible, that it exists.'

'As you were when you got engaged to Jeremy?' he countered coolly.

She flushed slightly, but said steadily, 'My mistakes were made in good faith—oh, perhaps foolishly, but at least there was, with Jeremy anyway, affection. This, us, doesn't even have to redeem it, and please don't quote what happened at Lover's Point to me again. Let's look at it from other angles or cover new ground if you prefer. I'm . . . a little tired of figuring as a . . . witless bird, or if not that, a bitch on heat,' she said deliberately.

His lips twitched. 'I apologise for that one.'

She looked him straight in the eye, then went on, 'Have you no faith in finding a woman to love?'

He was silent for a time. Then, 'You wanted me to be honest—no.'

Kirra shivered, and he noted it with a narrowing of his eyes. 'That disturbs you,' he murmured.

'Yes,' she agreed. 'I also find it a bit difficult to fit in with your . . . sermonising to me.'

'I don't go around leading people on,' he said quietly.

Kirra bit her lip, then surprised herself, 'Perhaps it's only through making some mistakes that you . . . expose the right emotions.'

He smiled coolly. 'Perhaps. Unless you get buried in the quicksand of the wrong ones.'

'So, you're not prepared to take the chance of that happening?' she queried.

'Were you?' Kirra hesitated. 'Perhaps I should tell you that your mother has favoured me with a brief version of your first engagement, Kirra,' he said reflectively. 'A fortune-hunter by the name of . . . Bret, I believe it was.'

Kirra paled and inwardly cursed her beloved mother.

'Wouldn't you say,' he continued softly, 'that Jeremy was your hedge against that ever happening to you again?'

'We're still . . . All right,' she conceded, 'that makes us even, *both* afraid of being hurt again—am I right?'

He shrugged and said amusedly, 'You've obviously heard about my father and . . .'

'So it was true,' she broke in.

'Oh, it was true all right. However, and I'm sorry to have to disappoint you if you were imagining I'm making you the object of all my cynicism on the subject, but I got over it years ago. I was only twenty-one at the time, she was older, and I was undoubtedly going through that period when older women are fatally fascinating.'

'Then why *are* you so cynical?' Kirra burst out. 'There has to be a reason, and don't try and tell me you're not!'

'I wouldn't dream of it,' he drawled. 'As for why, I think I honestly believe it's all a bag of moonshine. There are . . . attractions between men and women, friendships, but,' he looked at her meditatively, 'to quote the King of Siam if I may, "all the rest you hear is fairy-tale".'

Kirra sat transfixed for a moment, then she dropped her head into her hands.

'Which is why,' he went on after a moment, 'a sound business proposition with a dash of the physical thrown in, serves one much better, I think. For all concerned. And you'd be amazed at the number of women who agree with me.'

'*Agree* with you?' It was a hollow, muffled whisper.

'Why, yes. Since I made a lot of money, they've

actually been flocking to my door with business propositions, all manner of propositions.'

Kirra lifted her head. 'You can't accuse me of that,' she said hoarsely.

He smiled gently and said pensively, 'You did come to me with *something* on your mind, if you remember. Nor would we be having this conversation if I didn't have the money to redeem your parents.'

'Wouldn't we? This was all *your* idea.'

He thought for a bit, then said with a flash of amusement, 'You're right. You know, I do think I was getting a bit jaded and your . . . blow hot, blow cold approach was rather novel—it'll certainly add a bit of spice to the proceedings if you can keep it up, but I guess what really appealed to me was the opportunity to turn the tables for once.'

It occurred to Kirra that he wasn't serious, that he couldn't be, and she made one last effort. 'Do you . . . honestly believe it doesn't exist?' she whispered. 'Have you never seen two people in love, still in love after years of marriage?'

He stood up after a moment and walked over to the open sliding doors. 'Yes, I've seen it,' he said in a different voice. 'Recently, too. In fact, you're the living product of one such case, but how many do you see? One in a thousand?' He shrugged and turned. 'The rest of us do the best we can. Why don't you stop floundering around and say yes, Kirra?'

'Because I just can't believe . . .'

'Believe it,' he said drily. 'Look at it as one of life's nasty little surprises, if you like. Despite your—tangled love-affairs, you've had a charmed life up until now, but very few people escape life unscathed. How much *do* your parents mean to you?'

Kirra looked away, and thought of her father hearing that his last chance of emerging honourably from this débâcle had gone. She thought of her mother being so bright and brave, and how she'd failed them by being totally unaware in their hour of need. She remembered the crisis days after Bret when, although she'd spurned their advice, they'd lovingly helped her to pick up the pieces.

'All right—if you put it that way, yes.'

'Good,' he said unemotionally. 'How about a drink now? You look as if you could do with it.'

'Is that . . . all you can say?' she asked incredulously.

'What did you expect? That I'd go down on my knees and . . .'

'Oh . . .' Kirra jumped up and went to sweep past him, but he caught her wrist.

'On the other hand, if I thought you weren't going to fight me and only exhaust yourself and work yourself up into a state of hysteria . . . we could do this.' He released her wrist and pulled her into his arms, his hazel eyes glinting with mockery as he studied her outraged expression and felt the way she tensed convulsively.

'But then again,' he said very softly, his lips barely moving, 'that's half the charm of you, Kirra. The pleasure I'm going to get . . . taming the shrew.'

'You're . . . a devil,' Kirra hissed, 'and don't imagine I won't fight you.'

'I never did—well, not since we re-encountered one another. So fight away, my beautiful bride-to-be, I expect no less.'

Kirra closed her eyes and deliberately went limp in his arms, but her lashes flew up as she heard him laugh softly; then he picked her up and carried her over to the settee, where he set her down lengthwise on it, pushed a cushion behind her shoulders, and sat down beside her on the edge. 'I should warn you,' he murmured, pulling her skirt down over her knees, which she pressed together immediately, causing his lips to twitch, 'that passivity is a really hard act to maintain against a lover with a . . . slow hand and all the time in the world.'

Their eyes clashed, and to her horror Kirra felt a tinge of pink steal into her cheeks and her nerve-ends start to tingle, almost in anticipation of that slow hand. Her lips parted and the pulse at the base of her throat just above the blue fire topaz fluttered.

He observed all this with a narrowing of his eyes, and his face set in rather harsh lines, somehow remote and austere, and Kirra could feel herself shrinking beneath the weight of what she had unwittingly given away, like a flower fading and shrivelling.

He said then, with his hazel eyes completely unreadable, 'Unfortunately I don't have all the time in the world, so you're quite safe tonight—don't look so tragic.'

Kirra clamped her lips on the sob of despair and frustration that rose to her lips as she wondered if there was anything with which to dent his casual, supremely male arrogance.

'You were going to say?' he asked.

She forced herself to speak. 'Nothing—except, what does happen now?'

'We could make some plans.'

She struggled into a sitting position, bending her knees and pushing off her ivory kid shoes as the high heels dug into the upholstery. Her hair swung forward and she lifted a hand to tuck it behind her ear. She licked her lips, no longer painted petal pink, and looked at him at last, her blue-grey eyes shadowed and equally unreadable now. 'If you like. I don't quite see how we're going to spring this on my parents.'

'We won't. We'll lead up to it gradually. So long as it's a fact when the final papers are signed.'

'How long will that be?'

He shrugged. 'Time enough. There are contracts to draw up. In the meantime, it might be an idea to have some sort of a party to announce the merger. We could demonstrate our . . . shall we say, burgeoning interest in each other.'

'Start setting the scene, do you mean?' she said huskily.

He smiled faintly. 'Something like that.'

'Very well. Would you mind . . . I'm really tired now,' she said tensely.

'Not at all,' he murmured, standing up and staring down at her. 'We have all our lives in front of us, after all. I'll be in touch. Sweet . . . er . . . dreams, Kirra.'

And he left, swinging his jacket off her hatstand and slinging it over his shoulder carelessly.

Kirra stayed where she was for a long time, then got up and deliberately poured herself a neat brandy which she took back to the settee. Curling up in the corner, she sipped the brandy abstractedly.

'I can no longer not believe this is happening

to me,' she mused. 'I can no longer help but admit there is a sort of fatal fascination, quote-unquote, about him even now.' She stared into space for a long time. 'But there must be some way . . . of getting through to him. Oh God, I *am* tired. Too tired to think straight.'

CHAPTER FIVE

A WEEK later, he was as good as his word.

A reception-room had been hired at the new Gold Coast International Hotel, a cocktail party arranged, the highlight of which was to be the anouncement of a proposed merger between Munro's and Remington Enterprises.

Kirra arrived with her parents, and the photos of her in a stunning little black dress were to feature in Sunday paper social columns. Matt Remington, looking tall and distinguished and not at all remote, met them in the foyer. And he went out of his way from that moment to charm Naomi further, he also worded his speech simply, with no hint of a rescue operation being mounted but as if it were an honour to be associated with Sir Kenneth Munro.

Kirra could not help appreciating her parents' relief, which they were able to hide from all but her, and the fact that her father looked suddenly so much more buoyant. They even managed for the two-hour duration of the cocktail party to stop worrying about her and her broken engagement to Jeremy.

She also took the opportunity to observe Matt Remington in action socially. It wasn't a large crowd but, apart from the top management of Munro's and their wives, there were advertising agency executives, financial and business reporters, also a television crew in the wings, and some legal and banking representatives. And it occurred to Kirra that she'd never seen anyone accorded so much deference as her

father in this kind of milieu, yet her husband-to-be
—the thought made her quiver—certainly generated
it. He also, she noticed, had the sprinkling of
younger women in the crowd either simpering or
glancing at him furtively—apart from one, that was:
an upwardly mobile redhead who greeted him with
poise but a challenging look in her green eyes. When
she met the same redhead in the powder-room and
found herself to be on the receiving end of a
venomous green look, Kirra drew her own conclusions.

The only other incident of interest was when a tall,
excessively thin man in an exaggeratedly tailored suit
with a nipped-in waist and long-tailed jacket came up
to Matt and clapped him on the shoulder.

'Good to see you, old son,' he said jovially. 'Must
be ten . . . fifteen years?'

'At least, Morrie. What are you doing here?' Matt
asked, and, watching him, Kirra was aware of a
subtle change in his expression, a slight narrowing of
his eyes, the faintest hardening of his mouth. She
looked at the other man in some surprise and decided
he had a shifty look about him.

'Earning a quid, Matt, earning a quid. I'm into advertising these days,' Morrie said genially. 'So you're
extending the empire to good old Queensland these
days, eh? Can't say I blame you', he added with a
lascivious look around, letting his eyes linger on
Kirra. 'Always said the birds up here were beaut!'

'Your conversation was never edifying, Morrie,'
Matt replied with the coldest, most cutting look Kirra
had ever seen, and he turned away deliberately.

Morrie shrugged and drifted over to the bar.

But of course the *coup de grâce* to the evening
came when the party was starting to break up and

Matt said to her parents, 'I've persuaded Kirra to have dinner with me tonight. Would you mind very much if we slipped away now?'

Kirra had schooled herself for this moment, and when her parents turned to her simultaneously, she was able to smile ruefully, and say, 'It's true.'

'Not at all . . .'

'Of course you may . . .'

Sir Kenneth and Lady Munro spoke together, then looked at each other and laughed. 'Off you go,' Naomi said with a wave of her hand. 'We'll take care of the stragglers!'

Matt took Kirra's arm and led her away. She looked back once to see her parents staring at each other with raised eyebrows and identical expressions of bemused speculation that would have been comical in other circumstances.

The restaurant was luxurious and dim, and the *maitre d'* greeted Matt by name; then he recognised Kirra and was virtually bowled over with delight. 'Mr Remington and Miss *Munro*,' he said reverently. 'What a night!'

Matt grinned. 'I hope you've a table away from the limelight for us, Edward.

'Rest assured, I have,' Edward replied. 'Not even your best friends will know you're here, let alone any gossip columnists—if you so wish it.'

'For the time being, anyway—we may dance later.'

Kirra said nothing until the flutter of waiters unfurling cream damask napkins and presenting menus had subsided, and the two cocktails on the house had arrived.

Then she sipped hers and said, 'I still can't understand how I'd never even heard your name before

. . . before . . .'

'Before you ran into me again,' he supplied. 'Hadn't you?'

'No. And then I had to pump a friend for information.'

'Ah. The source of your knowledge about my father, I presume?'

Kirra nodded. 'Her husband is heavily into motor-racing, when he's not trying to design the perfect house. Had you no ambition to follow in your father's footsteps?'

He looked at her across the candle flame, and she noticed the little green flecks in his eyes. 'No.'

Kirra grimaced and stirred her drink with the straw. 'End of subject.'

'My father is not a subject I care to elaborate on,' he said drily. 'But in case you're wondering again, my disenchantment with him began when I was about six. He put my mother through hell and periodically dragged me around the race-tracks of the world with a gaggle of gorgeous girls in attendance.'

'And hangers-on like Morrie,' Kirra said quietly.

His hazel eyes narrowed, then after a moment he said, 'That was rather acute of you, Kirra.'

She shrugged. 'There was also a red-headed PR or something lady there tonight, with green eyes and, should we say, prior knowledge of you. I had this thought,' she went on as it was his turn to grimace, but with a glint of amusement, 'it crossed my mind to wonder, in fact, how often I would be bumping into . . . ladies like that.'

'So you could check them off a list?'

'So I could be prepared,' she said blandly. 'After all, you did quote the King of Siam to me, but I too know the musical version almost word for word, and the context of your quote I happen to know every word of. How does it go?' she said reflectively. ' "A girl must be like a blossom, with honey for just one bee . . . a man must live like a honey-bee and gather all he can . . . To fly from blossom to blossom, a honey-bee must be free. A blossom must not ever fly from bee . . . to bee . . . to bee," ' she finished gently. 'Is that how our marriage will be? Oh, I forgot the bit about the human male being pleased by many women, but the bee analogy says it all, really.'

His eyes never left her face, and she thought she detected a glint of admiration in them this time, which he confirmed, although making her want to hit him, by saying appreciatively, 'You're in good form tonight, Kirra. I'm glad we'll be able to stimulate each other mentally.'

'You haven't answered the question,' she said with irony.

'I suppose,' he said thoughtfully, 'that depends on the state of our marriage and how fulfilling it is. I may . . . er . . . have some faults, but I'm generally happy with one woman at a time, so the honey-bee syndrome doesn't altogether fit, wouldn't you say?'

'Perhaps,' she conceded, with a mocking little smile, 'if it's as you say. What I'm really trying to get at is, if the state of our marriage should become . . . unfulfilling in your estimation, and you decided you were justified in being unfaithful to me—even one woman at a time—would I be allowed the same privilege?'

He raised an eyebrow. 'Would you want it? It seems to go against your theories on love.'

Kirra laughed softly. 'I thought so. Had you considered that you might be more like your playboy father than you thought?'

In the silence that followed, Kirra knew she had hit home, had at last found a weak spot in Matthew Remington's defences, because for a second the world seemed to stand still as their eyes clashed, and it was her turn to receive that cool, cutting look, to see again that hardening of his mouth before he deliberately looked away. When he looked back, his hazel eyes were clear, but something in them made her shiver inwardly. A sort of enigmatic intensity that somehow made her think she was going to suffer a reprisal for her remark. She was to discover later that she was not wrong.

For the meantime, however, he said, 'We'll have to wait and see, won't we? I'm fairly certain it will be quite some time before you, at least, consider taking a legion of lovers.'

Kirra nipped her straw so sharply she thought she'd bitten it through. 'You've mentioned that before,' she murmured, keeping her temper with difficulty. 'You assumptions about women are quite nauseating, you know.'

'Are they?'

'*Yes*. We're not *all* pure sensualists, as you are, you know.'

'No?' he said idly.

'No,' she replied flatly. 'It takes a bit more than the old barefoot, pregnant and tied-to-the-kitchen-sink approach nowadays—and before you pick me up on the barefoot and tied-to-the-kitchen-sink bit, I'm sure one can feel equally imprisoned in the kind of luxury you no doubt have in mind.'

'Like a prisoner in a gilded cage. Have you quite finished, Kirra?'

She glared at him.

'Because I think you've done your avowed intention

of fighting me proud tonight. Have a break. Your digestive juices might appreciate it.'

What she might have replied was never uttered, as the first course was served. She'd ordered smoked salmon, and as she stared at it, atop a round crisp half of a lettuce by the look at it, complete with chives and thin, trimmed wedges of toast, she thought—temper, temper, Kirra! Don't be a fool, it will get you nowhere . . .

She picked up her knife and fork and sighed inwardly. The thing is, she mused, I still find it hard to believe this is not a nightmare I'm going to wake up from soon.

'All right,' she said. 'You choose something to talk about.'

He smiled faintly. 'Let's see—black becomes you. It makes your skin look . . . tantalisingly translucent.'

'Thank you.'

'Are you doing anything this weekend?'

'I . . . no.'

'I don't remember if I mentioned to you that I have a place on the Tweed.'

'You did.'

'Would you care to come down this weekend and see it?'

'Do I have a choice?'

'*We* . . . have a deal, Kirra,' he reminded her.

'Of course—how foolish of me to forget. Yes, I'll come.' She looked at him briefly, her eyes suddenly shadowed and strained, her face pale, and she put her knife and fork down with her smoked salmon only half eaten. 'I . . . I'm sorry but . . . you're right about my digestive juices. They seem to be tied in a knot if that's possible—well, something seems to be.'

Matt signalled the waiter, who removed their

plates, and he murmured something to him about delaying their main course, then looked at her. 'Have some wine,' he ordered.

She did, and by the time she had sipped half a glass some colour had returned to her cheeks. 'Sorry,' she said then. 'I'm fine now.'

But, although she managed to eat most of her main meal, and even follow his lead again conversation-wise, perhaps he saw the effort it was, because he didn't attempt to linger once they'd had their coffee, nor did he suggest they dance, although the band had struck up.

If Edward was disappointed at their early departure, he gave no sign, and bowed them out as if they were royalty.

Kirra couldn't help breathing a sigh of relief as the blue Rolls headed towards Main Beach, but her relief was to be short-lived when Matt parked it, got out and came round to help her out, and she knew he intended coming up to the apartment with her.

She thought of saying something, but could formulate nothing that didn't sound childishly petulant. She also felt exhausted and incredibly tense.

He took her key from her and opened the door, then stood back for her to enter. She hesitated briefly, then walked into the lounge, flicking on a lamp that shed a pool of soft pink light, and she dropped her bag on to the glass-topped table and said huskily the only thing she seemed capable of saying, 'What now?'

He came over to her and took her chin in his hand. 'What now?' he repeated, barely audibly, his eyes searching her face and his fingers roaming her jaw-line, the line of her cheek and throat. 'I think, as your prospective husband, it's my duty to try to relax you, Kirra. Like this . . .'

She made a stunned sound of protest, but he ignored it and she moved convulsively at what she saw in his eyes—a naked look of desire that made her skin shiver. And she knew suddenly that to fight him would be useless, that he would overwhelm her with ease, and tonight take pleasure in his victory—that this was to be his reprisal.

But there must be *some* way to resist this, Kirra, she told herself dazedly, as he drew her into his arms and slid one hand up her back to the nape of her neck beneath the heavy fall of her hair. I refuse to be treated like this . . .

She discovered not much later that her sentiments were like wishes on the wind against the almost mesmerising power he chose to exert over her. He didn't attempt to kiss her immediately, but his long fingers on the nape of her neck, stroking gently, unwittingly released a knot of tension; together with her awful confusion, and gradually reduced her to an almost trance-like state. But at the same time she was oddly conscious of how her body was resting against his, how her thighs felt against his and how her breasts were cushioned against his chest, how from straining every muscle to turn her body into a brick wall of resistance, she was achieving the opposite.

Oh God, I keep forgetting about this . . . how could I? I mustn't give way to it . . .

Perhaps her tortured thoughts were mirrored in her eyes, because he smiled slightly, a faint, cool movement of his lips before he bent his head and teased her lips apart.

It was a kiss she could not end, could only accept as if drugged with the feel and taste of him, her memories of the first time he had kissed her coming alive beneath his hands and mouth. How right she felt in his arms when he kissed her this way . . .

But if there was a spark of hope in her eyes, a supplication in the set of her parted, trembling lips when he lifted his head, he chose to douse it cruelly. 'Do you see now that you sometimes talk a lot of nonsense, Kirra?' he murmured, scanning the pale oval of her face beneath half-lowered eyelids.

She closed her eyes, and for a moment could only bury her face in his shoulder against the faintly rough surface of his charcoal jacket as she tried desperately to think. 'Yes,' she whispered desolately at last, and lifted her eyes to his to see that his face above his white shirt and dark green and black striped tie was set in harsh, uncompromising lines. She also discovered she felt curiously naked in her sleeveless black dress, and realised she was clutching the front of his beautiful tailored jacket like a hot-handed schoolgirl.

She opened her hand and put the back of it to her mouth. 'I . . . yes.' It came out muffled and sounded supremely vulnerable, and she cleared her throat and staggered slightly as he released her abruptly.

'Goodnight, then. I'll pick you up at ten o'clock on Saturday morning,' he said briefly. 'We can resume our love-hate relationship then.'

Kirra watched him go, then stumbled into her bedroom and sat down on her bed, gripping her hands together tightly and biting her lip hard enough to draw blood. For it had finally come home to her that Matthew Remington was not only disillusioned and very dangerous, but that he was also going to marry her come hell or high water.

The drive from Surfers' Paradise to Tweed Heads is

unexciting. The beaches that collectively make up the City of the Gold Coast are not really visible from the Pacific Highway, there are busy shopping centres all the way down it and usually plenty of traffic. Kirra had also driven the tedious length of it more times than she cared to remember.

She had never been driven down it in a magnificent late-model, dark blue Rolls-Royce coupé with cream leather trim, with the hood down, which distinguished the trip somewhat, she had to admit, although not favourably, and she thought once, I wonder where he keeps his battered Land Rover?

Apart from this, she also had her frayed nerves to deal with, for they had not stood the test of the intervening days well. In fact, it had taken a supreme effort of will not to do either of two things—confess to her parents the predicament she was in, or flee the country. Nor had her nerves been helped by the sight of her tormentor at precisely ten o'clock on this beautiful Saturday morning, standing outside her front door in jeans and a white cotton-knit shirt, looking freshly showered and shaved, but oddly lazy about those hazel eyes, as if he hadn't been up long.

Which he hadn't, he told her. He'd only arrived home from a business trip to Melbourne very late the previous evening and had slept in.

Kirra, who had been awake before dawn herself, had glinted him a taut, unsympathetic look. She'd also been mostly silent on the drive down, particularly after a verbal skirmish concerning his Rolls.

Because of the roof being down and the traffic which had frequently held them up, she had felt highly conspicuous, which had prompted her to say at yet another red light where people all around were craning their heads to look at them, 'Dad reckons these kind of cars are more trouble than they're worth. People enjoy scratching them and trying to steal the insignia, and they're also insanely expensive in Australia, and only a status symbol.'

'He's probably right,' Matt replied tranquilly. 'But I don't own racehorses or yachts, I don't go in for vast country or town mansions—as yet. I don't have expensive mistresses stashed about, I don't have my own plane, so I figured I could afford to shout myself one. The other thing is that they are an investment in that they hold their value better than most other cars, and you can't deny that, as a status symbol, they have a kind of class.'

'I hesitate to say this, but since you mentioned class again, do you see me as a status symbol or an investment? Or both?'

He considered. 'Both, I would say. I also think you're looking gorgeously windblown, which is an important consideration with this kind of car—a girl in a dowdy headscarf can spoil the image.'

Kirra ground her teeth secretly—one deal she had made with herself in the turmoil of the past few days was not to rise to the bait so readily, yet here she was, breaking that rule so soon. I shall play dumb for a while, she vowed.

But that didn't seem to faze him, either. He drove with almost negligent ease, seemingly totally oblivious of the quiet furore their progress was creating, but once they turned inland from Tweed Heads and left the traffic behind them, he upped the speed and the big car flashed along breathtakingly but with superb suspension.

The Tweed River, together with the Clarence and the Richmond, make up an area of New South Wales known as the Northern Rivers. It is in fact the most northern, and the town of Tweed Heads at its mouth is on the border of Queensland. But, while Tweed Heads is very much a holiday, tourist town, once you leave it behind and head inland, the magic of the river takes over as the road winds along beside its broad, peaceful reaches. It's sugar-cane country on the lower banks of the Tweed, and they turned off the highway before the Condong Sugar Mill, at Tumbulgum, a picturesque little village, and crossed the river by bridge.

It was a steep, winding drive on the other side, which the big car took in its stride, and before long they turned off the road and through a pair of white gateposts.

'Is this it?' Kirra asked, gazing around.

'Like it?' The car came to a stop beside what she first thought was a very old farmhouse. But it was the view and position that held her spellbound for a time.

'Oh,' she said, very softly. They were atop a foot-hill, a curved, grassy dome that swept smoothly down to the river, a hill that afforded a view up-stream to the town of Murwillumbah, itself clinging to the foothills of Mount Warning, a hill with the backdrop of the Lamington Range which, in the clear air, was tinted mysteriously purple. A hill with a view downstream, of the river broadening between patchwork canefields. His very own hill, by the look of it.

She turned to him at last. 'It's incredible.'

'Glad you think so.'

Something in his voice made Kirra narrow her eyes, something different, and it stirred a chord with-in her, but she couldn't put her finger on it. She turned her attention to the house and gasped as she realised it wasn't old at all, just built to look it out of red cedar which had weathered to a silvery grey. It was also more of a cottage, two-storeyed with a steep roof, dormer windows, a couple of tall stone chimneys and a veranda around three sides. There was a stone terrace below the front veranda with a brick barbecue, no formal garden but a flat area of lawn upon which several colourful chickens were picking unperturbed.

Behind the house there were some outbuildings beneath a clump of huge gumtrees: a garage, stables and what looked like a studio, with wide windows and a skylight.

'Do you paint?' she asked as he got out and opened her door for her.

'No.' He followed the direction of her gaze. 'That's where Min lives. She's a sculptress, so I converted an old shed for her. She should be around somewhere.'

'Min?'

'It's short for Minerva—the name her father was thoughtless enough to bestow on her at birth. She lives here, and in return for the studio, looks after the place for me.'

Kirra looked confused and surprised. 'On her own? Doesn't she get lonely?'

'Min likes being by herself from time to time. She won't stay for ever though, and speaking of her —here she is.'

A screen door on the veranda opened and out came a tall, attractive woman with very short, dark hair. As she got closer, Kirra saw that she was probably in her thirties, with a lithe figure fairly exposed in sky-blue shorts and a pink shirt tied to reveal her slender midriff, and intelligent, deep blue eyes—and a curl of suspicion awoke in Kirra's mind.

Then Matt was introducing them, and Kirra received a sweeping look from head to toe before Min said warmly, 'Welcome, Kirra. Matt was right—you're beautiful!'

Kirra blushed brightly, and could only murmur 'How do you do?' in return.

But if Min noticed her discomfort she only went on to say briskly that she'd set out lunch for them, that she'd done all the preparations for a barbecue for dinner if that was all right with Matt, and if there was anything Kirra needed, just to give her a call.

'Won't you join us for the barbecue?' Matt asked.

'Not tonight,' Min said decisively. 'I'm consumed with inspiration at the moment. But if you still want company for lunch tomorrow, I'll be around.' And walked away slowly towards the studio with a friendly wave.

'Min never changes,' Matt said with a grin. 'Care to come in?'

Kirra said she would.

He carried their bags in at the same time, and again Kirra was impressed—it was lovely inside. The walls were panelled with cedar, but this time a warm honey colour, and the floor was the same, although sealed and shining. Downstairs consisted of only three rooms: an open-plan lounge, dining and kitchen area about a turned, three-stage, timber staircase, a bedroom and a bathroom. But there was a warm, old-world charm to it, a comfortable sofa and deep chairs in front of an enormous stone fireplace, a long refectory table with some old, bentwood chairs, and the kitchen nook had copper pots hanging from hooks and an old-fashioned dresser for china. The bedroom wasn't large, but it had its own fireplace, a brass bedstead and a chintz spread.

Upstairs was even more fascinating, a loft really, just one large room with embrasures and window-seats around the dormer windows, a soaring ceiling with rafters, and it was furnished as a bedroom-cum-study.

'What a marvellous retreat,' she heard herself saying sincerely as they came downstairs again.

'Thanks,' he drawled. 'Coming from you, that's high praise, I'm sure.'

'I meant it,' Kirra said stiffly. Then, as he raised his eyebrows quizzically, she added, 'All right—but I did.'

'Am I to take it,' he was standing on the step above her, looking down at her amusedly, 'that your ill-humour of earlier has disappeared?'

She ran her forefinger along the banister, bending her head so that her hair hid her face, and said quietly, 'I wouldn't take anything for granted about me if I were you—*I* certainly won't be, because you see I'm just concentrating on getting on from moment to moment.'

'Yes, ma'am,' he said ruefully as she lifted her head and sent him a steady, blue-grey glance. 'Shall we have lunch? I don't know about you, but I'm starving.'

The lunch Min had set out was perfect for a hot day. Slices of rare cold beef with horseradish sauce, cold pork with mango chutney—Munro's, Kirra noted—tender, fresh asparagus, beetroot, tomatoes, hard-boiled eggs, warm, crusty rolls, and to finish, a bowl piled high with apples, oranges and grapes. Matt made tea for them.

Then he said, 'Why don't you slip a swimsuit under your jeans—do you ride, by the way?'

Kirra nodded.

'Would you like to ride down to the river for a swim?'

Kirra nodded again. 'But I'll clear up here first.'

'Min will probably appreciate that if she's creating. I'll change and get the horses ready.'

She heard him moving about above her as she cleared away quickly and competently. Then she went into the downstairs bedroom, where he'd put her bag, and closed the door.

She unpacked a few things and changed absently into her rose-pink swimsuit, put her jeans back on, tied her hair back—all the while deep in thought.

The implications of this weekend had been obvious, she had thought. By fair means or foul, she would end up in Matt Remington's bed . . .

'What do you mean—fair means or foul,' she asked herself beneath her breath. '*All* his means are . . . conniving to say the least, but I've got the feeling that *this* weekend the steel fist will be invisible beneath the proverbial velvet glove, and that, dear Kirra, is doubly dangerous.' She closed her eyes briefly, and then found herself wondering about Min. Surely he wouldn't . . .?

It was the sound of a horse harumphing outside and the jingle of bits that brought her out of her reverie.

'This is heavenly,' Kirra said idly as she chewed a stalk of juicy grass.

The swim had been refreshing and the ride very pleasant, not only because of the scenery but also because of her mount, a beautifully mannered and mouthed chestnut mare called Dandelion.

'Oh, isn't she pretty!' she had been moved to remark on first sight.

Matt had nodded non-committally and helped her into the saddle. He'd also kept a very close eye on her from his tall brown gelding with three white feet for the first few minutes, and ridden close enough to be able to grab the mare's bridle.

Finally Kirra had said indignantly, 'You don't have to *hover* like that. I told you I could ride, and anyway, anyone could ride her on a piece of cotton!'

'Anyone could not,' he had said. 'She responds to bad riding and heavy hands like the temperamental female of the species she is. But you'll do,' he'd added, and had moved away to take the lead down the path.

Kirra had murmured to Dandelion that she didn't believe a word of it, and weren't *males* of the species unbearable sometimes? Then the pleasure of the ride had taken over. And now she was lying on her towel, unable not to enjoy the sunlit afternoon, the smell of grass, the birdsong and the quiet murmur of the river. I must be mad, she reflected. I'm about to enter the most dangerous, unknown period of my life, I can come up with no plan of action which any strategist from Hannibal to my own father would not warn me is the height of folly . . . but I'm enjoying the birds and the bees, talking of which . . .

She sat up and squinted over to where Matt was sitting on his towel with his arms resting on his knees, staring across the water. His hair was damp and lying across his forehead, and his streamlined body still glistened with droplets of water, and she said abruptly, 'Are you expecting me to sleep with you tonight?'

He drew his gaze from the river to her, leisurely, and answered her question with another. 'Would you like to?'

'No . . . I . . . if it's a question of choice, no, I would rather not.'

'It's certainly not a question of rape,' he said wryly, 'if that's what you had on your mind.'

She laughed shortly. 'Not rape . . . perhaps seduction,' she suggested, plucking another stem of grass. 'And perhaps I should warn you I don't have a great reputation . . . in bed.'

He raised his eyebrows. 'It takes two to tango, Kirra,' he murmured, 'if you'll forgive the triteness. At whose hands was this reputation created, may I ask? Or perhaps I can guess,' he said softly. 'Fiancé number one.'

Kirra pressed her lips together as Matt regarded her steadily for a moment, then leant on his elbow and said casually, 'I normally don't believe in prying into what . . . has gone before, but I think you had better tell me about him. It . . . er . . . appears to me that a lot of what has followed might stem from him. He obviously conned you into believing he loved you for yourself, not your parents' wealth. Is that right?'

Kirra parted her lips, then took refuge in flippancy. 'Spot on! Bravo! In retrospect, he was one of those idle men, heavily into sporting achievements, but without the wherewithal to support his expensive tastes. He was also good-looking, fun to be with and very adept at hiding the fact that he was on the make. Women pursued him and . . . my heart used to go bang, bang, bang, whenever he was near. He assured me I had the same effect on him.' she said drily, and added, barely audibly, 'I shouldn't have been let out, I was so naïve.'

'How old?' he asked.

She grimaced. 'Nineteen.'

'And what burst the bubble?'

'I overheard him one day. He was talking to a friend of his, and it was only one those amazing co-incidences that I happened to be within earshot without his knowing. He . . . they were discussing me in . . . intimate detail.' She broke off and shivered. 'I gathered that I wasn't quite up to his standards in certain respects, but that I might just improve with experience. He laughed, and said that nobody could accuse me of being sophisticated or imaginative in bed, and that he might have to get that kind of fun elsewhere after we were married, but until we were, he was being very careful. It was, after all, he said, a minor consideration compared to all the lovely loot I represented and the fact that my parents doted on me, etc, etc!'

'Oh, dear . . .'

'There was more,' Kirra said bleakly, conscious of a fatalistic determination to tell him the lot now she had started. 'He also said he doubted if he was built to be faithful to any one woman, and it was fortunate that while I might not satisfy him, there was no doubt I thought the sun shone out of him, and if he could keep it that way, there was no reason he could see why I should interfere with his ability with women, the ability to lay them in the aisles begging for more.'

There was a short silence, then Matt said, 'What did you do? Break it off there and then?'

'No, I was . . . speechless. I couldn't believe not only what I'd been hearing, but the . . . coldness it represented. I was just stunned at how adroit he'd been and completely mortified at how right my parents had been about him. Although he charmed most people he met, he hadn't altogether fooled them. I . . . went home and planned to write him a letter ending it all so that I wouldn't have to see him again, but the next day he was killed in a water-skiing accident. For a moment, when I heard the news, I wondered if I'd wished it on him, and then there was the problem of everyone assuming I was heart-broken, when I was actually—well horrified but . . .'

'I know what you mean.'

'Do you?'

'Yes—it's pointless and tasteless to speak ill of the dead, so you had to accept all the sympathy and feel an utter fraud. Didn't you tell anyone?'

'Only my parents initially, then my best friend Pippa, and finally, Jeremy, that's all. He'd known Bret actually, and disliked him. He . . .' She stopped and sighed.

'Go on—tell me about Jeremy,' Matt prompted. 'For one reason, if no other—I'd like remove any stigma attached to my name in your mind concerning Jeremy. Do you think you would ever have married him?'

Kirra stirred restlessly. 'I don't know,' she said honestly. 'Because he *was* one of the few of us not to be taken in by Bret—he even tried to warn me once but I wouldn't be warned—because he understood, I suppose I . . . gravitated towards him because of that.' She shrugged. 'And he was so nice and so sure he loved me and so patient.' She grimaced.

'The antithesis of Bret.'

'I suppose so,' Kirra conceded.

'But instead of admitting that to yourself, you kept coming up with delays—you were delaying the wedding in your mind when you met me, weren't you, Kirra?'

Kirra looked across the water. 'Oh . . . yes!' She turned back, her eyes suddenly glinting fiercely. 'I was also wondering if I should inflict myself on him, for what it's worth. Can you not understand at all why . . . I was so mixed up?'

Matt sat up and frowned faintly. 'At nineteen—I guess we all go through some form of trauma or another with the opposite sex, but you're twenty-two, Kirra, a big girl now. You can probably look back on other follies you committed in your late teens, on the fact that you assumed you knew everything in those days . . . and laugh at yourself now. Why carry this chip on your shoulder?'

Kirra stared at him with a set mouth, then murmured, 'You're the last person I should be discussing this with.'

'On the contrary, the best, as things stand. And on the subject of how good you are in bed,' he said softly, 'why let the immature crowings of a two-bit louse influence you in your opinion of yourself?'

Kirra opened her mouth to reply tartly, but there was something completely unanswerable about his logic, no way to explain what a vulnerable area it was whether you were nineteen or thirty-nine, she suspected. So she said tautly, in an oblique cross-thrust, 'Tell me about Min.'

A smile twisted his lips. 'I've known Min for . . . let's see, sixteen or seventeen years now.'

'An old friend,' Kirra said ironically.

He held her gaze, then said deliberately, 'She was more than that—for a time.'

Kirra's lips parted. 'You . . . do you mean . . .?'

He nodded. 'It was also quite a long time ago, and we were able to remain friends when it ended.'

'Why are you telling me this?' she whispered, her eyes stunned.

He looked amused. 'You did ask me. Besides, it's

only what you suspected, isn't it?'

'All the same . . .'

He laughed at her openly. 'Anyway, you've just told me all your secrets, and as you've met her now, it's better that you *do* know, so there can be no misunderstandings in the future. I'm sure you'll find you'll like her. She's very kind and very sane.'

'I can't imagine why you didn't marry her, then,' Kirra broke in bitterly. 'I really not only hate you, but despise you s-sometimes!' Her voice shook and she jumped up tensely and ran down to the river, but he caught her and pulled her into his arms at the edge of the water.

'Still fighting?' he said softly, his eyes flickering from her mutinously set mouth down to her breasts beneath the rose-pink lycra.

'If you dare,' she said through her teeth, 'to try to kiss me after . . . in almost the same breath as parading your former love-life in front of me, I'll . . .'

'Jealous?' he broke in, his eyes gleaming with devilry. 'You needn't be. It's been over and dead for a long time.'

'No!' Her lips stayed parted in horror at the very thought. Then she said scathingly, 'That's like expecting me to believe you were jealous of Jeremy!'

'Oh, if you'd married him, I would have been.'

Her eyes widened disbelievingly.

'Kirra,' he said, as one would to a backward child, 'I'd have to be totally unmoved by you to have been jealous—which I'm not. There's be no point in marrying you if I were.'

'Not totally? How fortunate,' she murmured mockingly.

He grinned. 'Perhaps I could have put it better

—like this, for example.'

She tried to struggle out of his arms, but she slipped and they fell into the shallows, sending a spray of water arcing above them, and all she achieved was to be still in his arms, half submereged in the river with her skin fresh and satiny beneath his hands, her hair dark and streaming, and his mouth on hers . . .

When it ended, he picked her up and carried her out of the water, she was breathing erratically as he put her down on her feet and steadied her with his hands about her waist.

'Still hate me?' he asked.

Her eyes were dark and tormented. 'I . . .'

'I don't really mind what you call it—for the time being, that is.' He smoothed the wet hair off her face. 'Shall we,' he paused as she tensed, 'ride some more? Dandelion's getting restless.'

They rode the boundaries of the property, then washed the horses down together and stabled them for the night with their feeds. There was no sign of Min, but Kirra did see the elderly Land Rover parked in the shed.

'Your father's right,' Matt said as he noticed her staring at it. 'I keep that because there are times when the Rolls is a nuisance.'

Kirra grimaced. 'I have to be honest—Dad would probably love one, but Mum's not a very good driver, although she can't see it herself. Oh, she's all right in traffic, it's stationary things she has trouble with, like garage walls, fences and trees.'

Matt laughed. 'I like your mother.'

'She certainly likes you,' Kirra said quietly, staring again at the Land Rover, then she turned to him.

'Will you tell me one thing? What *were* you doing at Yamba? Do you do that kind of thing often?'

'I . . .' He stopped. 'Should we shower and change first? And I'll get the fire going for the barbecue . . .'

'You're not going to tell me, are you?' she broke in. 'That's not fair.'

'It's no deep dark secret, and yes, I will try to explain my . . . occasional bouts of wanderlust to you, Kirra,' he said. 'Over our meal, though. Coming?'

'I . . . yes.'

CHAPTER SIX

KIRRA put on a loose grey dress printed with yellow and white daisies after she had showered, then tied back her hair with a grey ribbon and slid her feet into yellow sandals.

She'd smoothed body lotion all over her skin, but other than that she'd used no cosmetics. Just the basic me, she thought.

There was music playing, and she recognised the stately but lilting *Rondo* from Mozart's 'Horn Concerto', which soothed her mental turmoil for a time. But when it finished there was silence, and no reason for her to delay leaving the sanctuary of the downstairs bedroom.

She stayed for a few minutes longer though, deep in thought because there were some things that were becoming increasingly hard to explain . . . such as how she could enjoy being kissed by a man who admired her body but not much else about her, or he wouldn't be bargaining with her as if she were a desirable chattel.

What's more, she thought, he has me in the most incredible corner and I can think of no way out, bar locking myself in here until he promises to take me home . . . A hunger-strike! Why didn't I think of that? And why, she smiled grimly, do I have the feeling he'd work his way round that one, too?

A knock on the door interrupted her thoughts, and she jumped, then called, 'Come in.'

He didn't come in, just opened the door and

started to say something, then stopped and frowned faintly.

As for Kirra, she was unable to tear her eyes away from him; he had showered and now wore jeans and a blue and white striped shirt, with his hair still damp.

'What's the matter?' he said abruptly.

She coloured and switched her gaze away angrily —in fact, that was what she reminded herself of, an angry cat flicking its tail. 'Nothing—I'm just fine,' she said sardonically.

He strolled into the room and paused to look at her searchingly. 'If you could relax, we might be able to make some progress.'

'Towards what? On second thoughts, don't tell me, I can guess.' She returned his look ironically.

'Towards being really good together—again. And I mean companion-wise.'

'Matt,' she said deliberately, 'I must warn you that, contrary to what my past history might have indicated, I'm no good at playing games.'

'Are we playing games?' he asked quietly.

'Yes. Cat-and-mouse games, and I'm the mouse.' She broke off and had to grimace ruefully, and mutter exasperatedly, 'I wish you'd make up your mind, Kirra!'

He looked at her quizzically, but she recovered quickly.

'The simple fact is that you're forcing me to marry you. You're also using your considerable experience and expertise with women quite deliberately and shamefully to play upon the fact that I once responded to you physically and in my book, *Mr Remington*,' she said scornfully, 'that makes you no better than Bret, although I suppose to call you a two-bit louse on the make would be inaccurate—a two-million-bit louse might be more appropriate.'

'Bravo, Kirra!' he said, his eyes glinting wickedly. 'This . . . cad of the first water stands utterly reproved. You're also quite sensational when you're angry, you know.'

'Oh . . . why didn't I just lock myself in?' she asked despairingly.

'Now that would have been childish,' he replied 'and I prefer you when you're firing straight from the hip. You'll feel better after you've had something to eat. It's beautiful outside and the fire's going well.'

He barbecued chops and sausages, and they ate them with the salads from lunch time plus a dish of ratatouille Min had made and left to be heated up. There was also a strawberry shortcake with ice-cream to follow, and he opened a bottle of wine.

It was unbelievably peaceful on Matt Remington's private hilltop, and as Kirra sipped her wine she watched the pale smoke of the fire swirling against the dark of the sky. There seemed to be a million stars out, and a prim little new moon descending in the west.

'Tell me about this wanderlust of yours,' she said at last.

He shrugged slightly. 'I think it stems from when I was a kid and I used to read Rider Haggard, Kipling, *Jock of the Bushveld*, *Memories of a Game Ranger* and later Robert Ruark—I used to dream about the Plains of Serengeti, the Mountains of the Moon . . . places like Etosha Pan and the Kruger National Park. It was my greatest ambition to be a big-game hunter or a game ranger,' he said wryly.

Kirra blinked and thought that if he had told her it had been a serious ambition with him to be a circus clown she would not have been more surprised.

'An odd amibiton for an Australian boy,' she said.
'My mother was South African.'

Kirra stared at him, wide-eyed. 'Tell me about her.'

'She met my father at Kia Lami—that's their grand-prix circuit outside Johannesburg—and was duly dazzled, although she did succeed in marrying him. Possibly because she had a lot of very large and moral male relatives,' he said drily, and added, 'She was a farmer's daughter and always stayed one at heart—I don't mean she was uncultured, but she was capable, loyal, stubborn, tremendously family-orientated and she had an affinity with the earth and growing things. And she paid dearly for the one mistake of her life.'

'Did she pine for South Africa?'

'Yes, but it wasn't only that. They were completely mismatched. All her qualities represented one thing to my father—being tied down. Oddly enough, and I think this was the one thing that made life a little bearable for her, she was a lot like the Remingtons and they liked and admired her. They're also a capable, cautious bunch . . . until Dad came along.'

'She also had you,' Kirra said quietly. 'Did she take you back to South Africa?'

'Every few years. I loved it, and my uncle, one of her brothers, was a game ranger with the Transvaal Nature Conservation Division.'

'How come your mother didn't divorce your father, if it was as you say?'

'She was very proud, perhaps too proud to admit the failure of her marriage, and anyway, he swore he'd never part with me. I couldn't understand it while I was growing up—it was pretty obvious whose side I was on, but I did work it out eventually. We,

she and I, were his one link with the Remingtons
. . . the rest of the family. If it hadn't been for us,
they'd have washed their hands of him a lot sooner.'

Kirra shivered. 'No wonder you're . . . so cynical.'

He glanced at her, then grinned. 'Actually, I'm a
lot less cynical about it since I've restored the family
fortune, our branch of it. And,' he sobered, 'for
what it's worth, my father and the former supposed
love of my life are still together, and to all intents and
purposes, quietly happy.'

Kirra stirred. 'She must—you said she was older
than you, but she must be a lot younger than he is.'

'Over twenty years, but for all that, she seems to
have reformed him. It's strange what works for some
people.'

'And you,' Kirra said, 'go on safari from time to
time in memory of your mother.'

'Something like that,' he agreed. 'Yes.'

Kirra watched him in silence for a while. He was
looking away from her, staring into the darkness with
the firelight flickering on his face and highlighting the
remoteness of his expression, the lines beside his
mouth, and she thought back to Lover's Point and
remembered how his smile had captured her heart, a
smile she hadn't really seen since. And as she studied
the way his fair hair fell, the set of his mouth, she felt
her heart contract and she was filled with a desire to
bring him back from wherever his mind was wandering.

'I don't know much about South Africa, apart
from the obvious, but after I saw the movie *Out of
Africa*, I read the book and it was just fascinating.
Not only because of Africa, but the way she wrote.
The images she created sort of leapt off the page,
they were so real.'

He looked at her at last. 'If you liked that, you'd have liked my mother. That's the kind of life she'd have loved.'

'Would you . . . no.' Kirra stopped.

'Go on.'

'It just occurred to me,' Kirra said slowly, 'that perhaps you—and your father until he got reformed, have a bit of Denys Finch-Hatton in you.'

It was strange, she reflected later, since it had been in her thoughts only minutes before—that heart-stopping smile that crinkled the corners of his eyes—and to see it again left her feeling oddly breathless.

'Perhaps,' he said. 'I did sometimes wonder if it was the elusiveness about my father that bound my mother to him against her will. I mean, if she'd been able to pin him down, she might also have been able to let him go. That sounds crazy, but . . .'

'I know what you mean. I'm sure it happens,' she said and found herself feeling curiously cold as if from an elusive premonition.

But in fact the breeze had strengthened and the fire was dying down. She sighed inwardly and said quietly, 'I'll clear up.'

'I'll help you.'

They did it in no time at all between them, and as he started the dishwasher, which ran almost sound-lessly, Kirra stood in the middle of the kitchen, wondering what to do next.

Matt straightened and glanced at her, then said abruptly, 'Bed for you, I think.'

'Thank you, I enjoyed that,' she said uncertainly.

'Goodnight. Will you be able to sleep?'

'Yes.' He was standing close enough for her to see the green flecks in his eyes, and she thought with a tremor, he'll kiss me and I'll feel like a . . . a foolish, star-struck girl.

He didn't. He studied her meditatively, the cotton dress with its brave yellow and white daisies, the ribbon in her hair, her shadowed eyes. He did put out a hand to touch her hair, but it was almost an absent-minded gesture as he said, 'Off you go, then.'

It was a long time before she got to sleep. Not only were the bed and the house alien, the small sounds different, the lack of noise compared to where she lived almost a noise in itself, but there were her alien thoughts to deal with. Such as why, instead of feeling she had been let off the hook, she should be feeling something different.

It was a blue and gold Sunday morning and they rode after breakfast, higher into the hills where the air was almost intoxicatingly pure and fresh, and alive with the smell of grass-seed and earth.

He made no comment about the faint blue shadows beneath her eyes, and she avoided mentioning anything that wasn't mundane.

But when they found a small pool in a tree-rimmed hollow and dismounted to rest the horses and give them a drink, she leant back against a gumtree, listening to the hum of insects and waving her hat to cool her face—and said unthinkingly, 'It's so beautiful here. If I lived here, I might never want to leave.'

'You wouldn't have to if that's the way you feel.'

She sighed inwardly and thought, I walked into that one . . . why not take it a step further? 'You wouldn't be able to spend much time here.'

He'd been tying the horses to a tree, and he came over and sprawled on the grass at her feet, pushed a hand through his hair and squinted up at her quizzically. 'That would be a problem wherever we lived, but naturally with a wife—and children eventually —I'd try to cut down my travelling as much as possible. Or you might like to come with me as much as possible—there are advantages about having one special place to come home to.'

Kirra stirred. 'Yes,' she said absently.

'We could always extend the house for kids.'

She was silent.

'Do you have anything against kids, Kirra?' he asked at length.

'No. I've never had much to do with children.' She looked down and encountered a searching hazel gaze which told her he knew she was simply going along with this conversation, and she looked away again. Did he *really* expect . . .

'I wouldn't expect you to rush into having a team of babies, Kirra,' he said deliberately.

'You know what you remind me of?' she said. 'That old adage about water wearing away a stone. Perhaps it's an old Afrikaans adage.'

He sat up and said with a faint smile twisting his lips, 'Come down to my level for a while.' He held out his hand.

She took it after a moment and slid down the trunk.

'You didn't sleep well after all, did you?' he said softly.

'No.'

'Do you know what I think?' His hazel gaze was curiously brilliant, and he raised a hand and touched the line of her throat, then let it rest on her chest, his fingers curled lightly about her neck. 'I think there's one way we understand each other perfectly, Kirra, and it's foolish to fight it.'

Her breath caught in her throat, and she trembled beneath the onslaught of the undoubted physical attraction he held for her. She thought how easy it would be to give way to the feel of his hands and mouth on her body, and she wondered how she would feel in the aftermath of his lovemaking, if that final intimacy—and the images of it flooded her mind—would release her from this torture, or chain her to it for ever.

'All the same, if I have a choice,' she whispered, 'I shall fight it.' And she took his wrist and returned his hand to his lap.

'Even when we're married?' he said, barely audibly.

She closed her eyes. 'I don't know yet. I can't visualise that somehow, but no—it would be foolish, and anyway, I'd be reneging on our deal. I won't do that. But until then, foolish or not, I prefer to fight it.'

'You think you can?'

Kirra opened her eyes but stared at her hands first, then lifted her lashes, uncertain of what she would see—that cold yet casual implacability, mostly masked this weekend? She'd found herself wondering last night if she was fighting herself more than him, until she had thought of his mother, enmeshed on a roundabout of love and pride and pain. And in the depth of the night she had come to one conclusion—that she could no longer afford to be disbelieving and distraught, nor could she allow herself to submit to the sensual hold he had over her without compromising her integrity. If she had to go to the altar of his disillusionment and desire for revenge, if she had to pay for her parents' peace of mind, she would at least do so fighting for the right to express her distrust of his motives.

'I think I have to,' she said, and realised the look in his hazel eyes was curiously critical, if anything. As if, although he was looking at her, he was examining something unseen, maybe even foreign to him.

Then his eyes glinted with familiar irony, and he said softly. 'May the best man win—no,' he added as she tensed expectantly, 'I'm not going to afford you the opportunity to fling my . . . considerable experience and expertise with women, quote-unquote, in my face.'

Kirra had lowered her eyes again, but she looked up and her blue-grey glance was steady but with a glimmer of contempt, causing him to break off and lift an eyebrow consideringly at her, and to say thoughtfully, after a while, 'Why do I get the feeling we have a whole . . . new ball-game going?'

'I told you before—I'm no good at games,' she said evenly. 'Believe it or not, this is for real.'

'Would you care to tell me about this new resolution?' he asked with a faint, dry smile.

'No,' she replied briefly.

'But,' he paused and it was there now, she saw, not so much the implacability but a coolly calculating look in his eyes that still had the power to make her feel nervous, 'you look as if you've come up with a secret weapon, my dear Kirra.'

'Perhaps I have,' she murmured, and wondered if she should tell him that it was a strange affinity she felt for a person she had never known, his mother, that had given her this resolution. 'Perhaps I know a bit more about you now,' she said with a faint shrug.

'Don't underestimate me, Kirra,' he warned quietly. 'Or the effect we have on each other.'

'It's not that; if anything, it's the opposite. That

doesn't mean I have to roll over on to my back and beg you to stroke my belly,' she said.

He looked faintly surprised at her choice of words, then absent-mindedly amused, and finally he said wryly, 'So be it.' And he stood up and gave her his hand to help her to her feet.

She took it with no fuss, and he didn't attempt to press any further attentions on her, although when he took the red bandanna he wore round his neck off and dipped it in the pool, he offered it her first.

She splashed her face, bathed her wrists and handed it back, and then they mounted and rode back to the house in silence. But Kirra found herself wondering if all she had achieved was to add fuel to the challenge.

Min was there like a genie, and she came out to greet them with a wave and a grin. 'Hope you're hungry, you two! I've made a traditional Sunday roast dinner.'

Kirra had a quick wash and brush-up, and they sat down to roast lamb with mint sauce, baked potatoes, fresh peas and carrots and a passion-fruit cheesecake to follow.

Fortunately, Min was in an ebullient, talkative mood—the result, she told them, of conquering a tricky piece of wood and persuading it into the shape she'd planned for it—so any deficiencies in communication between Matt and Kirra passed unnoticed.

She is nice, Kirra found herself thinking. I wonder if she has any idea of the true state of affairs between Matt and me? I wonder if he's told her he's going to marry me? She must be . . . curious, at least. Or perhaps she's used to him bringing different women down here . . .

It was after lunch that Min demonstrated she was

curious. Matt had disappeared towards the stables and Kirra was helping her with the clearing up when she said. 'You two . . . haven't known each other very long, have you? Oh, don't think I'm prying!' She rolled her eyes heavenwards, then grimaced and said honestly, 'Maybe I am. I . . . I've known Matt a long time, you see.'

'He . . .' Kirra hesitated, 'told me about you.'

Min's busy hands stilled on the sink briefly, then she started wiping it again. 'I'm glad,' she said quietly. 'Better to know now than find out later. If you're wondering what it means to us now, I can tell you that I shall always love Matt in a way, but not that way. That way,' she said with a sudden look of pain, 'is reserved for a man I can't have. That's why I'm here, trying to get myself together. Matt imagines I did him a favour once, and this is his way of repaying it. But if,' she paused, as if choosing her words with care, 'well, you find the situation bizzarre . . . I did try to explain to him when he rang me and told me he was bringing . . . someone down . . .' She stopped helplessly, then said very quietly, 'You're the first girl he's brought here, since I've been here, so I thought it must be . . . serious, and the last thing I wanted to do was . . . intrude.'

'You haven't,' Kirra heard herself say sincerely. 'This man—is there nothing—is he married to someone else?'

'He will be soon,' Min said carefully as she wiped and rewiped the already spotless sink. 'But not so long ago he was married to me.'

Kirra caught her breath and Min stopped wiping at last. And they looked at each other with the sudden and quite unspoken communion of two women in strife—as only women at the hands of men can be.

Kirra?' Min said uncertainly.

Kirra managed to smile shakily. 'I . . . I'm not very sure of myself sometimes, Min, that's all.'

'I'm sure Matt will help you to . . . overcome that. He . . . perhaps it's obvious I'm a bit of a fan,' Min said ruefully, 'but all the same . . .' She tapered off, then smiled suddenly. 'I'm sure he doesn't need me to speak for him! Would you like to see my work?'

'I'd love to see your work,' Kirra said, and went on to explain briefly what she did. 'I might be able to pass on some commissions or even find a buyer if you have any work for sale.'

Min tossed the dishcloth into the sink and said comically, 'Lady, you could be the answer to my prayers! Come, before you change your mind.'

Kirra bought three of Min's pieces on the spot, two statuettes and an intricately carved pair of bookends. They discussed what kind of work Min would be interested in doing if Kirra could pass it on.

'For example,' Kirra said, 'I know this sounds terribly commercial, but we're decorating a new house and the owner wants panels of frolicking dolphins set around the . . . er . . . jacuzzi—should I have even mentioned it?'

Min broke into peals of laughter and said finally, 'My dear Kirra, most artists are aware of the facts of life—dolphins about a jacuzzi are the bread-and-butter items that make it possible to go on and do your life's work. If you could send me some measurements, I'd be delighted to bone up on frolicking dolphins!'

Kirra left the studio after they had carefully packed

up the items she'd bought, and she left Min hunting through her books for pictures of dolphins.

There was no sign of Matt, and Kirra had a shower, changed into a primrose T-shirt and fresh jeans and packed her bag.

When there was still no sign of him, she wandered around downstairs for a while, then on an impulse climbed the staircase to his loft bedroom.

She hesitated at the top of the stairs, looking around. The big bed was made, the mulberry cover smooth, the desktop was neat and his bag stood open on a stool waiting to be packed. There was a stone fireplace at one end of the room surrounded by bookshelves, and she wandered over to it to inspect his literary tastes, which proved to be catholic, from Tolstoy to *The Hitch-Hiker's Guide to the Galaxy*—and there on one shelf all the books from his childhood.

She picked out *Jock of the Bushveld* and leafed through its yellowing pages and was enchanted by the drawings of animals on each page.

Then she wandered over to one of the dormer windows and sat down on the wooden window-seat with her feet up on it, knees bent, to savour the view.

How long she sat there she wasn't sure, but as she watched the afternoon darkened and heavy black clouds rolled down from Mount Warning, laying a shadow on everything and bringing an expectant stillness to the afternoon.

It was as the first spots of rain spattered on to the stone of the terrace that she heard the outside door below open and close.

For some reason she didn't move, and she wondered if it was a sense of defiance that prompted her to stay

She turned her head from the view at last to see Matt at the top of the stairs, pausing, just realising she was there.

His eyebrows lifted, but all he said was, 'I thought you must be with Min.'

'I was,' she said and went to get up, but he came over to the window. The rain was now spearing down and hammering on the roof, the gutters were beginning to gurgle and forks of lightning were splitting the sky.

'Not scared?' he asked as a clap of thunder reverberated through the house.

She shook her head. 'I've always loved storms.'

'Stay there, then. I might as well pack. We'll leave as soon as the worst is over.'

He moved away and switched on a lamp, dispelling the shadows in the room and creating a warm circle of light against the uproar outside.

Kirra watched the storm for a bit longer, then she rested her head back and watched him instead. He was packing neatly and precisely, and he closed the bag and looked up, catching her gaze before she could look away. 'Did you come up here for any particular reason, Kirra?' he asked, his eyes suddenly intent and direct.

She stared at him then shook her head. 'Not really. As a matter of fact, I was trying to examine my motives as you came in.' Her lips twisted ruefully.

'Perhaps it was just plain curiosity?' he suggested.

'Perhaps,' she agreed.

'Of the type Bluebeard's den might arouse?' His look was slightly ironic.

'Hardly ' she said drily.

'Sometimes you look at me as if that's not at all hard to imagine.'

'Do I?' She shrugged.

He sat down in the armchair and sprawled his long legs out. 'Could I make a suggestion?'

'If it's a . . . make-love-not-war type of suggestion, no.'

He grinned and glanced at the smooth bed. 'There's a certain . . . added intimacy about making love in the middle of a crashing thunderstorm. Ever tried it?'

Kirra looked away, feeling sudden patches of heat on her throat and a dew of sweat along her hairline.

There was silence, until she said presently, 'I think the worst *is* over now.'

'Worst of what?' he asked, barely audibly, and she knew his eyes had not left her, nor had he missed the signs of her agitation.

'The storm is passing,' she said as equably as she was able, but thinking, I'll be damned if I'll acknowledge . . . anything!

'Let's go, then.'

'If you want to.' She looked at him at last, and was unable to mask the glint of defiance in her eyes.

CHAPTER SEVEN

'DAMN!' Kirra said suddenly, breaking the uneasy silence of the trip home. Matt had appeared as pre-occupied as she was.

He turned his head and lifted an eyebrow. 'Forgotten something?'

'No. I mean, yes. It's Sunday . . . don't answer that.' She peered at her watch.

'It's five-thirty, it *is* Sunday—do you have a date?'

'Rupert and Mr Cassidy are coming over at six to . . .'

'Rupert? Mr Cassidy?' He shot her a laughing glance. 'Should I know about them as well?'

Kirra tightened her mouth, then said, 'Rupert is ten. He lives next door to me, with his parents and his dog—Mr Cassidy. We have a date to play Scrabble tonight. Any objections?'

'None. We should be there in plenty of time,' he said. 'I thought you said you hadn't had anything to do with children.'

'I said I hadn't had *much* to do with children—one child I baby-sit occasionally and play Scrabble with does not a summer make.'

'I stand corrected,' Matt replied gravely.

'Good,' Kirra said, but under her breath.

'What was that?'

'I'm glad you're capable of that, that's all,' she said sweetly.

'You must be feeling better,' he murmured. 'Either that, or there's something about my car that

120

brings out your fighting spirit.'

Kirra bit her lip and tried to force herself to relax. But she realised, as she turned her face to the window to watch the wet road reflect the lights as a premature, rain-laden dusk fell, that the weekend had taken a heavy toll of her, despite her resolution to indulge in no more histrionics or panicky manoeuvres. In fact, she felt as if her nerves were stretched to screaming-point, and it was almost impossible to squash the impulse to snap and be thoroughly bitchy.

'You don't have to come up,' she said stiffly when he pulled up outside her building.

'I don't intend to force myself on you,' he replied, and added with laughter lurking in his eyes, 'in this mood. All the same, you have rather a lot of stuff to carry, remember?'

She'd forgotten about Min's carvings. 'Oh . . . thanks,' she said briefly.

As they got out of the lift, two disconsolate figures further down the passage turned eagerly, one tail started to wag madly, then Kirra was besieged.

'You didn't forget!' Rupert cried enthusiastically.

'I'm afraid I did, Rupert—down, Mr Cassidy! I thought we had an arrangement about licking.'

'Then it's off.' Rupert's face fell, but almost immediately a spark of hope lit his eyes. 'Your friend could play with us! Three makes it even better, and I've added two new words to my list . . . one game, just one,' he entreated.

Mr Cassidy, who was small, black and white in some parts and brindle in others, and whose pedigree was hard to imagine, barked excitedly.

Matt said, 'I'm a fair Scrabble player myself.'

Kirra flashed him a look, then said resignedly, 'All right, inside you lot!'

* * *

'I know who you are,' Rupert remarked to Matt some time later.

'Oh?'

'You're the man with the smashing Rolls. I saw you pick Kirra up yesterday. Are you—oh, bother!' he said, noticing that Kirra had won the game. 'I didn't get the chance to use either of my new words!'

'Next time,' Kirra said consolingly. 'It was my turn to get all the good letters today.'

'She's pretty good at this game,' Rupert confided ruefully to Matt. 'Is she going to marry you instead of Jeremy?'

Kirra flushed and avoided Matt's wry look. 'Rupert,' she began but Matt said, 'Perhaps.'

Rupert grimaced. 'I was hoping no one would until I was old enough to marry her myself, but I don't suppose I can be expected to compete with a bloke with a Rolls-Royce, can I?'

Kirra closed her mouth, floored again in the space of a moment, but Rupert had suddenly turned bright red and was looking as if he heartily wished the ground would open up beneath his feet, so she put aside all other sentiments to say gravely as she ruffled his hair, 'Thank you for that, Rupe.'

'You don't . . .' He got stuck.

'I think, in fact I know,' she said with a slight smile, 'that all girls, even when it's not possible, appreciate a compliment like that, really they do.'

Rupert looked relieved then the phone rang once, his parents' signal that it was time to go home, and he and Mr Cassidy left, not without some good-natured grumbling.

Kirra closed the door on them and leant back against it, feeling exhausted. There was still Matt to be dealt with—he'd sent her the most wicked glance during Rupert's unexpected revelations, and she hadn't dared to look at him since.

He was standing with his back to her, staring out of the window, so she picked up the tray of refreshments she had provided and took it into the kitchen. But her nerves were beginning to get the better of her again, she discovered, as she put the biscuit-barrel away with unwanted force, rammed the glasses into the dishwasher and wiped the clean kitchen sink until she reminded herself of Min. She threw the cloth away disgustedly and, muttering beneath her breath, turned to march back into the lounge, only to bump into the subject of her ire—who was lounging in the doorway.

'Steady on,' he said softly, straightening and catching her about the waist.

'Let me go.' Her eyes were stormy.

'In a moment. So you have . . . another admirer?'

'Possibly a more genuine one!' she flashed at him.

He looked amused and drew her a fraction closer. 'Time will tell.'

'I'm sure you're right,' she said tautly. 'May I make a request?'

He thought for a moment, then said, 'Sure. I'm . . . definitely open to requests.' His words were husky and almost caressing, as were his hands, moving up from her waist to span her back beneath her shoulders. She tried to break away, but he pulled her closer and leant back against the door-frame, eyeing her mutinously set mouth with a perfectly grave expression that was a mockery in itself. 'Fire away.'

'I would . . .' she said raggedly, 'I would like you to go away and leave me alone for a while.'

'Is the strain getting to you, Kirra?' he asked.

'I . . .'

'Or would you like a little time to . . . reconnoitre?' He lowered his eyelids as he inspected the hollows at the base of her throat just above the neckline of the primrose T-shirt.

'Yes,' she said before she could stop herself.

His lashes lifted leisurely and her heart started to beat faster, but he smiled faintly and said placidly, 'I'll be interested to see what you come up with between now and Friday. I'll be in Melbourne until Thursday, by the way, but I thought we might go out on Friday night.' He lifted an eyebrow at her.

'If . . . if you want to,' she said helplessly.

'Oh, I do. Incidentally, what kind of a ring would you like for your third engagement ring? Do you like sapphires?'

'I hate sapphires,' Kirra said precisely. 'My first engagement ring was a sapphire, as it happens.'

'Dear me,' he replied, 'it hadn't occurred to me but that's obviously a problem for such a much engaged lady as yourself. Let's see . . . if we rule out diamonds and sapphires, what's left? A ruby? Or an emerald?'

'I've a much better idea,' Kirra said through her teeth. 'Why don't you get me a ring replica of a ball and chain?'

He laughed softly and bent his head to kiss her lightly on the lips. *'Touché*! See you Friday.' He released her and left without another word.

'Darling, I'll be fine,' Kirra said into the phone on Wednesday evening. 'I think it's a great idea for you and Dad to have a break, and if he's agreeable, you should definitely strike while the iron's hot so to speak. He could change his mind.'

'Well, I know it's a bit of an out-of-the-blue

decision,' Naomi said down the line, 'but I do think
he needs to get away, and we thought we'd just get
into the car tomorrow morning and head for
wherever the mood takes us.'

'Sounds lovely,' Kirra said warmly. 'Just don't
spoil it worrying about me or anything. There
isn't——' She paused. 'There's nothing to worry
about any more, is there?' She tried to sound casual.

'Not a thing,' Naomi replied, 'but sometimes it's
very hard to wind down, if you know what I mean.'

'Mmm . . . Of course, it's not all completely
finalised yet, is it?' said Kirra. 'I mean, it must take
time to draw up all the contracts and so on.' For
some reason she held her breath as she waited.

Naomi chuckled. 'Actually, it's all signed and
sealed, pet, and what's more, Matt has already sunk
a substantial amount of capital into Munro's.
Apparently it's a well-known fact in the business
world that once he decides to move, he moves very
swiftly, but I must say your father was quite
surprised at the speed of things. But then . . .'

'Mum,' Kirra stared at herself in the mirror above
the phone table and saw she was white with shock,
'when . . . you didn't mention this . . .'

'About the contracts? Didn't we?' Naomi said
vaguely, then, on a sharper note, 'You haven't been
worrying still, have you, Kirralee? The contracts were
a formality once we had his word. He . . . he's that
kind of a man, my dear, and . . . well, I suppose we
just never guessed you might be afraid . . .'

Kirra didn't hear the rest of what her mother was
saying nor, as she put the phone down, did she
remember what she had said in reply, but it must
have reassured her mother because her parting words
had been cheerful, that she did know. But as she

stared at her still pale, shocked and disbelieving face in the mirror, a tide of understanding began to course through her, and a tide of rage . . .

CHAPTER EIGHT

'OH . . .'

She moved away from the phone at last, breathing heavily, and discovered that her hands were shaking and her thoughts were flying in a dozen different directions, only to be pulled back like a ball on a string . . .

'All along it *was* a game, a cold, cruelly calculated game of revenge, but he must have known I could have found out . . . he can't have cared! Perhaps he counted each succeeding day I remained in ignorance as a bonus after the initial fright he gave me, and he had a few weeks up his sleeve, anyway . . . oh! And he was probably clever enough to realise my old-fashioned parents would place more trust in his word than pieces of paper . . . I could have gone on in ignorance for *weeks* longer! But *why*?'

She stood in the middle of her lounge, examining all the answers she could command. 'He's a devil, a cold, cynical . . . devil beneath the charm and the . . . He had to be, because what I did to him was nothing compared to this. What did I do, anyway? Get a bit carried away for a few hours, but *this* . . .'

She started to pace the room agitatedly, trying to bring some order to the angry chaos of her thoughts, some logic to his actions. 'To think,' she whispered, 'That I even began to wonder if I'd fallen in love with him . . . Oh, I see, damn you, Matthew Remington!' she breathed. 'That's what you were planning to achieve, not for the pleasure of having me chained in a one-sided marriage to you, but for the pleasure of being able to walk away from me. How subtle and tortuous, but don't imagine . . .'

The phone rang, and for a moment she was tempted to ignore it, then she strode across the room and lifted it impatiently. It was a long-distance call, and an operator asked for Miss Kirra Munro, then connected her to Mr Remington.

Kirra's eyes flashed with fire through a series of clicks, then narrowed almost calculatingly.

'Kirra?' His voice came down the line.

'H-hello?' she said unsteadily, because she was thinking furiously.

'Were you asleep?'

'No! I mean, no . . .'

'You sound bemused.'

'I didn't think you knew my number,' she said lamely.

'I didn't, but it was simple enough to find it. Do you mind me ringing you?'

'I . . . are you still in Melbourne?'

'Yes—and thinking of you.'

Kirra was silent, amazed that, despite all she now knew, her skin was prickling, not only at what he had said, but because she thought he sounded tired.

'Kirra?'

'I'm here.' She cleared her throat. 'Have you been very busy?'

'Yes. Have you?'

'No . . . uh . . . just normal.'

'Have you come to any more conclusions about us?' he queried.

Kirra clenched her free fist, but managed to say, 'There doesn't seem to be any point, does there, beyond . . . upsetting myself.'

'I'm glad to hear you say so. I thought you might have decided to leave the country after our last encounter.'

'What would you do if I did . . . do that?'

'I think you know that,' he said after a pause.

'Of course.' Her eyes gleamed. 'Just . . . checking the state of the art.'

'If we were together, the state of the art would be . . .'

'Don't,' she broke in wearily.

'Would be infinitely pleasing, as we both know, and despite your intention to fight it,' he said deliberately. Then he added flatly, 'I'm missing you for what it's worth.'

Liar, she found herself wanting to say, to shout. She said instead, 'What's that supposed to mean?'

He took his time about answering. 'That I'd like to be with you, holding you, touching and exploring . . . making love to you. That's all.'

'All?' Her voice quivered, and not only with scepticism, but because his words had undoubtedly exposed a nerve, damn him again, she thought.

'Is there more?' he asked. 'Something I missed?'

'You . . . ' She took a breath. 'Why don't you go to bed? You sound tired.'

'So do you—tired and scratchy. We could be missing each other. Personally, I think I'm going to stay up and work. If six o'clock suits you, I'll see you then. Sweet dreams, Kirra.' The phone clicked in her ear.

She put it down slowly and carefully, lost in thought. Then she shook herself mentally and went to bed, but there were no sweet dreams for her, there were too many plans to be made, too much to review. For example, having made the decision that two could play games, and that it might even be possible for a late starter to turn the tables, there was also to be decided how she should carry on so that he wouldn't suspect she knew, until it was too late.

On the whole it would be wisest not to change too much, she told herself. If you suddenly become all sultry and seductive, he's going to smell a rat. No, Kirra, it's your turn to be . . . subtle.

It wasn't until the early hours of the morning, when she was light-headed with tiredness, that the irony of the situation occurred to her. Instead of being immeasurably relieved, she was immeasurably hostile and hell-bent on revenge.

'But why shouldn't I?' she asked herself, turning her cheek to the pillow wearily. 'Why should I weakly and spinelessly accept being made such a fool of?'

At six o'clock precisely on Friday evening, her doorbell rang, and it was more by accident than design that her plan of action received the boost it needed. She had actually planned to step out of the shower to answer the door; what she hadn't anticipated was that she would have had an exceedingly busy two days, that she would be genuinely delayed at work by a talkative client, genuinely feel the need to dive into the shower because it had been a hot, muggy afternoon, and genuinely feel rushed and tense and tired as she opened the door with dripping hair and a damp robe clutched awkwardly round her equally damp body.

In spite of that, he managed to surprise her.

'Hello . . . oh!' she said, blinking as she took in the fact that he was wearing shorts and sand shoes, and that he appeared to be laden down with packages,

Not only that—he looked casual and carefree, younger, bigger . . . but not in the least like the satanic monster her overwrought imagination had turned him into.

He raised an eyebrow lazily. 'You look surprised to see me, Kirra.'

'I'm not . . . I'm . . . I just got home and it's been so hot. Um . . . come in,' she said confusedly, turning away and leaving him to close the door with his heel.

There was evidence of her late arrival home in the form of her bag, open and spilling its contents, and two carrier-bags tossed down on the settee, a pair of earrings and her sun-glasses on the glass-topped table, her elegant navy shoes discarded on the carpet, her mail, still unopened lying on the floor beside them where she had dropped it in her haste. She knelt down to gather it up, muttering beneath her breath.

When she stood up, he had deposited his packages on the dining-room table and was standing right behind her, causing her to mutter something else as she turned and bumped into him.

His lips twisted as he took her by the shoulders to steady her, and he murmured, 'Busy day, by the look of it,' as she juggled the mail and the sash of her robe which had slipped loose.

She nodded perfunctorily. 'I'll just go and . . . get decent.'

'Decent?' he said softly, his hazel eyes following the little trails of water sliding down her neck and trickling into the valley between her breasts which were now outlined quite clearly beneath the damp, clinging silk.

Kirra swallowed and knew she could do one of two things—break away now, or pretend to be mesmerised and let him have his way . . . up to a point.

She trembled and stared up at him, hoping no flicker of her indecision showed in her eyes, yet wondering what he would expect to see—how she could project a genuinely helpless submission to this moment that had somehow exceeded her plans and expectations.

'I . . .' It was only a breath of sound and her lips closed then quivered as he slid one hand down her robe and laid his forefinger unerringly on the slight mound of her nipple beneath the silk.

If he had branded her, she thought later, the effect could hardly have been more electrifying. All her senses leapt and both her nipples hardened into taut peaks, her eyes widened in surprise, and she dropped the mail again.

'Like that?' he asked, his hazel gaze capturing hers as he circled the throbbing bud of her nipple with his finger and slid his arm around her shoulders.

Kirra closed her eyes and unwittingly laid her head back against his arm. 'Yes,' she gasped as his fingers moved to her other breast, caressingly, circling first then touching the peak so that she shuddered.

'And this?' He bent his head and kissed her throat, sliding his lips down the smooth skin to the hollows at the base of her neck, tasting her at the same time as he slid his hand through her hair, exploring the tender skin of her nape and behind her ears. And his other hand left her breasts and slid around her hips, drawing her into him, moulding her body to the strength and hardness of his.

Kirra whispered something inaudible, perhaps despairing, as she felt herself softening against him, and she tried to concentrate on the fact that she must retain some control, however subtle, of the situation.

But her mind seemed to be moving very slowly, as slowly as his hands were moving on her body, and it was almost impossible to concentrate on anything but the lovely sensations that were running through her, the feel of *him*, the need to respond . . .

She raised her arms and spread her hands on his back, feeling the long muscles through his thin shirt, and she opened her eyes as he lifted his head, and knew he was going to claim her mouth, and that she would not resist.

It was a kiss that left her shuddering in his arms, every nerve-ending quivering, a kiss that left her mouth feeling bruised but her body aching for this intimacy to continue, as if it were a primitive force flowing between them that could not be denied. What surprised her dimly, as she stared up into his eyes, was the absence of any look of triumph.

'Kirra?' His lips barely moved.

'What?' she whispered, but she knew the exact nature of the enquiry in his eyes—or perhaps it was a statement, she thought then, of his undoubted desire for her. He was breathing heavily, she could see, and there was a nerve beating in his jaw, and he was holding her against him still, as if the feel of her body on his was irresistible.

I've got him right where I want him, the thought skimmed her mind, but it was followed immediately by a more honest one—we're in the same boat, and what I'm going to do now is, curiously, what I would have done before I found out, and for the same reason . . .

She lowered her head and rested her brow on his shoulder for a brief moment. Then her body slackened and she dropped her hands to her sides. And she returned his gaze with her blue-grey eyes sombre but steady.

His mouth tightened into a hard line for a second, then he released her abruptly and stepped back and said, 'Is this where I take refuge in a cold shower?'

Kirra licked her lips and stared down at the sash of her robe which she'd started to pleat unconsciously. 'We could go for a swim,' she said with an effort.

He smiled without humour. 'In the dark?'

'It won't be dark for another half-hour.'

'I should have had the foresight to bring some togs,' he said ironically.

'What . . . what did you bring?'

'Dinner,' he said laconically, glancing at the packages on her dining-room table. 'Take-away Italian we could heat up. All right, if you don't mind me going around in damp shorts, let's go.'

'I . . .'

'This was your idea, Kirra.'

She saw the merciless glint in his hazel eyes and turned away defensively.

It was beautiful on the beach, and by mutual, un-spoken consent they walked for a while first, before taking the plunge. The water was cold at first, then the buffeting of the surf was refreshing yet relaxing at the same time. At least, when they came out, at the western horizon was a pure fiery orange streaked with feathery dark clouds, Kirra wrapped her towel around her and found herself feeling tense, although they still had not exchanged a word.

She stared around as Matt dried himself then slung the towel round his neck, and she wondered if the swim had achieved anything for him. And she explored the errant thought that she couldn't help wishing things were simple between them, as clean cut and beautiful as this beach in the sunset, the sea, the sky . . . two people with this undoubted craving for each other's bodies. Surely, she thought, there must be an answering hunger in our souls. But . . .

Her lips parted as a sudden flash of fear gripped her heart, the forerunner of a curious premonition which caused her to plead with herself . . . no, oh, no, not that. *Remember* all he's put you through . . .

'Kirra?'

She blinked and looked up at him, and he took her chin in his hand, his hazel eyes acute and very probing, and the irrational fear that he might be able to see into the depths of her soul, might even be able to mould all her fears and uncertainties into the consequence she knew she could only dread and regret, gave her back her spirit of defiance and hostility, although she was quick to veil it from her eyes.

'I don't know about you, but I'm hungry,' she said huskily. 'I missed out on lunch.'

His eyes narrowed and his fingers on her chin tightened briefly; she shivered slightly but inwardly, because she knew the gauntlet she had thrown down had been picked up, and that the rest of the evening would be a battle of wits from which she could emerge mentally scarred and bleeding if she wasn't cool and cautious—and committed to her cause. She knew, and it gave her a moment's pause, that one of the reasons they could fight this battle at all was that they were beginning to know each other rather well, perhaps too well . . .

She wasn't sure why this should disturb her, like some dark wings brushing her mind, and anyway the thought was so elusive, she had to let it go. And she waited, with patience, for his reaction.

He released her chin. 'Let's eat, then, Miss

Munro,' he said.

'I think I'll have another shower, a quick one,' she said casually when they got back. 'To wash the salt out of my hair. Would you like one?'

He looked at her speculatively. 'No. Just a dry towel, thanks.'

'Oh!' She glanced at his damp shorts. 'If you give those to me, I'll put them in the dryer—they won't take long.'

'Thank you,' he said with a slightly ironic look. 'If you're sure your . . . principles won't feel compromised if I wander around for a while in only a towel?'

'No, they won't,' she replied with deliberate lightness. 'Nor will any of my chairs bear damp patches. Do you think your poor, wounded masculine pride will ever recover?'

She couldn't help the secret little smile of amusement that curved her lips at the cutting hazel glance that flashed her way, but if she thought she'd scored a direct hit, he made an almost instantaneous recovery. He grimaced and said wryly, 'I know now how Mr Cassidy must feel.'

Kirra raised her eyebrows.

'Yes,' he said softly. 'What was it you said to him? "Down, dog—I thought we had an agreement about licking." Or words to that effect. Is that the same technique you used on Jeremy?'

'Jeremy . . .' Kirra bit her lip. 'Let's leave him out of this,' she said quietly.

He shrugged. 'If you prefer. Why don't you go and have that shower? I'll start heating up our dinner.'

Kirra hesitated.

'I'm quite domesticated,' he murmured.

She turned on her heel and left him.

She put on a pair of white shorts and a blue and white sleeveless sailor blouse after her shower, and left her hair loose to dry. While she was tidying up the bedroom, she heard the dryer going on and was annoyed for a second at the thought of him making himself at home in her laundry as well as her kitchen, but she resolutely banished any suggestion of pettiness, and paused to wonder what she had achieved so far tonight. And, with a feathery feeling of apprehension, it occurred to her that rejecting Matt was like playing with fire. But at least I've stated my case, and the fact that he's not forcing me to marry him is immaterial. Once more, though, how to go on? Perhaps I can only play it by ear . . .

When she emerged from the bedroom, it was to see the low glass-topped table in the lounge set with cutlery and two napkins, wineglasses, a dish of parmesan cheese and a salad. She raised an eyebrow and went into the kitchen.

He'd bought canelloni and he was dishing it out of the foil containers as she came in. She couldn't help sniffing appreciatively.

'Smells good, doesn't it?'

'Smells delicious,'she agreed.

'Do you mind if we eat in the lounge?'

'Not at all. We can watch the news or whatever's on. I'll bring the wine.' He had even, she noticed, filled her silver bucket with ice, and the wine was in it, already opened.

They ate sitting side by side on the settee, and thanks to *The Good Life*, which happened to be on television, Kirra was able to relax and even laugh a little.

'That was an old one but a good one,' she said,

pushing away her plate and leaning back with her wineglass.

Matt stood up and collected the plates.

'I'll do the dishes later,' she said, but he took no notice, leaving only the wine behind, and she heard the tap running in the kitchen as he rinsed everything.

She stood up herself after a couple of minutes, to change the television channel, but nothing appealed and she switched it off and listened to the relative silence. This was broken by the sound of the dryer door opening, and she wondered if he was leaving.

He certainly re-appeared wearing his shorts instead of a towel, but as their gazes caught and held across the room her skin prickled and she felt the tension building up again, and she knew the second—or was it the third—round of this bout was set to begin.

She bent her head briefly, then looked up at him and said quietly, 'What now?'

He strolled over to the settee, poured more wine into both their glasses and sat down with his. 'You choose—I'm easy.' He raised his glass in a mocking little toast.

Kirra tried to compose her thoughts, and finally could only fall back on honesty. She pushed her hair back wearily. 'It would be nice just to relax.'

He raised an eyebrow. 'Do you think it's possible?'

'I . . . it *should* be,' she said with a sudden intensity that took even her by surprise.

'Care to sit down and elaborate?' he queried.

'If you intend to,' she started to say tautly, 'to . . .'

'I don't intend to *force* my attentions on you, Kirra,' he drawled.

She bit her lip frustratedly, then sat down with a fair length of the settee between them, and picked up her glass. 'Perhaps what I'm trying to say is this,' she stared down at the glass in her hand then raised her eyes to his, 'if a marriage is not to be the kind of shambles your parents had, there have to be times when you can relax together in tenderness and affection and . . . tolerance and humour.'

'Sure,' he agreed. 'After the loving—and it's possible to have those things between a man and a woman outside of marriage . . .'

'We're not talking about that,' Kirra broke in.

'If I am, it's to make you aware I am capable of that,' he said deliberately.

'But only *after* the loving,' Kirra said ironically. 'Or to be more specific, the sex.'

He shrugged. 'It's generally what generates those other feelings.'

'If,' Kirra said slowly, 'we went to bed now, say, and we found it didn't generate the rest, would you release me from our . . . contract?'

'No.' His gaze was slightly amused, mostly enigamtic.

'Just . . . no?'

'I'm afraid so.'

'And you're not at all afraid it will be that kind of a shambles?' she asked meditatively.

He thought for a moment, then said, 'The elements of my parents' marriage that made it such a mess will be lacking in ours, Kirra, because we're making a commitment to marriage.'

She laid her head back. 'Not to each other, but to the institution, in other words. Wouldn't it be strange if we fell in love one day?'

He was silent for so long, she turned her head to look at him at last, to surprise an oddly grim look in his eyes. 'Of course, you don't believe in that, do you?' she said softly. 'It's sentimental fairy-tale to you, whereas to me . . .' She paused. 'Do you know what the main difference between us is?' she asked then, and went on without waiting for a reply, 'You mistrust the emotional side of love, while I mistrust the physical side. If ever the twain were to meet . . . who knows what the outcome would be.'

'What are you trying to say, Kirra?' he said at last with a faint frown.

'I'm just . . . meditating, I guess. Just as I can't help meditating about sleeping with you, sometimes, to be perfectly honest. And how my famous inhibitions would react. Whether you could turn my rather timid inexperience into the kind of naked desire that would match yours.'

'There's one way to find that out,' he said, barely audibly.

'Yes,' she agreed, but almost absently. 'Do you ever wonder what it will be like to have the responsibility for the well-being, the real well-being of a woman on your hands? Have you ever thought of it like that?'

'Have you?'

'Yes, I have—lately I've thought of it quite a lot. Perhaps they're not very emancipated or liberated thoughts to have, but then in my case, I'm not in a very liberated situation. You're expecting me to . . . put my life in your hands, to regard you as my anchor, my solace through the years and pain of childbearing and rearing and growing old. If I were to tell you that the thought of going through all that without the prospect of you finding any joy, real joy in me, is . . .' She broke off and shivered, and sat up abruptly.

'Kirra,' he said harshly, 'you were all set to do that

to yourself only months ago.'

'Yes,' she whispered and turned to stare at him gravely. 'You've certainly . . . taught me a few lessons about myself one way or another, Matt,' she said huskily, and added, 'the hard way. Would you like a cup of coffee?'

'No.' He reached over and took her wrist. 'Don't run away now.'

'I'm not. Where is there to run?'

'Tell me this, then—if I weren't forcing you to marry me, would you sleep with me now, Kirra?' His eyes held hers and they were grim again, and his fingers hard on her wrists.

'Is that all you ever think of?'

'And you don't? You just told me you did.'

'I . . .' She took an uncertain breath.

'Would you?' he persisted.

'No.'

'Just . . . no?' he mimicked.

'I'd be mad to, wouldn't I, Matt?' she said very steadily, suddenly finding her thoughts crystallising to a degree of stunning clarity. 'What then would be the difference between me and all those women who latched on to your father, all the women, for all I know, who've done the same to you? What prospects would I have of not being loved and—left?

'You know, all the lessons haven't only been self-revealing. They've taught me something else—you've despised a lot of women for doing just that—sleeping with you in seemingly casual circumstances, but perhaps hoping to pin you down. Oh no, and with all I know, of you were asking me to marry you, I'd be mad to do that as well.'

'Those are very lofty sentiments, Kirra.'

'What's the point of going through the mill if you

don't aim for something higher?' she retorted and added, 'I gather you're not going to defend the charges.'

He smiled for the first time, a cool, slow smile. 'No. What you said is probably true to a degree. Incidentally, you're putting up a great fight, my dear.' He released her wrist, and added softly, 'Even better than I expected. There is just this to consider. You're going to have to sleep with me sooner or later —don't make things too hard for yourself when the time comes, will you?'

Kirra stared at him and said equally softly, and with a curious glint in her blue-grey eyes, 'I'll make things as hard as I can—for both of us.'

His lips twisted. 'That's my Kirra,' he said and stood up. 'I'm off to Adelaide for a few days, incidentally. I'll be in touch as soon as I get back. Any . . . last thoughts you'd care to add?'

'No. Have you?'

He narrowed his eyes and searched her still, slightly pale face probingly. And when he said he hadn't, Kirra got the impression he'd been about to say something else and changed his mind, and for some reason her skin prickled again and those same elusive thoughts she had encountered on the beach brushed her mind but remained as elusive.

He left without attempting to touch her, although something, she thought, had flowed between them. Some indefinable current that she could only dimly identify as the binding of two enemies locked on a collision course and, even in their discord, or perhaps because of it, acutely aware of each other.

She took the thought to bed with her, turning it over and over in her mind and asking herself why she should be preoccupied with it instead of, for instance, how well she was succeeding in turning the tables on him.

The days passed until nearly a week had gone by with no word from him and as they passed she became restless and edgy, and even began to wonder if he was playing hard to get. That it should occupy her thoughts to the degree it was concerned her, but, when his secretary rang her and spoke to her with distant hauteur, another possibility occurred to Kirra —and had the effect of temporarily enraging her.

CHAPTER NINE

'MISS MUNRO? Miss Kirra Munro?'

'Yes?' Kirra said into the phone, just before she was due to leave for work.

'It's June Daly here, Mr Remington's private secretary. He's asked me to advise you that he's been delayed in Adelaide—not to mention indisposed.' The last part was said reprovingly.

'Indisposed?'

'Er . . . yes, a virus by the sound of it. What he needs is a holiday, but he doesn't take the slightest notice of me. Be that as it may, he said he would call you when it was possible.'

Don't call us, we'll call you . . . The phrase shot through Kirra's mind. I wonder . . .

'Is . . . is he on the coast?' she asked, managing to sound almost diffident as her brian worked overtime.

'He gets in at lunch time.'

'Well, thank you . . . oh! I wonder if I could have this address.' How ridiculous, she thought. I don't even know where he lives.

'I'm afraid it's not my place to hand out Mr Remington's address,' said June Daly stiffly.

'I was only . . . thinking of sending him some fruit to . . . cheer him up,' Kirra said, improvising madly.'

'If you'd like to send it to the office, Miss Munro, I'll see it gets passed on.'

'How kind of you!' Kirra said brightly. 'Thank

you,' But it was with a great effort that she restrained herself from slamming down the phone. Yet it was more than June Daly's manner —although Kirra did think briefly, How dare she? Who the hell does she think she is? that caused Kirra's eyes to glint with anger and her fists to clench so that her nails dug into her palms. It was the thought that Matt Remington might be choosing to end the farce before she'd had the pleasure of getting her own back.

'Well, well,' she whispered, 'we'll have to see about that.' And she picked up the phone again and rang Stanley.

'Stanley—do you think Dad would have made a note of Mr Remington's home address? I—er —I've been invited to a party and I'd like to ask him.' This was true enough––it was Marcus and Pippa's house-warming on Sunday night, and they would undoubtedly be delighted if she took Matthew Remington—they just didn't know it yet.

'I can tell you that, Kirra,' Stanley said down the line. 'Your father got me to deliver some papers to him one night. Uh . . . it's the Biarritz building, Old Burleigh Road, and it's number . . .'

Kirra wrote the number down carefully. 'Fancy that,' she murmured. 'I know it well.' Then she thanked Stanley and mentioned she'd had a card from her parents and that they seemed to be enjoying themselves.

She thought for a bit after putting down the phone, then went off to work.

The Biarritz apartment building was situated slightly removed from the high-rise jungle of Surfers' and the streets around it were quiet and leafy. As the sun set, Kirra entered the luxurious lobby and took the lift to the fourteenth floor with a distinct feeling of *déjà vu*. The feeling was heightened as she stepped out of the lift and looked around, because she was almost sure the number she sought would be on a door that would open up to marble floors faintly pink-tinged in the lounge and dining-room, a wall of mirrors, marble tables, beautiful rugs, a plain white couch and two Chinese chairs with brass inlays and yellow velvet seats, duplicated in the dining-room suite, a pristine white kitchen.

She knocked on the door and waited, wondering what she would do if he wasn't home.

He was.

It was hard to say who was more taken aback as he opened the door. Kirra was certainly surprised at the way he looked, his eyes heavy-lidded, his face lined in a way that made him look older, blue shadows on his jaw. He'd discarded the jacket of a dark blue suit, and his shirt sleeves were half rolled up untidily, and his tie loosened.

He also, after a blink of surprise to see her on his doorstep, looked distinctly unenthusiastic, which caused her to tighten her lips momentarily as he said, 'Kirra—what are you doing here?'

'I heard you were . . . indisposed.'

'Who the hell told you that?'

'Your Miss Daly—or perhaps it's Mrs Daly. She sounded cross because you always disregard her advice, about taking holidays, for example.'

He looked irritated beyond words. 'She tries to mother me, and I didn't ask her to tell you I was sick which I'm not.'

'You don't look very well.'

'That's none of her business, and besides . . . '

'Oh, don't worry. She wouldn't reveal your address. I had to scrounge around for that! But seriously, you don't . . .'

'Now, don't *you* start, Kirra.'

'Do we have to conduct this conversation on the doorstep?' she broke in. 'We are engaged to be married, after all,' she added sweetly.

He stared at her, then moved aside to let her in.

Nothing had been changed in the main rooms, she saw, which struck her as ironic. And an open leather briefcase stood on the floor beside the dining-room table which was littered with papers.

'You're not still working?' Kirra asked, observing this together with the silver pen and his gold-rimmed glasses, which looked as if they had been flung down impatiently.

'Why not?' he countered. 'If you've come to play Florence Nightingale, I told you I'm not . . .'

'Were you sick?' she asked coolly.

He shrugged. 'It was only one of those twenty-four hour viruses.'

'Which leaves you feeling like death warmed up, and looking it,' she supplied. 'Have you eaten this evening?'

'Not . . . yet.'

'Then I'll make you something,' she said quietly. 'And don't argue with me, please. If it's all right for you to take out my splinters—and feed me—it's all right for me to do this. Call it reciprocity, if you like.'

He grimaced, then grinned twistedly. 'I don't know that I've got anything much to make.'

She lifted up her string bag and put it on the kitchen counter. 'I came prepared,' she said calmly. 'Provided it doesn't take too long, you could finish off what you're doing—then clear it up.'

He hesitated briefly, then said ruefully, 'Yes, sir.'

Kirra had bought seasoned chicken breasts which she fried until they were crisp and golden, and a carton of cooked rice and raisins and nuts that she warmed up. She made a fresh salad, then looked around for a cheese-board but had to make do with a large platter for the smoked cheese she had bought with biscuits, two juicy nectarines and a bunch of grapes. The state of his cupboards and fridge spoke volumes—he rarely ate at home. Her other purchase had been a crusty loaf of bread.

She went unerringly to the linen cupboard for a tablecloth and napkins and just before she dished up, to the guest bathroom.

'You seem to know your way around here, Kirra,' he said thoughtfully, as she set the meal out on the table.

'I do. I helped decorate it.'

'So,' he said, unfurling his napkin and shooting her a hazel, lazy glance, 'I've virtually been living with a part of you ever since I bought the place—it was newly decorated when I bought it. That's rather ironic, isn't it?'

She could only agree, but said, 'I didn't do it all. But I did find the Chinese chairs and the lamps and —if it's still in the main bedroom, the painting.' She stopped abruptly, because that particular painting was of a half-naked woman with only a gauzy skirt on, rising up out of a flowery meadowland. It had been a half-humorous touch on Kirra's part, but she'd also thought it was beautifully done, hazy but with a lovely quality of light and pearly skin tones.

For the first time that evening, as she looked across at him with a tinge of defiance, she read genuine amusement in his eyes, and he said softly, 'She's still there to tantalise me from time to time.'

Kirra coloured and, to cover it, implemented the next part of her plan. 'Do you think you'll be one hundred per cent by Sunday?'

'Of course. Why?' He looked at her enquiringly.

'I've been invited to a party.'

He pushed his plate away. 'That was very nice. Thanks.'

'Well?' she asked with a challenging gleam in her eye that she couldn't quite hide.

He leant back in his chair, one hand on the table fiddling absently with a spoon. 'What kind of a party?'

'Very elegant, I've no doubt.' She caught herself sounding sardonic and went on swiftly, 'It's a house-warming, they're rather good friends of mine. He's an architect and she's an old school-friend.'

'Have you told them about us?'

'No.'

'Do you intend to?'

'Not on Sunday night. Is there some reason why you'd rather not come? They know a lot of the best people.'

For an instant she thought she saw a flicker of contempt in his eyes, then it was gone. Still, it was with a rather dry smile that he said, 'It appears to me you've changed tactics, Kirra. If I seem reluctant, it's because I can't help wondering what you're up to.'

'Tactics?' she said softly, but with a little flame of anger causing her eyes to look bluer. 'I can't imagine why I didn't think of indulging in them sooner! Still, I'm learning. It must be,' she smiled, 'from . . . associating with a master tactician like yourself.'

He said nothing, but studied her dispassionately for a time. Then he remarked almost grimly, 'If you're regretting the physical closeness we achieved last time we met, in spite of our differences . . .'

'Oh, I am,' she broke in. 'You've hit the nail on the head.'

He didn't respond, just kept turning the spoon over and over in his long fingers. Then he dropped it and rubbed his forehead briefly.

Kirra stared at him, then said reluctantly, 'Have you . . . got a headache?'

He shrugged.

'Have you *taken* anything for it?'

'I will . . . all right, I'll come to the . . . party.' Something glinted in his eyes she couldn't decipher. 'What time would you care to be collected, Miss Munro?'

Kirra bit her lip, then shot him a dark look. 'Seven, but only if you feel up to it.' She got up and gathered some plates. 'Would there be anything like a simple aspirin around?'

He looked amused and pointed to a kitchen cupboard. She got out two and took them to him with a glass of water. 'Don't . . . just don't argue,' she warned him wearily. 'Is there anything else you'd like? A cup of tea?'

He nodded after a moment.

She was just pouring it when she heard his chair scrape back, and tensed as he came into the kitchen. But he didn't touch her, just leant back against the counter and folded his arms.

Then he said, with a smile twisting his lips, 'So you came here to fight with me tonight, not smother me with tender loving care, Kirra.'

'I did cook you a meal,' she pointed out. 'Here's your tea. Why don't you take it into the lounge while I clear up?'

'I would certainly hesitate to do anything else with you in this mood of extreme militancy,' he said. 'Except to assure you that by Sunday I should be . . . fighting fit.'

Kirra looked at him expressionlessly.

'Unless,' he said softly, 'you'd like to come to bed with me now? That might restore me better than anything else.'

'Take your tea and go,' she advised him.

'Small comfort,' he said with a wry twitch of his lips, but he did as he was told.

She watched him as he strolled into the lounge, put his cup down and pulled off his tie. Then she switched her gaze back to the task at hand.

Ten minutes later, she glanced over the counter again to see that he'd fallen asleep sprawled back on the settee. She finished off as quietly as she could and moved around switching off all the lamp but one, then stood staring down at him.

Sleep, she saw, had smoothed away the lines of weariness and strain, and it occurred to her that her rush of emotion as to whether she was being 'brushed off' might have been misplaced. Well, in this instance, at least, she mused. He's obviously been ill and he's just as obviously very tired. He also might be one of those men who genuinely hate being fussed over when they're sick.

Then she discovered how hard it was to tear her gaze away and her heart started to beat heavily, so heavily that she sat down in the Chinese chair beside the settee where she could watch him, and for the first time admitted the possibilty that despite whatever she might say to herself to the contrary, however she might try to rationalise her feelings, and his, she was trapped. She was fighting this battle, in other words, not to avenge herself, but because she was falling deeper and deeper in love with him—she was fighting for her life.

She moved restlessly, then looked at him anxiously, but he didn't stir and she asked herself how, why? The answers were plain enough. Why else had she been like a cat on a hot tin roof this past week, if it wasn't because she'd actually missed him? Why else would she be so anxious not to join the list of women he despised, and be able to understand why it was that way for him, and be able to hate his cynicism . . . but not him?

'Oh God,' she whispered, 'that's what's been eluding me, I'm fighting this for real. Does he know? Is *he* aware of this dangerous closeness that I can't change, even if it's often bitter? Or is he still playing me like a fish on a line?'

She closed her eyes on tears of confusion and despair, then left very quietly.

Sunday was a tense uncomfortable day.

Away from him, she was uncertain again and almost feverishly trying to persuade herself that she could not have fallen in love with a man who didn't believe in it.

Then, early in the afternoon, she suddenly realised she had forgotten to get a present for

Pippa and Marcus, and she racked her brains for a solution to the problem, until she remembered Min's beautifully carved bookends. She dashed over to the office, praying no one else had nabbed them. But they were still there, and she left an IOU for them and rushed home with them thankfully.

But why am I *rushing* everything? she wondered, back in her apartment with the afternoon stretching emptily ahead of her. Everything about me is off key, out of tune, and I'm so afraid it's because . . .

But she wouldn't allow herself to think that thought. She *couldn't*. The prospect was too humiliating.

She started to get ready quite early, earlier than necessary—anything to pass the time. She was never quite sure what prompted her to wear what she did. At least, afterwards, she couldn't help wondering if she had surrendered to some subconscious urge, although at the time she'd only been determined to look her best.

She washed and blow-dried her hair, and for a change put it up on top of her head in a simple knot. It looked elegant, she decided, and made her look, if not older, more mature, somehow, more serious, although there was one disadvantage, it made her eyes look larger. And if your eyes are the window to your soul, she reflected rather grimly, that could be a serious disavantage. But she tightened her lips and left it up.

The next step was her underwear, and it was blatantly seductive—an all-in-one black lace garment that combined the functions of bra and suspender-belt with delicious, sensuous frivolity, that caressed her skin and caused it to gleam enticingly, and surprisingly had been a gift from her mother. In fact, Kirra had thought she'd got over being surprised by her mother, but this gift had proved her wrong. It was a crime not to wear this kind of thing while you'd still got the figure for it, her mother had said with a naughty little twinkle in her eye.

This was probably why it was hard for Kirra to associate the garment with any kind of sin, and anyway, she discovered she loved wearing the sheerest of stockings with it rather than tights.

The dress she put on was a deep shade of corn-flower-blue, figure-hugging with narrow shoulder straps, a tantalising little opening between her breasts, and a slash up the front from ankle to knee-line. It was a dress she'd worn before and not considered particularly daring.

She sat down to do her face, but even this procedure, done carefully and delicately, still left her with about forty-five minutes to kill. She looked around despairingly, but her bedroom was tidy, the rest of the apartment was tidied within an inch of its life, witness to a punishing bout of housekeeping yesterday, and there was nothing for her to do but sit and wait.

She shrugged and slipped on her grey kid shoes that were several shades darker than her stockings and wondered if she needed a drink to steady her nerves, but the thought annoyed her acutely.

So it was that all in all, by the time seven o'clock came around, she had worked herself into a state of simmering hostility and resentment.

'Come in,' she said carefully, opening the door to him. Her bare skimming glance took in his beautifully tailored grey suit, paler grey and white striped shirt, and blue tie. 'We have time for a drink, if you like.'

'No, thanks.' He followed her into the lounge. 'But . . .'

'Then I'll get my bag,' she said abruptly.

'Won't that make us early?' he asked idly, catching her hand as she went to sweep past him.

'Who cares?' she asked, staring at him tautly, hating him for his tall, cool composure when she felt the way she did.

'If that's the case,' he said abruptly, 'why are we bothering to go to this party at all?'

'Because it's better than sitting here, feeling trapped.' Her blue-grey eyes were defiant and her voice bitter.

'Trapped?' he questioned softly and with something like a glint of anger in his eyes. 'Or . . . wanting to do something else altogether? Such as this.' He released her hand and drew her into his arms.

Kirra shivered with a mixture of apprehension and anger, and he felt it and pulled her even closer with a mocking little smile. 'So fresh and perfumed and gorgeously groomed,' he marvelled. 'And as furious as a beautiful tigress wanting to be tamed, wanting it all to be undone, wanting to be stripped naked and thrown down on a bed, wanting to fight but be overpowered and . . . taken.'

'You . . .' she hissed, one hand unwittingly curling to claw his eyes out. 'That's disgusting!'

'Is it?' He released her and stared down at her sombrely. 'I think it's often the nature of things between men and women, whether we like it or not. Love is often savage and a lot of things we like to think it isn't.'

'You're talking about lust!'

'Call it what you like,' he said indifferently, 'just don't try to deny it exists between us by whatever name.'

'Right now, I'm prepared to deny it to the grave,' she said through her teeth. 'I . . . I'd rather consort with a . . . with a . . .'

'Snake?' he offered, barely audibly but with a glint in his hazel eyes that frightened her suddenly, made her catch her breath and wonder how he would retaliate, because she knew instinctively that he would.

She turned away jerkily.

But all he said, dispassionately she thought, was, 'Go and get your bag, then.'

She went with every nerve jangling and the heart-stopping, humiliating thought that he might have been right, that her feelings *had* descended to a savage desire for physical expression.

She stared at her bed and felt her cheeks begin to burn as the images he had triggered swept through her mind. 'No,' she whispered, appalled at what she was thinking, and she reached for her bag clumsily—and heard one of her sheer, beautiful grey stockings go ping.

She looked down and saw the ladder climbing to her knee. '*Damn*!' she muttered furiously.

She threw her bag back down on the bed and undid the stocking through the silky material of her dress. Then she hunted through a drawer, but the only grey ones she could find were a new pair and much lighter, which meant she would have to change both stockings. She kicked off her shoes and discarded the wrapping of cellophane and cardboard on to the floor, then started to peel the others off in a fever of irritation.

She never knew what alerted her, he'd made no sound on the thick carpeting, but just as she was standing on one foot with her dress hitched up around her hips, and just as she was securing the second of the new stockings on the leg poised on the end of the bed with her foot arched, she glanced up and he was there, standing in the doorway, watching her.

Her hands stilled and her heart started to beat erratically at the way he was watching her, and she followed his gaze to where her hands rested, to where the gauzy grey stocking gave way to the ivory, satin-smooth skin of her inner thigh.

Her lashes lifted and she looked over at him again, to see that curiously heavy-lidded gaze move up her. She glanced down, to see that because of the way she was standing with one shoulder slightly forward, the creamy and black-lace-shadowed curve of one breast was exposed where the opening at the front of her dress had fallen forward.

She looked up again and their gazes caught and held; she felt oddly naked but hypnotised beneath that all-encompassing hazel gaze. Then she forced herself to break the moment. She closed the last suspender unhurriedly and stood upright, smoothing the cornflower-blue silk as it slid down her body. Finally, she raised her chin and stared at him coolly.

But as he moved and strolled across the carpet towards her, she began to regret her hauteur and recall the instinctive feeling she'd had that he wouldn't allow her last insult to pass unavenged. She was not proved wrong.

He stopped right in front of her so that she had

to tilt her head back to look up at him.

'When we're married,' he drawled and raised a hand to trail his fingers very lightly down the valley between her breasts, then smooth the material closed, 'you'll need some new clothes.'

Surprise made Kirra blink, which he observed with his lips twisting into a cool smile, although his eyes were not smiling. 'Yes,' he added thoughtfully. 'Because I don't think I'll enjoy other men seeing your breasts and . . . lusting after you, from my own point of view, but also from yours—you who have such an inbuilt dislike of it, or so you tell me.'

Sheer shock held Kirra rigid, her lips parted, her eyes darkening, but that only brought another cool smile to his lips and a glint of mockery to his eyes. Then he said casually, 'Shall we go?'

'Darling!' Pippa breathed into Kirra's ear some time after they had arrived. 'Why didn't you tell me?'

Kirra stiffened and said warily, 'Tell you what?'

'Why you were so interested in Matthew Remington!'

'Oh, that,' Kirra said lamely.

'Yes, that,' Pippa said ruefully. 'Do I detect an air of mystery in your manner?'

'Not . . .' Kirra broke off and bit her lip.

Pippa narrowed her eyes thoughtfully. 'He is . . . well, he almost defies description, doesn't he?'

He does that all right, Kirra thought bitterly.

'Or to put it right, Kirra thought bitterly. one stumbles through this jungle of life, one observes from time to time a king of the jungle, a man among men for whom you'd gladly sell your soul, despite the fact that you love your cuddly little husband.'

Despite *her* state of mind and the unfortunate allusion to jungles, Kirra couldn't help smiling, not only at Pippa's extravagant imagery, but because while Pippa was lean and elegant, Marcus was short as well as short-sighted, alternately earnest and playful, and bore no resemblance to the tiger king. But her smile was short-lived.

Pippa watched her expression change and she said slowly, 'Perhaps not an easy man to know, though. Want to tell me how things . . . stand between you?'

'Oh, Pip,' Kirra said, suddenly unable to hide the distress in her eyes, 'I wish I *knew*.'

Pippa looked concerned, then pressed Kirra's hand. 'If ever you do need a good listener, I'm always willing,' she said gently. 'Why don't you just relax and enjoy yourself for now?'

It was a successful party.

The new house was a dream, but then with Marcus and Pippa's combined talents it would have been surprising had it not been.

What surprised and amused a lot of people, although not Kirra, was their hosts' touching pride in it all—everyone got a complete guided tour of even the bathrooms, linen cupboard and laundry.

What did surprise Kirra was how many people seemed to know Matt, mostly men, admittedly, but their wives or girlfriends were obviously flattered and impressed to be introduced.

They ate caviare and lobster, drank champagne and danced on the red-flagged terrace beneath the stars—some even went for a swim in the floodlit pool.

Kirra visited one of Marcus's pride-and-joy bathrooms and, coming back, lingered for a moment just inside the lounge, where she could see Matt dancing with a languorous blonde, without being seen. And, as she watched, she saw him say something that made her laugh with no trace of languor.

Is that *expertise,* or just because he's *nice*? Kirra thought with a stab of resentment. He's certainly not making her feel like a tramp. I bet he would only have to snap his fingers and she'd leap . . . Oh hell, Kirra, you're not jealous, surely?

After midnight the party got livelier and noisier, but Kirra merely got more tired. It was an unbelievable strain dancing with Matt—it was a strain dancing with anyone, because she kept wondering how the front of her dress was behaving and kept getting angry with herself for bothering. Will this night never end? she asked herself wearily.

He chose to end it, for them at least, at about one-thirty. He said, 'You look as if you've had enough.'

She nodded, keeping her eyes veiled. And for the first time that evening he displayed some possessiveness. He took her hand and kept it in his while they made their farewells. And he held it as they walked down the driveway to the car, then he raised an eyebrow at her. 'Up or down?' He indicated the hood.

'Oh, down, I think,' she said. 'It's a beautiful night.'

She didn't protest when it became obvious they were not going straight home. Nor did she say anything when he parked the car beside a moonlit stretch of beach. She sat for a time watching and listening to the surf, then she put her hands up to her hair which was windblown and coming adrift, and eased the pins out and with a sigh of relief ran her fingers through it and laid her head back.

He turned to her and propped one arm along the back of the seat. 'You've been very quiet tonight, Kirra.'

'Sometimes champagne has that effect on me. Dulls the edges.' Something has dulled the rage anyway, she reflected. Was it the thought that it could have been the reverse side of a compelling desire to . . . submit?

'So it has nothing to do with what I said to you before the party?'

She turned her face to him without lifting her head. 'Of course it has,' she said with no anger, just sounding drained and weary.

'I'm sorry.'

'Are you?' she whispered after an age, staring at him, at the way the moonlight glinted on his fair hair, the lines of his face, the way he was tracing the spokes of the steering-wheel and watching what he was doing so that she couldn't read his eyes.

'Doesn't that help?' he said, looking up at last.

'It doesn't help the way I feel about myself.' She said it slowly and quietly, and a spark of irony flickered in her blue-grey eyes, then they focused on him again, her lashes forming perfect dark crescents, her face pale and curiously young looking.

'Are we getting closer to naming the day?'

Why did I ask that? she wondered immediately, and as soon as he spoke, knew.

He said drily, 'I'll consult my diary.'

She closed her eyes and thought, I was hoping you'd be honest with me and end this farce right now—that's why I asked that. Why don't I end it? What am I hoping for—a miracle?

She sat up abruptly. 'Could you take me home now?'

'Kirra . . .'

'*Please*—I'm tired.' Her voice was hoarse with sudden urgency.

He captured her chin and forced her to look at him, but some lingering spark of defiance made her lower her lashes and clamp her lips together until he smiled as drily as he'd spoken earlier, and released her to start the car up.

The drive home was swift and silent, so silent that she thought she could hear the clock ticking.

He didn't get out, he didn't even switch the engine off in the forecourt of her building. And all he said was, 'I'll be in touch.'

Kirra slipped out of the car and ran inside without a backward glance.

CHAPTER TEN

MIN surprised her the following morning by arriving unexpectedly.

She popped her head around Kirra's office door and said gaily, 'They're finished, done, and I hope to God you like them, otherwise I'll take them out and drown them!'

'Min! Glory be, that was quick work! Come in, it's great to see you. And I'm sure you won't have to drown them—how do you drown dolphins, anyway?'

Min chuckled. 'I'd have found a way. I brought one panel in to show you,' she had a heavy-looking parcel under her arm, 'and the rest are in the car.'

Min's dolphin panels were a great hit, and she secured two more commissions on the spot.

'Come and have lunch with me,' Kirra said impulsively.

'It should be my shout after . . .'

'Nonsense! You did all the work the last time we met—it's definitely mine!'

They chatted idly for a while over lunch, then Min said, 'How's Matt?'

'Fine. You haven't seen him since . . .?'

'No. It goes like that. Sometimes I don't see him for months. Are you . . . is he . . . are you two still together?' Min asked awkwardly.

Kirra studied her quiche rather attentively, then she sighed and said, 'As together as we're ever likely to be.'

'Would you like to tell me about it?' said Min gently.

'I . . .' Kirra hesitated.

'There would be no question of me ever repeating anything to Matt. He may be my friend, but you and I . . . well, I regard you as a friend, too.'

Kirra smiled at her and said quietly, 'Thanks. Well . . .' And to her surprise, she found herself telling Min everything. '. . . and when I discovered the contracts *were* signed, that he'd only been toying with me, I was . . . I was——' She broke off and grimaced. 'There's an old saying about hell having no fury like a woman scorned—I can vouch for it.'

'Because you'd fallen in love with him?' Min queried.

'That condition is something I've only fairly recently admitted to.' Kirra pushed her plate away. 'It was relatively easy to pretend otherwise while I thought he was forcing me to marry him. But much as I'd still like to think I hate him, I . . . I . . . it's as if my whole being is *centred* on him. It's very hard to explain,' she said helplessly. 'It's just as if he's the focus of my existence. When he's not around I can't settle to anything, when he is I alternate between . . . wanting him desperately and feeling as if I could kill him—anything.'

She winced and looked away, but when she looked back Min was only looking extremely thoughtful.

'Sorry,' said Kirra shakily. 'I didn't mean to sound so dramatic, nor do I always feel quite so violent about it. But I think,' she said slowly, 'there's only one thing I can do now, and that's put as much distance between us as I can.'

'There's something I don't understand, though,' Min said. 'If it's as you say, he's gone to extraordinary lengths either to teach you a lesson or to avenge his masculine pride, don't you think?'

Kirra shrugged. 'Perhaps he thought—well, here's one witless bird I *can* teach a lesson.'

'Do you honestly believe that?' Min asked softly.

'If I knew what to believe, I might not be in this mess. I can't help but believe women don't stand very high in his esteem.'

'That's true—*certain* kinds of women, and probably for all the usual reasons that good-looking, wealthy men are rather wary. But I happen to be . . . living proof, if you like, that he doesn't despise all women. You know,' Min paused, and there was suddenly a far-away look in her eyes, 'I sometimes wondered if it wasn't himself he despised.'

Kirra stared at her with her lips parted.

'For,' Min paused again, 'inheriting his father's fatal attraction for women. Perhaps, despite himself, *that's* the root of some of his cynicism.'

'I . . . oh!' Kirra said, barely audibly.

'Yes,' Min agreed.

Kirra was silent, then she said, almost to herself, 'He is . . . the only time or one of the very few times I've got beneath his skin has been in relation to his father. I mean, he told me quite readily he didn't like him and why, but . . . once, anyway, I thought there might be more to it, although I couldn't put my finger on it. On the other hand,' she said with a frown, 'he hasn't exactly gone out of his way to . . . do things differently from his father, has he?'

'Hasn't he?' Min murmured. 'He's committed himself to no one—sure, he's played the field and probably often with the sort of indifference that's tantamount to a calculated insult. Perhaps it's even been a test,' Min moved her hands, 'a sort of standing back and saying, if all it takes is a bit of physical expertise . . .' She grimaced, then went on, 'I can't believe it was indifference that prompted him to do this to you, though, Kirra. I think you must have hit a nerve.'

Kirra put a hand to her mouth. 'If I thought understanding would help . . . And I do understand, but how to get across that I do?'

'Maybe you can only love him,' Min said wisely.

Kirra thought about what Min had said all that afternoon, and that evening she stayed at home in case Matt rang, but he didn't.

Instead, he took her to lunch the next day. He simply turned up at her office doorway much as Min had done the day before, and the unexpectedness of looking up and seeing him caught her off guard, so that a tide of pink rose up in her cheeks, her pulses started to hammer and she got up jerkily, knocking over a glazed pottery urn standing on her desk.

It was he who strode forward to catch it before it hit the floor.

'Oh . . . thank God,' she breathed.

'Valuable?' he asked.

'Very, and very old. I don't know how I came to be so clumsy.'

He said gravely, 'I didn't mean to startle you so.'

'You didn't,' she said, then coloured because that was patently untrue.

But he didn't comment, and he put the urn down carefully and ran his hands over it. Then he stepped back and studied her thoughtfully, until she smoothed her buttercup linen dress uncomfortably and said foolishly, 'Did you want to see me about something?'

A faint smile twisted his lips. 'I just wanted to see

you. Can I buy you lunch?'

She stared at him and felt her stomach churn with the knowledge that here was the opportunity to do what she knew she had to—if she was brave enough.

'Thanks,' she said quietly. 'It so happens I've got the afternoon off.'

He took her to Nicolini's at Mariner's Cove, and they sat outside on the veranda beneath the awning, with the Broadwater stretching away from them, dancing in the sunlight and studded with millions of dollars'-worth of boats at their moorings.

They both chose prawns Nicolini and a salad—and Kirra could think of nothing to say, no way to begin . . .

Nor did he make any move to push the conversation until they were half finished, when he said idly, watching her as her gaze rested on a sleek, gleaming, fly-bridge cruiser, 'Would you like a boat for a wedding present?'

Kirra averted her gaze hastily. 'No, thank you.'

'That's a pity—we could have called it the *Lady Kirralee*,' he drawled. 'What would you like? You could have almost anything in reason, you know.'

'Is that . . .' her voice quivered, 'why you asked me to lunch? To insult me?' Their eyes clashed, and hers were more blue than grey, like the water beside them, and suddenly very steady as she added, 'To continue to insult me, I should have said.'

He raised an eyebrow. 'I gather this is where we . . . deal in the truth. What, as a matter of interest, decided you to show your hand at last?'

'You knew I knew?' she queried incredulously.

'I guessed,' he murmured. 'You had to find out sooner or later.'

'Your . . . sheer cold-bloodedness is almost

unbelievable,' Kirra said with an effort.

'Is it?' he said softly. 'The offer is still open, by the way. Will you marry me, Kirra?'

'If this is another . . .'

'It's not. Will you?'

She searched his eyes dazedly. 'I don't understand.'

'That I want to marry you?'

'No—no, I don't.'

'You don't agree that we're rather well matched?' he said, and his hazel eyes were suddenly compelling.

'Have I . . . have I passed some sort of test I wasn't even aware of?' she asked huskily.

'Perhaps,' he said very quietly, and now his eyes were hooded, she thought, unreadable and sombre, and beneath the smooth, thick fair hair the lines of his face were harsh. And just to look at him hurt her, not only because she loved him and could never deny it to herself again, but also because she knew him now as she thought she would never know another man or want to—but knew she couldn't change him.

'Tell me something, Matt.' She fiddled with the salt-cellar, turning it round and round in her slim, beautifully manicured fingers. Then she put it down and lifted her eyes to his. 'Why did you . . . issue that ultimatum under such false pretences?'

He sat back in his chair. 'I did it on the spur of the moment. You were so haughty—and so beautiful.' Their gazes locked and held. 'I thought it could be a way to find out what really made you tick, Kirra.'

'And now you have . . . at least, you've found out I won't go to bed with you. Was that the test I passed?'

He was silent, but she saw the ironic little salute in his eyes, and closed her own briefly.

'That . . . disturbs you?' he asked.

Kirra stared down at her hands, and at the two delicious prawns on her plate she knew she could not eat. 'Yes. Yes, it does,' she whispered.

'It seemed to be very important to *you*,' he said drily.

'It was—but all the same we were at cross purposes. And we still are. I don't believe your . . . test was conclusive of anything other than a deeply rooted cynical indifference . . . which, I grant you, you've never tried to deny. But I couldn't live with that. That's why it was so important to *me*.'

'On the other hand, Kirra, don't you think we've forged a kind of unity throughout this . . . contest, if you like? We want each other and no one else. We . . . we can even read each other's minds,' he said with a grim little smile, and when her eyes flew to his, he went on, 'I knew that night I phoned you from Melbourne that you'd found out the contracts had been signed. You knew, if you're prepared to admit it, from not much later that I was only humouring you.'

Did I? she wondered with an inward tremor. 'Humouring me?' she repeated, however, and her eyes were bitter.

'Don't tell me you didn't know that the game was no longer a game,' he said roughly.

She coloured, but said steadily, 'I could be forgiven for thinking it was always a game to you.'

His gaze was sardonic.

'All right,' she said quietly. 'Although I didn't admit it to myself, I think I must have . . . I did know it wasn't a game. Not for me, at least,' she said barely audibly.

'Or for me,' he insisted.

'All the same,' and her voice was unsteady now, 'I can't marry you, Matt. Foolishly or otherwise, I want more than you can give.'

'You still don't know what I *can* give you, Kirra,' he said harshly.

'Yes, I do,' she whispered. 'A marriage composed of tests—I'm bound to fail one sooner or later.' She dashed at the tears on her lashes. 'I've done some stupid things since I met you, Matt, but as I mentioned once before, I've also learnt a lot. The answer is no, and nothing you can say will make me change my mind. I . . . I think I'd better go now.'

He stood up and dropped some money on to the table.

'I can get a taxi home,' she said shakily, but he put out a hand to help her up. Nor did he let go of her arm until they were at the car. But he said nothing on the short drive to Main Beach.

Then he switched the engine off and turned to her. 'If it's a declaration of undying, eternal love you want, Kirra, I have to tell you the words alone mean nothing, and if someone else ever says them to you, just remember this, I never swore anything to you or made you any false promises, but I think I know you better than any other man ever will.'

Her breath came in a surprised little jolt as his words echoed her earlier thoughts.

'And to me, that's what it's all about. I'm sorry . . . we differ there.'

He put out a hand and touched her hair, then his lips twisted as she looked away, then back at him, and said simply, 'So am I. Goodbye, Matt.'

'Goodbye, Kirra.'

Hours later, she sat in her apartment, dry-eyed but

feeling incredibly bereft, and in her agony she'd been over everything he had ever said and done to her and all her reactions and responses, as if searching for a truth that still eluded her. The conviction, for example, they each held that they understood one another better than anyone else would—should that be enough to base a lifetime commitment on, as he had suggested? Did her conviction that it wasn't stem from an over-emotional, sentimental view of love?

'Whatever,' she whispered at last, hugging a cushion to herself, 'I made the decision . . . because I can't change myself.' And the tears came at last, but they didn't heal the feeling of loss, and she wondered if anything ever would.

CHAPTER ELEVEN

THREE months later Kirra got home from work and withdrew a slim folder from her bag, then sat down to study the contents—brochures, stickers and an airline ticket, destinations Hong Kong and Singapore.

Her date of departure was a fortnight away.

She studied them for a few minutes, then with a sigh put them away, because she knew this trip was not going to excite her, it was more in the nature of a desperate attempt to forget.

She had seen and heard nothing from Matt, although she'd heard of him through her parents and been on the receiving end of their delicate probings as to why such a promising beginning had apparently died such a swift death. These she'd parried as well as she was able to, and she had also gone out of her way to hide from them the fact that she had lost some weight and was still, three months on, not sleeping well. She'd done this by being as active as possible socially, but there were times when her mother looked at her assessingly and seemed set to say something, but changed her mind at the last minute.

It had been on the last of those occasions that Kirra had decided she had to get away.

'Well, now I'm going,' she said to herself, getting up to draw the curtains on a cool, autumn evening. 'I've always wanted to see Hong Kong and Singapore —surely I can dredge up some enthusiasm?'

* * *

The foyer of the Mandarin Hotel, Hong Kong, was a symphony of gold and black, and Kirra was immediately impressed by the air of elegance, and more particularly by the absence of flurry which had formed her first impressions of Hong Kong since her Cathay Pacific flight had landed a few hours ago. In fact, it would be accurate to say that the traffic had been mind-boggling, and she had gazed out of the window of the car that had transported her from Kai Tak airport to the hotel, via the Harbour Tunnel from Kowloon to Hong Kong Island, with wide eyes. Not only the traffic but the people, and even now she stared over her shoulder out through the main doors to the chaos of Connaught Road, and wondered if she would ever be game to leave the sanctuary of the Mandarin.

But perhaps that's exactly what I need, she mused, a challenge—something to get me functioning properly again. After a good long sleep, though, she added to herself. I feel as if I've been on that plane for nineteen hours instead of nine . . .

'Miss Munro?'

She turned from the reception desk where she was registering with a little start of surprise. 'Yes?'

'Miss Munro, may I introduce myself? I'm the manager, and I've had the pleasure of welcoming Sir Kenneth and Lady Munro to the Mandarin several times.'

'Oh,' Kirra smiled, 'I know. They were quite adamant I should stay here and nowhere else. How do you do?'

'Miss Munro . . .' The man in the pin-striped black suit hesitated, and Kirra's smiled faded after a moment.

'Is something wrong?'

'I'm so sorry to have to be the bearer of these tidings, but your mother has been taken ill, Miss Munro.'

'Ill,' Kirra said dazedly. 'Seriously?'

'Rather seriously, but please, would you come into my office? We can . . .'

'But I've got to get home! Right now . . . oh, please,' she said desperately. 'I . . .'

'That's what I hope to be able to arrange for you. Please come this way, Miss Munro.'

If her first flight had felt prolonged, the one she caught home after a stay of only eight hours in Hong Kong—all of them wide awake—seemed never-ending. She couldn't sleep, she barely ate, and for the first time in her life suffered acute claustrophobia on a plane. And she couldn't concentrate on anything other then the vision of her mother, the victim of a stroke and in intensive care.

Fortunately, she flew direct to Brisbane instead of via Sydney as the flight to Hong Kong had taken her. And when she landed, feeling terrible and no doubt looking it, the prospect of the long trudge through Customs and Immigration made her feel like screaming. But someone must have alerted the authorities, because she was processed first, and, although she was very grateful, she couldn't help wondering if it was an ominous sign.

The last person she expected to meet her beyond the swinging doors and the barrier was Matt; Matt in a dark suit and a white shirt, his face unreadable.

'Have . . . have you come to meet me?' she stammered.

'Yes.'

'Oh, how is she?' she whispered, her control

breaking at last and tears streaming down her face. 'Is . . .' She realised to her embarrassment that she was clutching the front of his jacket.

'She's holding her own, Kirra,' he said quietly, scanning her pale face with a frown in his eyes, and he put an arm round her. 'Come.'

She hid her face in his shoulder for a moment, then took a grip on herself. 'How are you?'

'Fine,' he said briefly, and for an instant, as they stared at each other, everything that had fascinated and tormented her about him rose up in her heart in a living tide of despair. He looked exactly the same and she remembered suddenly how, right from the beginning, she'd rejoiced in his looks, although her vision of him had been false. Or was it? she wondered. Even then you knew he was a loner at heart.

She tore her gaze away and bent to pick up her bags, which were absurdly light, but he took them from her and remarked on the fact.

She grimaced. 'They say you should go to Hong Kong in only what you stand up in, because things are so cheap there—I took them at their word.'

He smiled faintly, and led the way to the car.

It was a swift trip to the coast, and Kirra's desperate concern for her mother had swept all other emotions away again.

Matt told her all he knew of her mother's condition, and half-way there he pulled out a silver flask and handed it to her. 'Brandy,' he said, his eyes flickering over her. 'Have some. Have you eaten lately?'

'I couldn't.'

'You must eat,' he said gently. 'It will help no one if you collapse.' And he pulled into a road-house and bought her a toasted chicken sandwich and a chocolate bar. To her surprise, she ate both and then had another sip of the neat brandy.

'Thanks,' she murmured. 'I do feel a bit stronger now.'

He took a hand from the wheel and put it over hers.

That night was the longest night of Kirra's life, as she and her father comforted each other and kept a vigil over her mother.

'I don't know what I'd do without her,' her father kept saying. 'She means more to me than anything.'

'I know, I know,' Kirra kept answering, wincing at his anguish added to her own.

But the early hours of the morning brought good news.

'She's been very lucky, Sir Kenneth,' the doctor told them. 'There may be some slight paralysis, but she's definitely out of danger now, I'm happy to be able to tell you.'

Kirra clung to her father, weeping tears of joy, as was he, and Matt, who had not intruded on their vigil but kept them supplied with coffee, sighed with obvious relief.

Then Matt and her father spoke together quietly for a while, and her father came over to her and said, 'My dear, Matt is going to take you home.'

'But . . .'

'Darling, you must be exhausted.'

'So are you!'

He smiled tiredly. 'I haven't flown half-way across the world and back in the last two days, but they're going to fix me up a bed here. Go home and have a sleep, so that when she's more lucid, you'll be fresh and rested.'

It was raining outside and she nearly fell asleep in the car, but when they got upstairs to her apartment she felt wide awake again.

'Thanks,' she said awkwardly as he unlocked the door for her. 'You don't have to . . . stay.'

'Yes, I do,' he replied with a critical look at her, and he followed her in and closed the door. 'Why don't you have a bath? I'll make some breakfast.'

'Well, but you must be tired too, and I haven't got anything to make for breakfast.'

'Kirra,' he said with a wry look, 'don't argue. Just do as you're told. I'll go and get something to make for breakfast.'

The bath was heavenly, more so because it was a chilly grey morning and the rain was teeming down now. And as she lay in the steaming, scented water she felt her nerves beginning to unwind. She also sniffed appreciatively as the aroma of grilled bacon filtered into the bathroom.

They ate the bacon and eggs in a queer sort of harmony, as if they were curiously insulated from all that had happened between them.

She told him about her confused impressions of Hong Kong, and he told her it had taken him two trips before he had got the hang of the place. He mentioned that Min had decided she was brave enough to come out of seclusion, and Kirra said warmly that she was happy for Min. Then she asked him what he would do about the horses and the house, and he said he would board the horses out on a neighbouring property and shut up the house.

All so natural, one small portion of Kirra's tired brain marvelled, but in no way could she come to grips with this phenomenon.

He made them coffee and she closed her eyes and drank it slowly.

'To bed now, I think,' he said quietly.

'Yes,' she murmured, finding it hard to keep her eyes open.

'Off you go—I'll clean up.'

She stood up and stared down at him for a long moment, not knowing what to say, and in the end said only, 'Thanks.'

He didn't reply, but he looked away first.

She fell asleep almost immediately—only to wake in minutes, with her heart pounding, her mouth dry and her nerves tightened to screaming-point. And when she managed to calm herself a little, it occurred to her that she wasn't going to be able to sleep—that she should not have rejected the mild sedative the doctor had offered her, that she was dangerously over-tired and over-wrought.

That was how Matt found her, sitting up with her head in her hands, and it was the quiet opening of the door that made her look up.

'What is it?' he asked, coming over to the bed.

'I can't sleep,' she whispered helplessly. 'I'm . . . a nervous wreck.' She tried to smile, but it didn't come off; and then she was crying, silently.

He sat down and took her in his arms and stroked her hair. 'Yes, you can,' he murmured. 'I'll help you.'

'I feel such a fool,' she wept.

'Why? You're only over-tired.'

'I know that, but . . .'

He released her and brushed some wet strands of hair off her face. 'Lie down,' he said.

'W-where are you going?' she stammered, sliding

down.

'Nowhere,' he said, lying down beside her and adjusting the covers so that, although he was on top of them, he could put his arms around her. 'I'm tired too. We might as well be tired together. You smell like a rose.'

'That's my bath oil,' she said dazedly.

'Comfortable?'

'Mmm . . .'

'Close your eyes, then.'

'I . . . I'm afraid to.'

'No, you're not. Think of something nice. Roses, seeing as you smell like one. Slim little salmon-pink buds wrapped in cellophane, or—lovely blowsy full-blown cream ones with bees buzzing around them, mysterious dark velvety red ones . . .'

Kirra never knew afterwards whether it was the roses he brought to mind so vividly, or the safe strong feel of his arms, his breath on her cheek, his quiet, deep voice that mesmerised her into slipping unknowingly into sleep, a deep, dreamless sleep for hours.

When she woke, the rain had stopped and the sun was shining, it was well after mid-day, and she was alone.

Or so she thought when she reached unthinkingly across the bed before she was properly awake, then sat up, pushing her hair back and looking around, still drowsy and disorientated.

He was standing in the doorway, leaning against the frame with his jacket hooked over his shoulder, his tie undone and his hair lying across his forehead.

She said his name uncertainly, and he straightened and started to speak, but she interrupted him.

'Don't go, please,' she whispered.

'I must,' he said, his hazel gaze sombre as it swept over her briefly, her hair, her bare shoulders beneath the narrow shoulder straps of her grey silk nightgown, the outline of her breasts, then back to her eyes. 'If I stay,' he said, barely audibly, and with a nerve flickering in his jaw, 'I might do something we . . . could regret.'

'No,' she said equally quietly. 'There could be no regrets. I . . . need you, Matt. Please stay . . .'

CHAPTER TWELVE

'HOLD it!' the photographer said enthusiastically. Then, 'Excellent. Now if I could just take one last one of Mrs Remington and the baby.'

It was a small christening party, comprising Kirra's parents, Pippa and Marcus, Min and her escort—a big, quiet-spoken man who was obviously in love with her, and Stanley, who had made the cake and insisted on acting as butler and chief nurser of André Remington, who, at just three months, had slept through the proceedings so far.

But although small in numbers it had been a lively gathering at the house on the hill overlooking the Tweed River, and Kirra glanced around with deep affection as she accepted André from his maternal grandmother, whose only visible after-effect of the stroke she'd suffered was a slight limp.

She didn't notice Stanley charging everyone's glasses as she sat for the last photo; in fact, she'd transferred her gaze to her sleeping son, who was so like his father that it still amazed her. And her thoughts were on the fact that he was due for a feed and would soon wake and indicate this to her with a determination that was also reminiscent of his father. Nor did she look up immediately when the camera flashed, and for a moment no one said a word, as they all watched her sitting there in her wistaria-blue dress with a small white voile collar and cuffs, her hair loose and lying on her shoulders, and her obvious preoccupation with her son.

Then Sir Kenneth cleared his throat and proposed a simple toast. 'To Kirra,' he said, raising his glass.

She looked up at last, taken unawares, and went faintly pink as almost everyone echoed her father's words, and she looked directly at Matt, the only one who had not participated, but as their eyes met he raised his glass in a silent, lingering salute, and she saw in their hazel depths a look she was now very familiar with. A look that told her he would with great diplomacy end the party soon, and after she had fed his son he would make love to her in a way that even after nearly two years of marriage made her tremble to think of it.

The sun had slipped behind Mount Warning and Murwillumbah, and its fiery splendour was fading when Kirra prepared to go downstairs, having bathed and fed André and put him to bed.

She had changed into an ivory and red silk caftan with a tissuey gold border on the wide sleeves and hem that brushed the floor. Matt had bought it for her in Hong Kong, where they had spent part of their honeymoon, after a wedding which had taken place only a few days after she had returned from her first, abortive trip there. But she lingered a while, fingering the gold tissue on her sleeve and staring out over the darkening landscape, thinking about their marriage and how it had taken place by mutual, almost unspoken consent, as if it had been inevitable—the unalterable consequence of their physical union. And thinking that what was between them was still unspoken. Apart from their marriage vows, they had made no undying declarations to each other, but somehow he had bound her to him more closely each succeeding day. She sometimes wondered if he would ever say the words she had longed to hear, she sometimes longed to say them herself, but never did. Instead she accepted his passion and matched it, as she had accepted his care and compassion through a rather arduous first pregnancy and birth, and she had told herself she didn't need the words, she was content and at peace, she would never press him—it was the nature of things between them . . .

He was waiting for her in the lounge with a tray of smoked-salmon sandwiches set on the low table before the stone fireplace, and two glasses of wine poured, and he had changed too, into jeans and a navy blue sports shirt. His fair hair was damp and awry, and his feet were bare as he lounged on the leather settee.

'Settled?' he asked with a lift of an eyebrow.

'Yes.' She smiled faintly. 'I don't think being christened made any impression on him at all.'

'He's a young man with rather a one-track mind, I've noticed,' Matt said with a grin. 'The curious thing is that we share . . . that track.'

'*I've* noticed that,' Kirra murmured. 'Must be what that old saying—like father like son—is all about.'

He reached for her hand and pulled her down beside him. 'How does it feel to have,' he paused, and his voice was curiously husky as he went on, 'the absolute devotion of two males with one-track minds?'

Kirra went still, and when she turned her head to look at him, her blue-grey eyes were wary and startled. 'You don't,' she cleared her throat, 'you don't have to say that.'

'Don't I?' He bent his head and fiddled with her

gold wedding band, the only ring he'd ever given her. 'Personally I think it's long overdue,' he went on, and raised his eyes at last.

'Matt,' she whispered and realised she was shaking, 'I . . .' But she couldn't go on for a time, and they could only stare at each other until she said, 'Why now? Is it . . . because of André? Or have I passed . . .'

She stopped as his grasp on her hand tightened almost unbearably, and he said with barely suppressed savagery, 'The only test applicable between us is the gauge of my insanity, my inability to understand that nothing is ever going to make me stop loving you. You once said to me something about joy . . . watching you this afternoon filled me with pride and joy and something else, the knowledge that I could never let you go.' His lips twisted wryly. 'So from being a disbeliever,' he said with obvious self-directed mockery, 'I've become . . . perhaps the worst kind of believer: possessive, obsessed, all those things I swore never to be. Do you think you'll mind?'

'Oh God,' Kirra said hoarsely, her throat working and tears starting in her eyes.

He swore beneath his breath and pulled her into his arms. 'I didn't mean to sound flippant,' he said roughly. 'I'm deadly serious. I love you, Kirra . . . and if it's been too long in coming, I'm sorry, so sorry. I saw you,' he said with an effort, 'after André was born, when you were exhausted and hurting, look at me for an instant as if you were searching for something, and when you didn't see it, you closed your eyes briefly, but then you looked at me again and smiled . . . That's when I knew it had happened. That I loved you not only because you were beautiful and proud, but strong and committed and faithful.'

'Why . . .'

'Why didn't I say so then?' He sighed. 'If the truth be told, I've never known how to put into words how I felt about you. And even then—even now—it's much deeper than the words can say it. I . . . asked you to marry me several times in several ways, and when we did, we didn't say much at all. Would you think I was crazy if I said this time was for real?'

She stared at him with her lips parted, until he grimaced and he murmured, 'No, my darling Kirra, I haven't gone round the bend, but along with every-thing else I've become, all those things I mentioned, I've also discovered a streak of pure sentimentality. Which was why I thought this might be a fitting occasion to,' he reached down between the cushions and withdrew two grey velvet boxes, 'give you these.'

Her eyes widened.

'This one,' he said, handing her the smaller box, 'is an engagement ring. Open it.'

She pressed the catch and couldn't contain a gasp of delight at the ring nestled in the white satin lining. It wasn't large or ostentatious, and it wasn't the conventional diamond or sapphire. In fact, it was the most unusual and beautiful engagement ring she had seen: an amethyst in an antique gold setting and flanked by two small, milky opals that nevertheless gleamed green and gold and pink as they caught the light.

'It's exquisite,' she said huskily.

'Like it?'

'It's just beautiful. Thank you.' She blinked away some tears.

'I thought you might prefer it to a ball and chain,' he said with a wicked little glint in his eye, 'although I got one of those, too. As a memento.'

She looked at him and then down as he flicked open the second box and revealed another amethyst, a round one, a lovely pure violet-pink stone rimmed with gold and attached to a fine gold chain.

'Oh Matt,' she breathed, picking it up between her fingers.

'If I'm any judge,' he said, capturing her face in his hands, 'it will be a very private memento, this one . . . I'll show you what I mean in a moment, but can I put the ring on?'

She held out her left hand and he slid it on in front of her wedding band, then lifted his eyes to hers. 'Do you feel married to me now in every sense of the word, Kirra?' he queried.

She stared at him with all her love for him showing in her eyes at last. And she said, 'I do.' And raised her mouth for his kiss.

It was later when she stirred in his arms and remembered the amethyst ball and chain. 'You were going to show me something,' she said softly.

'Ah, yes.' He reached out a hand and switched on a lamp, and took it from her. 'Just one thing—you'd have to get undressed.'

'Why is that?' she asked innocently.

'That's the private nature of it.'

'I see. Well, perhaps you'd like to . . . do the honours.'

His eyes gleamed, but he said formally, 'Very well, Mrs Remington, if you insist.'

But he undressed her very slowly, stopping frequently to slide his lips and fingers along the smooth, glossy hollows and curves of her body that he now knew so well, and as always his touch was so light, she couldn't understand why it was like a trail of fire . . .

When he took her dress off, he eased her upright on the settee so that she was kneeling with her hands curved about his neck, and one by one he undid the long row of tiny buttons down the front, and when they were all undone she dropped her arms so that the material could slide off her shoulders with a soft, sibilant shush.

Their eyes caught and held, but he didn't immediately undo her bra. He cupped her shoulders in his palms instead and his long fingers slid beneath the straps, playing over her skin. He drew her close, and she tipped her head back so that he could kiss her throat, then lower and lower, until it became a sweet kind of torment that her breasts weren't free.

'Please,' she whispered, and he obliged, sliding his hands under her arms and releasing the catch and drawing it off her.

Then he took his hands away and she knelt with her ivory and gold dress clinging to her hips, her eyes solemn and a little questioning when his hands didn't come back to her.

But he had picked up the amethyst again, and with grave intent put it round her neck, fumbling a little with the catch, then, when it was done up, straightening the chain and the stone so that it hung between her breasts.

Kirra looked down at last, then up into his eyes.

'I thought,' he said softly, 'you might like to wear it only when we're going to make love.'

'I think that's a brilliant idea,' she whispered, her lips curving into a smile.

'Do you remember,' he said not quite evenly, playing with the amethyst, 'when you thought you might not be very good at . . . that?'

'Making love? Yes,' she said gravely.

'You were dead wrong, you know. I say that because I still want you beyond all belief.'

'Can I say what I think?'

'Please do,' he invited, moving his hands over her caressingly.

'I wasn't wrong. It's you. You've wrought the miracle. And it's because I love you and always will.'

'Kirra, darling,' his eyes were bright in the moment before he drew her into his arms and held her as if he would never let her go, 'that's my line.'

THE MARRIAGE DEAL

CHAPTER ONE

A CAR door slammed, and high heels clicked across the paving stones with brisk impatience. As the glass doors of the towering office block swung open, the security guard got to his feet, his usually impassive face registering faint surprise.

'Miss Landon—we weren't expecting you back for another ten days ...'

He was left gaping after Ashley Landon's retreating back as it pursued an openly stormy passage to the lift, and with a shrug he returned to his cubicle.

'Someone's for it,' he remarked to no one in particular.

The lift stopped at the sixth floor, and the doors glided open to release the sole passenger. She was a slim girl, slightly above medium height, the sculptured lines of her elegantly bobbed black hair giving emphasis to her pointed chin and high cheekbones. Her clothes were expensive, but sat awkwardly on her body, as if she'd had other things on her mind when she put them on. And the muted beige of her skirt and jacket did nothing for her clear, pale skin, or her green eyes, glinting now like an angry cat's.

When she reached the door marked 'Company Secretary' she flung it open and walked in without knocking with the air of one who has the right, past the startled typist, and straight into the inner office.

Henry Brett was on the telephone, and he looked up frowning at the unceremonious opening of his door, his face clearing instantly when he saw his visitor.

He made a swift excuse to his caller, and replaced his receiver, coming round his desk, hand outstretched.

'Ashley, my dear, you're back already. That's wonderful!'

'Hardly the way I'd describe the disruption of my first vacation in three years,' Ashley rejoined crisply. 'But the signals seemed too urgent to ignore. What the hell's going on?'

Henry Brett sighed, steering her to a chair. 'A takeover,' he said succinctly. 'Marshalls are making yet another bid for our shares.'

'They must be mad,' Ashley said, dropping her bag to the floor beside her. 'They got a very conclusive answer the last time they tried it, and nothing's changed.'

'I'm afraid it has,' Henry said levelly. He pressed a buzzer on his desk, and spoke into the intercom. 'Jean, could you rustle up some coffee?'

'Not for me,' Ashley cut in.

'I think when you've heard me out, you're going to need some stimulant,' said Henry, his genial face sober. 'I can't hide it from you, Ashley. This time they mean business, and they could succeed. According to the recent soundings I've been taking, they could have a majority of our board on their side.'

There was a brief appalled silence, then Ashley said, 'Henry, you can't be serious! Why, last time, every member of the board was solidly one hundred per cent behind Landons.'

'They were solidly one hundred per cent behind your father,' Henry said grimly. 'But Silas has been dead for two years, my dear. And you must remember that quite apart from the fact that his personality could carry anything through, most of the board owed him a great deal. After all, he'd put the majority of them where they were, and that counted—then.'

'But not any more.' There was a painful constriction in Ashley's throat. 'My God, Henry, I know I'm not my father, and never can be, but I've done my best to run the company exactly as he would have done ...'

'No one would deny that.' Seated on the edge of his desk, Henry sent her a compassionate look. 'You've done everything and more that anyone could expect, but the fact remains ...'

'The fact remains I'm not a man,' Ashley said with a mirthless smile. 'And the board—hidebound traditionalists every one of them—have never believed a woman of my age is capable of running a property development company the size of Landons.'

Henry looked embarrassed. 'Hang it all, Ashley, it was Silas' own view, and you know it.'

'Yes,' she said in a low voice. 'But Henry, I've tried so hard to be the son he wanted—I really have ...'

'No one could have done more,' he assured her warmly. 'But it was a responsibility Silas never wanted you to have. It was that damnfool rule of your grandfather's that only a member of the family could become company chairman that had him hidebound. That was why ...' He stopped in sudden embarrassment. 'Oh, damnation!'

'It's all right, Henry,' Ashley said in a level voice. 'I won't fall apart at the seams if you talk about it. My God, it was over three years ago!'

'All right then,' Henry said quietly. 'That was why he wanted you to marry Jago Marrick. As his son-in-law, Jago would have become chairman after Silas—the strong man at the top the board wanted.'

'Oh, Jago was that all right.' Ashley bit her lip. 'It was as husband material that he failed to meet requirements. But that's all in the past. He's settled in the States now, and probably on his way to his second million.'

'Or even his third,' Henry said wryly. He paused. 'But I'm glad to hear you've managed to put the whole sorry business behind you. I had to think very hard about bringing you home at this time.'

'But why?' She looked at him blankly. 'This is an emergency. Where else would I be?'

Henry cleared his throat. 'You see, there's another factor. Giles Marrick died very suddenly, only a few days after you left for the Caribbean.'

'Jago's cousin?' Ashley frowned. 'I'm sorry. He was a kind man.' She stopped abruptly. 'Oh, I see—Jago came back for the funeral.'

'And not just for the funeral,' said Henry with a trace of heaviness. 'Rumour has it that he intends to stay. He's Giles Marrick's heir, of course, so the Manor and the estate now belongs to him, although I believe the widow has some kind of life interest in it.'

'Yes.' She managed the monosyllable from a taut throat. 'At least, until she remarries.'

'Which probably won't be long,' Henry conceded. 'Good-looking woman, and years younger than Marrick himself, of course.'

'Years,' Ashley agreed quietly. Although Jago had explained the position to her during their brief engagement, it had always cost her a pang to think that when he finally owned the beautiful Georgian house, Erica would still have the right to live there—Erica, with her sultry blonde good looks and malicious tongue.

Mentally, she gave herself a little impatient shake. The Manor was no longer any concern of hers. The loss of Landons was.

She said crisply, 'Don't look so concerned, Henry. I got over Jago a long time ago. Let's get back to the main priority. How did you know Marshalls were sniffing round again?'

'Movement of shares. And then Clive Farnsworth advised me privately that he was being pressed to sell his holding, and warned me that a majority of the board would be in favour of accepting Marshalls' offer.'

'It's unbelievable!' Ashley made a small sound of disgust. 'Why, everyone knows what my father thought of them. He said they were sharks— jerrybuilders creating modern slums.'

'He was right,' Henry said bitterly. 'Which is why they want Landons, of course, to confer a cloak of respectability on their operations. It's the company name they want as well as its assets. But their real ace in the hole is their new managing director, a real dynamo by the sound of him. I gather he reminds some of the older board members of Silas when he was young. That's the enticement—the kind of strong male leadership they're used to.'

'My God, what an attitude!' Ashley expelled her breath in a small harsh sigh. 'It belongs in the Ark.'

'I can't deny that, but we can't dismiss it either.' His gaze met hers squarely. 'We have a real problem here, Ashley. The board aren't just a set of dyed-in-the-wool male chauvinists. They're anxious about our recent performance.'

He broke off as the door opened and Jean Hurst came in with a tray of coffee.

It was what she needed after all, Ashley discovered

wryly, as she accepted a cup of the dark, fragrant brew, and sipped it gratefully.

When they were alone again, she said, 'Was it deliberate? Did Marshalls wait for me to go to Barbados before they made their move?'

Henry looked slightly taken aback. 'It's possible. They must know that loyalty to Silas' memory still exerts quite a hold.'

'So—we fight.' She lifted her chin. 'What am I up against, if it came to a straight boardroom battle?'

'I think you'd just lose,' he admitted, and she winced.

'I can't bear it! To see everything Grandfather and Silas worked for just—handed over to a cowboy outfit like Marshalls. My God, I'd do anything—anything, to stop it happening.'

'I hope you're not contemplating a sex-change,' Henry made a heavy-handed attempt at humour.

Ashley grimaced. 'Coupled with an operation to make me ten years older? Don't tell me that isn't part of the problem.'

'You're just not what they're used to,' Henry said tiredly. 'To most of their generation, women are wives or secretaries, cast in the mould from birth.' He paused. 'And I'm afraid many of them see your—repudiation of your engagement to Jago Marrick as a sign of—feminine instability. They worry that it might break out again some time.'

'Oh, no,' she said with soft bitterness. 'My brush with Jago was a one-off thing—never, I pray, to be repeated.' She put her cup down on the desk. 'When I broke off my engagement, I don't think Silas ever really understood, or forgave me. He thought the end justified the means, and that I was just making a silly fuss about some trivial disagreement. He didn't know ...' She stopped.

'Didn't know what?' Henry prompted sympatheti-cally.

She was silent for a moment, then, 'Didn't know how totally unsuited Jago and I were,' she said stiltedly. She smiled faintly as she got to her feet. 'I'm going home now, Henry. I need to think. But thanks for the timely message. I'd have hated to have been voted out of existence in my absence.'

'That's what I thought,' he said unhappily. 'They're pressing for an emergency board meeting next Thursday. Between now and then I'll see what I can do in the way of persuasion or pressure to change a few minds to our way of thinking.' He sighed. 'But it's going to be an uphill struggle.'

'We'll win,' she said. 'We have to.'

Her words evinced a confidence she didn't feel. Her mood as she drove to her flat was one of dejection.

She'd never envisaged becoming chairman of Landons, but that didn't mean she was prepared to see the company taken away from her.

Oh, Silas, she thought fiercely, why didn't you prepare me better?

Perhaps he would have done, if he'd lived to the ripe old age his bounding energy had seemed to promise. If he hadn't collapsed with a heart attack while exploring a possible site for development, and died in intensive care an hour later, before Ashley could even get to his bedside. Her first act on assuming control of the company had been to complete the deal for the land. Nothing spectacular, but surely a sign to the rest of the world that it was business as usual.

Her flat occupied the top floor of a purpose-built block, which Landons had erected some ten years previously, and was the nearest to a real home she had ever had.

Her mother had, unbelievably, died giving her birth, and Silas, dazed by grief, had instantly sold the house they had lived in together. Ashley's earliest memories were of a changing landscape of hotel suites, and a shifting population of nannies. Silas travelled the country, and she, perforce, travelled with him until she was old enough to be despatched to boarding school.

She had understood quite early in their relationship that she seemed to make her father uncomfortable, and had assumed it was because of some painful physical resemblance to her mother. Gradually she came to realise that, whether he was aware of it or not, Silas resented the fact that his only child was not the boy he had planned on. Yet he had never made any attempt to alter the situation by marrying again, although he had enjoyed various discreet liaisons over the years, seeming perfectly content with his nomadic existence, the only awkwardness occurring when he was obliged to have Ashley with him.

She had spent many dull hours reading, watching television, wandering round strange towns, watching other people's lives from a distance, until at last, when she was sixteen, she had rebelled, and insisted on accompanying him on to site. He had been openly reluctant at first, but when he saw she was adamant he had acceded, and slowly a new relationship had been forged between them. He had started by being sceptical about her interest, but he answered her questions with total frankness, and she had learned a great deal simply by being with him.

But he had been by no means preparing her to take over from him. His plans for her future had been very different, as she had suddenly, and painfully, discovered.

In her small elegant bathroom, she stripped and showered slowly, letting the water pour through her hair and down her body. She dried herself without haste, and wrapped in a fresh towel, sarong-style, wandered back to the bedroom and stretched out on her bed.

She felt infinitely weary, but sleep eluded her just the same. There was too much on her mind, she thought, punching the pillow. And if she was honest, the problem about the takeover wasn't foremost in her thoughts as it should have been.

Jago, it seemed, was back, and possibly planning to stay. She had banked very heavily on never having to see him again, but if he was really going to be around as a permanent feature, she didn't see how this could be avoided. It wasn't that large a town. Nor could she leave. This was where Landons had its head office, so she couldn't run, no matter how much she might want to.

Not that there was any logic in that, she castigated herself scornfully. There was no reason why she and Jago should not meet in a perfectly civilised manner. She'd got over that heartbreaking, desperate, adolescent love for him a long time ago. He couldn't hurt her again, so what was she afraid of?

The million-dollar question, Ashley thought ironically.

She bit her lip savagely. As a future wife for a man like Jago Marrick, she'd been a disaster, but as Silas' successor, she thought she had enjoyed a modest success. She had felt desperately isolated at first in her new eminence, but she had listened carefully, and made full use of all the experience and expertise which had been offered.

She sighed. Yet in spite of all her efforts, the board still didn't trust her, or have any real confidence in her, and all her buried insecurities were burrowing to the surface, nagging and gnawing at her mind. She was not quite twenty-two, after all, and not very old to be doing battle for her share of the market place—a fact of which Marshalls were clearly well aware. Their board obviously regarded the present takeover attempt as no contest, and if she was honest, she could see little way of stopping them.

If it was any other company, she thought ruefully. But stories of Marshalls' shoddy dealings and poor workmanship were rife in the industry, and they had already brought a libel action against a well-known satirical magazine which had lambasted them over a new shopping centre, threatened with structural collapse. They had won their case on a technicality, but with derisory damages.

Yet they were still wealthy enough, and endowed with sufficient clout to be bidding for Landons. They knew that their only chance of success was appealing to the inherent greed of human nature. And shareholders, in this respect, were just as human as anyone else.

The sudden trill of the phone beside the bed startled her, and she stared at it resentfully, wishing she'd had the foresight to disconnect it. She waited for the caller to get tired of waiting, and ring off, but it didn't happen. Few people knew she was back, she thought, so perhaps it was Henry calling to apprise her of some new development. And it was clear he wasn't giving up, so she lifted the receiver.

'Hello,' she said grudgingly.

'So you are back.' Jago's voice, low, sardonic,

and totally unmistakable. 'I presumed old Henry would have pushed the panic button by now.'

'I think you have the wrong number,' she said wildly. 'I don't know what you're talking about ...'

'Yes, you do, Ash, so don't play games. According to the hints and rumours in the financial columns, Landons have a serious problem. I think we should talk.'

'Well, I don't.' In spite of herself, her voice sounded ragged, his deliberate diminution of her name rousing memories she would rather have denied. 'I don't need your help.'

'I thought three years might have matured you, Ash,' he jibed at her. 'But it seems you're still the same prickly schoolgirl, nursing your hurt pride. And for that, you're prepared to see Landons go down the drain. You amaze me!'

'That isn't true,' she said stiffly. 'If you have any helpful suggestions, then you should get in touch with Henry. I'm sure he'd be glad to hear from you.'

'Although you're not.' Jago gave a low laugh. 'Well, I suppose that was too much to expect under the circumstances. But you will be hearing from me, Ash, and sooner than you think. I had the greatest admiration for Silas, and I'm not prepared to see his company go to the wall for the sake of past differences between the two of us.'

'I like "past differences",' Ashley said contemptuously. 'It's a good blanket term to cover your mercenary agreement with my father, and your flagrant infidelity!'

'Oh, it covers a damned sight more than that,' he said pleasantly. 'But I'm glad you approve. It's a start anyway. I'll be seeing you, then.' The line disconnected briskly.

He had never, Ashley thought, as she replaced her own receiver, been one for prolonged farewells.

She sat up, nervously hitching up her towel, as though Jago was in the room with her, his tawny hazel eyes observing her state of disarray with that overt sensuality which had so disturbed her during their brief, ill-fated relationship.

He'd called her a prickly schoolgirl, and she supposed he had a certain amount of justification, remembering how she had nervously shied away from any physical advances he'd made to her. Not even the fact that she had fallen head over heels in love with him had been able to mitigate her panic-stricken recoil from any real intimacy between them during their engagement.

And if she had been frightened by the unknown passions she had sensed were tightly leashed in his lean male body, then she had been utterly terrified by the wild unbidden reaction of her own innocent flesh to his lightest touch. And there was no one to help her understand or cope with these new and overwhelming sensations. The sex education lessons at her school had described the mechanics, but said nothing about the emotions which should accompany such experiences, and Ashley's housemistress had given muddled, embarrassed talks about the problems inherent in 'leading men on', quoting current rape statistics, and advising 'keeping oneself decent for marriage'.

And Silas' values, she had discovered when she had nerved herself to mention the topic to him, were equally rigid. Purity was what a man looked for in his future wife, he had told her flatly, and she could learn anything she needed to know from her husband when the time came.

When Jago held her close, she felt totally

confused, her body at war with her mind, which insisted that such an intensity of emotion must be wrong, even in some way abnormal.

Eventually, it seemed easier to keep Jago at arms' length. Or at any rate simpler, she amended hastily, because it had never been easy.

She had supposed naïvely that Silas was right, and that once they were married everything would be different. That wearing Jago's ring, having the right to call herself his wife, would bring about some fundamental sea-change in her. Only she had never had the opportunity to find out.

The wedding had only been a few weeks away when she had finally found out the truth about the kind of man she was marrying. She hadn't seen Jago for several days, not since they'd spent an evening at the theatre together. Afterwards, he had suggested she go back to his flat with him for a nightcap, and she had shrunk immediately. It was altogether too secluded and intimate an environment for her to cope with, feeling as she did, and she'd heard herself babbling some feeble excuse. That Jago had recognised it as such was evident, although he had said nothing. But his mouth had tightened, and he had driven her home with almost exaggerated care, depositing her on her doorstep with chilly courtesy, not even bothering to bestow the most chaste of goodnight kisses.

Ashley told herself he was being unreasonable, and that she wasn't going to be the first to make amends, but as time passed without a word from him, her need for reassurance got the better of her pride, and she tried to telephone him. When there was no reply from the flat, she told herself he was probably staying at the Manor, as Giles liked him to do from time to time.

But when she drove out to the Manor that evening, she found only Erica Marrick at home. She was sitting in the big drawing room, stitching at a piece of tapestry set up in a frame in front of her, and Ashley, who had no skill at sewing, watched in fascination as the needle pierced the canvas over and over again.

Later, when Ashley allowed herself to recall that terrible evening and its aftermath, she was to remember above all that shining needle, stabbing in and out, and feel as if it was her own flesh that it was wounding.

'I'm sorry you've had a wasted journey,' Erica said, when the usual social pleasantries had been observed. 'It might have been wiser to ring first, and check where he was.'

Ashley forbore to mention that she'd been trying to contact Jago for two days. She said, trying to sound casual, 'I suppose you've no idea where he could be?'

Erica chose another strand of thread. 'None at all, my dear. Giles is only Jago's cousin, not his keeper. Jago's an adult male. He comes and goes here as he chooses, and we don't ask any indiscreet questions. Much the best way, I assure you.' She threaded her needle. 'Jago doesn't actually live here yet.'

'I know,' Ashley said huskily. 'But I thought—I got the impression he was spending more time here these days—using the flat rather less.'

'I hardly think so.' The needle stabbed again. 'After all, it's the one small piece of bachelor independence which hasn't been eroded yet, and he'll be anxious to hang on to that as long as possible, I would imagine. He's sacrificed quite a lot already,' she added almost casually. 'I hope he finds Landons is worth it.'

Ashley's brows drew together. 'I don't quite understand ...'

'How wise of you,' purred Erica. 'It's always so much better to respect the conventions in these matters, and pretend the marriage has been arranged—such a telling phrase, I always think—for personal rather than business reasons.'

Ashley felt as if a hand was slowly tightening round her throat. 'Are you insinuating that Jago is marrying me only to gain a stake in Landons?'

'Hardly a stake, my dear.' The deadly needle went in and out, doing its work. 'After all, you're an only child with neither the physical nor mental capacity to become a—a captain of industry. Your father, naturally, needs someone he can trust to run the company eventually, and who better than a son-in-law and as you were—gratifyingly ready to marry him, and Jago is extremely ambitious, everyone's satisfied.'

There was a silence. Ashley said flatly, 'I don't believe you.'

Erica laughed. 'Of course not. Why should you? And you have nothing to worry about. Jago will never forget that you're Daddy's daughter, and be less than attentive, but you must remember to allow him—a little leeway now, before the noose tightens for ever. So why don't you go home like a good girl, and wait for him to call you. I'm sure he will, eventually. He tends to have a fairly strict sense of duty,' she added blandly.

Some guardian angel must have protected Ashley on that nightmare drive to his flat, because she remembered nothing about it.

All the way there, a voice in her head was whispering, 'It can't be true—can't be true ...'

And yet suspicion, once planted, was growing like a weed in the sun, sending out deadly tentacles to smother and choke. She had to see Jago, to confront him, and find out once and for all the real truth behind their marriage.

Because, she had to admit, the romance had been a whirlwind affair. She hadn't seen a great deal of Jago while she was growing up, but after Silas had decided to seek a permanent home base near the company headquarters, they had begun to come into contact with each other.

At first, she had been full of shy admiration, gauche and tongue-tied whenever he was around. As he shared her father's professional interests, it was inevitable that they should meet. Sometimes he was kind to her, at others, he teased her unmercifully. Gradually, almost in spite of herself, her admiration turned to a kind of hero-worship, and then, bewilderingly, to something much deeper.

Ashley had found she was aching for a glimpse of him, and agonising when this was denied her. She was ecstatic when he noticed her—once he gave her a lift home from the library, and she lived on it for weeks—and miserable when the passenger seat in his car was filled by one of the leggy blondes he seemed to favour. Not that he was always at home by any means. A lot of the time he was away, pursuing his career, immersed in one of the civil engineering projects for which he had trained at university.

'He's going straight to the top, that lad,' Silas had remarked more than once with unveiled satisfaction.

But Jago's ambitions and professional abilities counted for little with Ashley. For her, he was the focus of all her romantic dreams, and when, right out of the blue, he had rung and invited her to have dinner with him, she had thought she would die of delight.

But she had lived, and it was the start of an idyllic period in her life. Jago dined her, and danced with her, partnering her at tennis, taking her on picnics, and visits to the theatre and cinema.

And when, after six heady weeks, he had asked her to marry him, she had said 'Yes' eagerly, with no thought of dissimulation. 'Gratifyingly ready,' Erica had said mockingly, she recalled with a shiver of nausea. But it was no more than the truth. She'd been foolishly, blindly ready to allow herself to be handed over in exchange for the Landon empire.

As she drove, a lot of pieces seemed to be coming together in an increasingly terrifying pattern. She remembered the impatience in him, coiled like a spring, when she had drawn back from the growingly explicit demands of his mouth and hands, so different from the gentle restraint he had displayed during the early days of their courtship.

Before he was sure of her, said a small icy voice in her brain.

If he'd really cared for her, wouldn't he have been prepared to make allowances for her inexperience? she asked herself.

And more troubling still, he had never actually said in so many words that he loved her. He wanted to make love to her, in any way she would permit, but all he had said when she agreed to be his wife, was, 'Darling Ash, I'll try and make you happy.'

She'd been more than content with that at the time, but now it seemed a disturbing omission.

At first when she rang the doorbell at his flat, she thought he was still out somewhere, and she was just about to turn away in defeat when she heard the sound of movement inside.

The door opened, and they faced each other. He looked terrible, was her first thought. He was pale, and his eyes were bloodshot, and he seemed to be wearing a dressing gown, and nothing else.

She said anxiously, 'Jago, are you ill?' She took a step forward, to be arrested by the sour reek of spirits on his breath. It was something she hadn't encountered before with him, and it alarmed her.

In his turn, he was staring at her as if he didn't know who she was, and then she saw a dawning horror in his eyes.

And in the same instant heard a girl's voice saying with plaintive impatience, 'Sweetie, aren't you ever coming back to bed? Get rid of whoever it is and ...' She appeared from the bedroom, wearing nothing but the coverlet from the bed draped round her, none too effectively.

The hand was round Ashley's throat again, tightening, squeezing ...

The girl came forward to Jago's side. Her eyes, blue and hard as nails, flicked over Ashley dismissively.

'They say three's a crowd, don't they, darling? Or is that the way you like it?'

Jago slumped against the door jamb with a muffled groan.

Ashley wanted to stamp her feet. She wanted to kick, to lash out with her hands, and tear with her nails, and scream. She wanted to damage them, both of them, physically. Mark them as they had smashed her emotionally.

Nausea rose, hot and acrid, in her throat, and she turned and ran down the stairs, not waiting for the lift, and out into the chill of the night air. She leaned against her car, retching miserably, uncaring who might see her or what conclusions they might draw. Then, as soon as she was sufficiently in control of herself, she climbed into the driving seat, and started the engine. She didn't go home. She drove out of town, and down to the river, parking in the very spot where Jago had proposed to her, sitting white-faced and burning-eyed until dawn.

When she finally returned home, she brushed aside her father's reproaches and anxious queries, saying merely that she'd had some thinking to do, and needed to be alone. When she'd added that she was no longer going to marry Jago she and Silas had the worst row of their lives.

'But you can't throw him over for some whim!' he'd raged at her. 'My God, girl, only last week you thought the sun, moon, and stars all shone out of him! And I need him. I need a strong man to run Landons after I'm gone. As your husband he can become chairman after me. As soon as I met him, I knew he was the right man.'

'Right for me?' she wanted to ask, wincing. 'Or merely right for Landons?' But she'd never voiced the query.

Her magnificent solitaire diamond ring she'd sent back to Jago by company messenger, with a note stating bleakly that she never wanted to see him or hear from him again.

And nor had she, Ashley thought wearily, until now. Until that phone call, like a bolt from the blue.

Not only was her company at risk. With Jago's return, her precarious peace of mind was threatened. And that, frighteningly, seemed a great deal worse.

CHAPTER TWO

AFTER a while, when she felt a little calmer, she lifted the telephone and dialled.

'Martin Witham, please,' she told the receptionist who answered. 'Tell him Miss Landon is calling.'

She was put through with flattering promptness.

'Ashley!' Martin sounded pleased and surprised. 'Why on earth are you back so soon?'

'Clearly, you haven't been reading the financial pages,' she said lightly. 'Let's just say a state of emergency's been declared and it seemed better to return.'

'My poor sweet!' His voice was warm and concerned. 'Want to tell me all about it over dinner at the Country Club tonight?'

She laughed. 'That's exactly what I hoped you'd say,' she teased. 'Pick me up at eight?'

'I'll be counting the minutes,' he promised.

She felt better after that. His voice had reassured her, helping to take away the sour taste the earlier call had left.

She'd been seeing Martin for a couple of months, since he'd arrived from London to join a local firm of solicitors. After Jago, Ashley had tended to steer clear of any kind of involvement, but Martin had persuaded her to think again, although he had made it clear from the first that he was in no hurry to rush into any kind of serious relationship. He'd been divorced, he told her, and was still licking his wounds, but he would be glad of some female

24

companionship.

It was an arrangement which suited them both very well. Since Silas' death, Ashley had been lonelier than she cared to remember, and Martin's friendship had buoyed her up, just when she needed it most.

And she needed him now, she thought ruefully.

Martin had not told her very much about his marriage, and she was equally reticent on the subject of her broken engagement. Now, she supposed, she would have to tell Martin that her ex-fiancé was back in town, throwing fresh attention on an episode she had hoped was behind her for ever.

She felt depression closing in on her like a cloud, and gave herself a swift mental shake. Sleep was what she needed, and food. She made herself an omelette in her compact kitchen, eating every scrap, then curled up on the living room sofa, emptying her mind, and relaxing her muscles until her intrinsic weariness had its way with her.

When she woke, she felt perceptibly better, refreshed and even relaxed. Which seemed, she thought, to bode well for the evening ahead. She applied her usual light make-up, sprayed herself lavishly with *Amazone*, then zipped herself into a new dress she'd bought on impulse during her West Indian holiday. It was the colour which had attracted her originally—a clear, vivid emerald, enhancing her eyes.

Her one beauty, she thought critically, as she turned and twisted in front of the mirror, trying to decide whether the dress was too extreme for the sedate delights of the County Club. Certainly, the crossover bodice plunged lower than anything she had worn before, and the back of the dress bared her from the brief halter round her neck almost to the base of her spine. For a moment, she was tempted to change into something more demure, something that reflected the muted businesslike image she tried to project these days. Then she tossed her head, making her glossy hair swing challengingly.

To hell with it, she thought recklessly. Since the night of Jago's betrayal, she'd lived a kind of half-life. Perhaps it was only right that his return should signal her emergence from her self-imposed chrysalis—proclaiming to the world at large, as well as himself, that she no longer carried even the flicker of a torch for him.

She'd been a fool to react like that to his call, she told herself angrily. She should have been civil but indifferent, instead of letting him know he could still get under her skin. Well, she would know better at their next encounter—if there was one.

Martin's expression when she admitted him to the flat was evidence, if she needed it, that her change of image was a success. And it reminded her too of how little thought she'd given to her appearance over the past couple of years.

'The new me,' she explained. 'Do you approve?'

'I'm not sure if "approve" is the word I'm looking for,' Martin said carefully. 'May I kiss you, or will it spoil your make-up?'

Ashley went readily into his arms. She was accustomed to the light embraces they exchanged on meeting and parting, and when Martin deliberately prolonged and deepened the kiss, she made no demur. Perhaps it wasn't just the outer shell she needed to change, she thought, submitting passively to the ardent pressure of his mouth on hers.

She waited for some answering surge in her own

blood, but it didn't happen. Probably she was still too tired and caught off-balance by the past twenty-four hours to be able to conjure up much of a response, she excused herself, as they left for the Club.

It was already quite crowded when they arrived. Martin had booked a corner table, away from the dance floor where a three-piece band played quietly.

'The usual wide choice, I see,' he said wryly, handing her a menu. 'Steak, steak, scampi or steak.'

Ashley smiled at him. 'And I keep telling you that's the height of sophistication in this neck of the woods,' she teased.

'So you do,' he muttered. 'What's it to be, then?'

'Melon, please, followed by a fillet steak rare to medium, and a side salad.'

'And I'll have the same,' Martin told the waiter. His hand reached for Ashley's across the table. 'We never seem to ask for anything else. Maybe we should make it a standing order.'

'Maybe,' Ashley returned neutrally. She returned the pressure of his fingers, but his words troubled her, seeming to signal a permanence she wasn't ready for. She was relieved when the conversation took a less personal turn. Martin was engaged in litigation work, and he gave a droll description of some of the cases he'd been defending while she way away.

Ashley leaned back in her chair, enjoying the fragrance of the white wine she had asked for as an aperitif, her eyes idly scanning the room as she did so.

'And when the magistrate asked if he had anything to say, the idiot came back with "But the car always stalls if I drive at less than sixty, Your Worship",' Martin was saying, then his voice sharpened.

'Ashley, what is it? Are you all right?'

Her whole body had tensed, and she could feel the blood draining from her face. Standing in the doorway, looking round the room, was Jago Marrick.

Her first, instinctive thought was how little he had changed in the intervening years. The breach between them had left no mark on him as it had on her, but then why should it? she asked herself bitterly. No doubt he'd regretted the loss of Landons, but he was a success in his own right as Silas had always predicted. Ashley had been nothing more to him than a means to an end.

But it was unfair, she thought, digging her nails into the palms of her hands, that his physical appeal should not have diminished. Outwardly, he was still the man she'd fallen so helplessly in love with.

The lean, graceful body, the lightly curling brown hair, still worn rather longer than convention demanded, the cool, incisive lines of nose, mouth and jaw, had lost none of their impact, thrusting her into sudden unwelcome turmoil.

With a superlative effort she fought for control.

'It's all right,' she said, forcing a little laugh, and inwardly thankful for the comparative seclusion of their table. 'I—I'm jet-lagged still, I suppose. Perhaps I should have had a quiet evening at home.'

'Well, you still can,' Martin assured her promptly. 'When we've eaten, I'll drive you back.' He smiled at her. 'Some cosseting's what you need.'

She doubted whether she needed anything he had in mind but now was not the time to be talking about that. She felt suddenly like an animal, caught in a snare with the hunter drawing closer ...

Get a grip on yourself, she adjured herself, silently and savagely. So he's here. It's a public place, and he has as much right to use it as you.

But there's nothing he can do to you any more—nothing …

Martin said with a faint groan, 'Oh, hell! One of the firm's most important clients has just come in, and he's heading this way. I shall have to be civil at least.'

Ashley knew with a sense of sick inevitability who it would be, and nerved herself, her hands clenching into fists in her lap, her face schooled to impassivity.

'Good evening, Witham.' Jago stopped beside their table. She made herself look up, her face stretched into a polite smile which felt like a grimace. He wasn't alone, she saw. Erica was beside him, ethereal in black chiffon, clinging to his arm. The grieving widow's first public appearance, Ashley decided ironically.

Jago was looking at her now, his brows lifting with faint cynicism as he assimilated her appearance.

'Ashley,' he said softly. 'What a charming surprise.'

'You know each other?' asked Martin. 'I was just about to introduce you.'

'No need,' Jago assured him. 'Ashley and I are old—acquaintances, aren't we, darling?'

'You could say that,' she said shortly. She looked past him to Erica. 'Please accept my condolences on your sad loss, Mrs Marrick.'

'Such a terrible shock,' Erica sighed delicately. 'But life must go on. That's what dear Giles would have wanted.'

Remembering the big, bluff man with his booming laugh, Ashley thought this was probably true. At any rate, it absolved Erica from most of the conventions of mourning, she decided cynically.

'Won't you join us?' Martin offered, to Ashley's

horror.

'We'd be delighted,' Jago said smoothly, and she had to bite back a gasp of sheer anguish. But nothing could be done; a waiter was already hurrying to lay two extra covers. Ashley's sole consolation was that Erica seemed no better pleased by the situation than she was herself, judging by the expression she had seen fleetingly cross the widow's lovely face, and the way her fingers were curving possessively on Jago's sleeve.

Well, everyone looks for consolation in their own way, she told herself, and turned an artificially radiant smile on Martin.

The meal was a three-dimensional, Technicolored nightmare, with full stereophonic sound. The steaks, when they arrived, were excellent, but Ashley might just as well have been chewing her way through an old handbag for all the enjoyment she derived from hers. Tautly, she declined a dessert when it was offered, and coffee too, praying that Martin would take the hint, and whisk her away as he'd promised.

But Martin wasn't in the market for hints. Oblivious to any undercurrents, he was leaning back in his chair, being expansive and thoroughly enjoying himself. Taking the opportunity to impress an important client, Ashley thought, then chided herself for being unkind.

She glanced up, and found Jago's eyes on her. He, she realised resentfully, wasn't even making an attempt at pretence. Openly and unashamedly, he was staring at her, insolently studying the shape of her breasts under the flimsy bodice, and to her shame and horror she found her body reacting to the calculation of his gaze, the nipples hardening and thrusting against the soft cling of the fabric. And, worst of all, she could tell by the slow smile curling his firm-lipped mouth that her involuntary arousal had not gone unnoticed.

Mortified beyond all bearing, she stared down at the table. What kind of person was she to allow herself to be excited by a look from a man who had treated her as badly as Jago had done? She swallowed, remembering that he had always had that effect on her, no matter how hard she'd tried to resist it. Even in company, one lingering glance from him had been enough to melt her bones, and send sweet fire coursing through her veins. It was only later, alone with him, that the problems had started, shame at her body's own urgency freezing her into frightened rigidity when he tried to kiss and caress her.

But that was something she neither needed nor wanted to remember, and she tried to turn her attention elsewhere, gazing at the couples moving round the dance floor in time to the music.

Jago leaned towards her. 'Would you like to dance?' he asked courteously.

Her voice was stony. 'No, thank you.'

'Oh, go on, darling,' Martin urged jovially. 'You know you love this tune.'

Had she really admitted that to him? she asked herself despairingly. How could she—when it was a song she'd danced to with Jago over and over again in those first heady days?

'Then that settles it.' Jago was standing beside her chair, reaching for her hand, drawing her inexorably to her feet before she could utter any further protest.

She couldn't free herself without making some kind of scene, and her spirit quailed at the thought of that, so numbly she allowed him to guide her through the encircling tables to the dance floor.

'I'll try not to touch any bare skin,' he said sardonically, as he drew her into his arms. 'But the design of your dress makes it rather difficult.'

She flushed angrily. 'Don't!'

'Why so sensitive?' he jeered. 'You can't help being the way you are, any more than I can. And you certainly never wanted to be touched—by me, at any rate.'

Ashley shrugged, trying not to flinch from the clasp of his cool fingers, making herself move to the music with him. 'Why drag up the past?' she asked shortly. 'It was a long time ago. I've changed. Probably we both have.'

'In your case, the change is formidable,' he said softly. 'What's brought about this new sophistication? Witham?'

'Perhaps,' said Ashley, lifting her chin. 'If it's any of your business.'

The tawny eyes glittered down at her. 'Going to marry him, Ash?'

'Now that really is none of your business.' Ashley bit her lip. 'I'd like to go back to the table, please.'

'When the dance is over.' He swung her round, gently but inexorably, making her realise it was impossible to be free without undignified hassle. 'And isn't it natural that I should be interested in your plans for the future? After all, they once involved me quite intimately, if you recall.'

'I'm not likely to forget,' she said scornfully. 'I'd have said you'd totally forfeited any right to enquire into my private life. And while we're on the subject, how did you get hold of my phone number? I'm ex-directory.'

'Let's say a little bird told me,' he said. 'You seem rather besieged at the moment. I thought you might welcome a friendly call.'

'Then you miscalculated,' Ashley said bitingly. 'I don't need your interest in my affairs, business or personal. In future, kindly leave me alone.'

Jago gave her a meditative look, his eyes hooded. 'That isn't as easy as it sounds. I'd say we were bound to run into each other in a place this size. Don't you think we should at least practise being civil to each other?'

Ashley tried to quell the inner dismay his words evoked. He seemed to be confirming that he would not, after all, be returning to the States, just as Henry had suggested.

'It's a small town indeed,' she said.' And rather limiting, I'd have thought, for someone of your ambition. I imagine you can't wait to go back to America.'

'Then your imagination is playing you tricks,' he said pleasantly. 'I'll be happy to discuss my plans with you, Ashley, but now is not the time. I didn't ask you to dance in order to have a serious talk.'

'No? Then I can only assume you intended to annoy me.' She shook her head. 'I'm sorry, Jago. The most I can call on where you're concerned is indifference. If anyone's suffering from any kind of aggravation here tonight, then it's probably your cousin Erica.'

'Oh, I think Witham is managing to keep her entertained,' he said casually. 'Although he's a bit of a dull stick.'

'He's a decent person,' Ashley said levelly. 'Although I suppose decency is a quality that couldn't be expected to have much appeal for you.'

'Or to you, my sweet vixen.' His mouth curled. 'But I asked you to dance, Ashley, to find out if the change in you is any more than skin deep.' His hand at her back increased its pressure suddenly, forcing her towards him across the slight decorous distance that separated them. Bringing her body into intimate, objectionable contact with his.

Ashley gasped, her eyes flashing green fire at him, as she tried unavailingly to pull away. Her lips parted in a protest which was fated never to be uttered as Jago's mouth came down on hers, warm, firm, and shamelessly sensual.

Her senses reeled under the suddenness of the onslaught. Her body seemed to be melting, her legs no longer able to support her properly, the blood in her veins moving slowly, thick and sweet as honey, as she fought for control.

The kiss seemed endless and she had to curb the instinct to yield, to respond, to explore his mouth as avidly as he was seeking the secrets of hers. It was a temptation that had to be resisted at all costs, and she knew it, even though her body was overwhelmed, trembling with the surge of unsatisfied longing within her.

But she had to remember that he cared no more for her now than he had three years ago, a small desperate voice in her head warned her. He was trying to score points, that was all. To let the eyes watching them know that the breach between them, once a nine-day wonder, was either healed or no longer important.

When at last he took his mouth from hers, it was with open reluctance. The music had stopped, and only a smattering of applause from the other dancers filled the amazed and questioning silence around them.

Still dazed, Ashley let Jago lead her back to the table, aware of the barrage of fascinated and curious looks and murmured remarks following them. She was aware too that the couple awaiting them at their table didn't share that general fascination and curiosity. Martin looked bemused and sullen, and Erica was plainly furious, although she was smiling graciously enough.

Muttering an excuse, Ashley grabbed her bag, and made her way to the refuge of the powder room. Luckily it was deserted, and she sank down on one of the padded stools in front of the mirror and stared at herself. Her eyes looked twice their normal size, and she hadn't a scrap of colour left. She touched the bare, swollen outline of her mouth with fingers that shook slightly.

Jago had made no concessions at all, either to the passage of time which had separated them, or to the fact they were in a public place. His behaviour, by any standard, was unforgivable. She opened her bag, fumbling a little as she retrieved her compact and lipstick and tried to repair some of the damage he had wrought, while shame and anger built up inside her.

How dare he behave like that! she raged inwardly. His arrogance was appalling. But so, honesty reminded her, had been her own reaction.

She couldn't go back in the dining room, she thought restlessly, to face the stares and speculation, and Jago's silent triumph. She would have to get a message to Martin, telling him she had a headache and wanted to go home.

But when she emerged, she found Martin waiting for her.

She pinned on a smile. 'Ready to go?'

'More than ready.' His voice was pettish, and she smothered a sigh. His hand gripped her elbow almost painfully as they walked to the car park, but he said nothing more until they were in the car, and on their way.

Then, 'What was that all about?' he wanted to know restively.

'Do we have to discuss it now?' Ashley stared in front of her.

'I'd say so. I don't appreciate being made to look a fool in public.'

'If it's any consolation, I don't think that was the main intention.' Ashley bit her lip. 'Jago was trying to—prove a point, and he chose a rather drastic way of doing it, that's all.'

'Old acquaintances, he said.' Martin's mouth turned down at the corners. 'It seemed more than that to me.'

His tone demanded an explanation. Ashley hesitated for a moment, then said reluctantly, 'As it happens, Jago Marrick was the man I was engaged to a couple of years ago.'

'Good God!' Martin, always the most careful of drivers, actually took her eyes off the road to gaze at her while he assimilated the information. 'I hadn't the slightest idea ...'

Ashley sighed. 'I thought someone would probably have mentioned it.'

'I suppose everyone assumed you would have told me yourself.' Martin sounded injured. 'Didn't you think I'd want to know you'd been—involved with one of our top clients?'

Ashley looked down at her interlaced fingers. 'Frankly it was a period of my life I preferred to put out of my mind altogether. Jago was in America, and Giles Marrick could have lived for another thirty years, as far as I knew.' She moistened her lips with the tip of her tongue. 'But what does it matter, anyway? It's over, and has been for a long time.'

After a long pause, Martin said carefully, 'A

casual observer tonight might query that.'

Ashley forced a smile. 'I think tonight was a cross between Jago's idea of a joke, and his wish to tell the world there's no longer any bad feeling between us.'

'And is that the case?'

She bent her head in affirmation, trying to push out of her mind the memory of that cynically passionate kiss, and her unsought reaction to it.

He said judiciously, 'Well, it's never easy to get over these things, as I know to my cost. Were you very much in love with him, darling?'

'I'm not sure I even knew what love was,' Ashley said tonelessly.

He seemed content with that, and to her relief, didn't insist on accompanying her into the flat as she had half-feared. He accepted her excuse that she was still dog-tired after her flight, and went off, promising tenderly to phone her the next day.

Ashley fell into bed like an automaton, but still she couldn't sleep. She lay for what seemed like hours, staring into the darkness. Didn't she have enough problems? Jago's re-entry into her life was a complication she didn't need.

Or perhaps the trouble she felt brewing through him was simply a figment of her overcharged imagination. He had his own life and responsibilities now, with Erica not the least of them, judging by tonight's showing. He wouldn't have time, let alone the inclination to bait his ex-fiancée.

Surely their lives could run on parallel lines, never crossing the path of each other. And on this comforting reflection, she finally dozed off.

She was woken the next morning by the prolonged ringing of her doorbell. Groggily, she pushed back the covers and grabbed for her robe, trying through the clouds of sleep to remember if the milkman needed paying.

As she opened the door, she stiffened, her whole body taut with outrage as she recognised her visitor.

'You again!' she exclaimed furiously, and tried to slam the door in his face, but Jago was too quick for her. His arm clamped round her waist, lifting her totally off her feet as he stepped into the narrow hall. As he set her down again, the door was already closed behind him.

Ashley gritted between her teeth, 'There's really no end to your presumption! May I know how you discovered my address—or have I the same little bird to thank?'

Jago tutted. 'You sound very crotchety, my sweet. I don't think late nights agree with you. Are you alone, or should I lurk discreetly in the sitting room while Witham makes his escape?'

'If there's any vanishing to be done, you'll do it,' she said tersely. 'Get out!'

'When I've said what I came to say.' The hazel eyes looked her over mockingly. 'Or did you think last night was all there was to it?'

'It seemed more than enough for me,' Ashley snapped. She caught sight of the long case clock in the corner. 'My God,' she said falteringly, 'it isn't even eight o'clock yet! What the hell ...'

Jago produced a carrier bag, 'I thought we'd have a working breakfast,' he said briskly.

'You thought what?' Words failed her.

'A working breakfast,' he repeated kindly. 'They have a lot of them in the States. I'm supplying the food.'

'Well, don't expect me to cook it. I never eat breakfast anyway.'

'Then you should.' He gave her another more

searching look, and her hands moved instinctively to tighten the already secure sash of her robe. 'It occurred to me last night, you can't afford to lose any more weight. Will you show me where the kitchen is, or shall I find it by trial and error?'

'You'll get out of here now!' Ashley raged. 'And take your lousy food with you!'

'Your ways of expressing yourself don't seem to have improved over the years,' Jago said coolly. 'The food is fresh—grapefruit, eggs and bacon, and bread for toast. You don't have to lift a finger. Just eat—and listen to what I have to say.'

'There's nothing you have to talk about that I want to hear.' Eyes sparkling ominously, she faced him, her head held proudly high.

'Not even when the subject under discussion is Landons—and its questionable future?' he asked.

'There is no question about Landons' future,' Ashley denied sharply.

'Now there we differ,' he said quite gently. 'I'd say that without some pretty fancy footwork on your part, Marshalls are going to snap you up, and cheap at the price. Is that what you want?'

'Of course not,' she said impatiently. 'But it's no concern of yours.'

'It's my concern.' There was no amusement in his face. The hazel eyes were cold and inimical as they rested on her. 'Silas was my good friend, remember?'

'I'm hardly likely to forget. I've often thought it a pity you couldn't marry him yourself.'

'And I've often thought it a pity you weren't smacked, as a child, until you couldn't sit down for a week,' Jago said bitingly. 'Now go and get dressed, unless you want to spend the morning in that travesty of a dressing gown. I'll call you when the food's ready.'

She said shakily, 'If I were a man, I'd throw you out.'

'Don't be silly, Ash.' He tapped her hot cheek lightly with his forefinger. 'If you were a man, I wouldn't be here, period.'

She wanted to tell him not to call her 'Ash', but it suddenly seemed infinitely safer to go to her room, and put some clothes on as he'd suggested.

She dragged on jeans, not new, and a sweater which had seen better days, dragging a comb ruthlessly through her black hair. Cosmetics she left severely alone. Jago was not to think she had taken any trouble with her appearance on his account, she told herself vehemently.

The kitchen was full of the scent and crackle of frying bacon and percolating coffee, and in spite of her anger, Ashley's nose twitched in appreciation as she entered. Jago was standing by the hob, slicing tomatoes. He too was wearing jeans, she noticed, the close-fitting denim accentuating the length of his legs and the leanness of his hips. The cuffs of his shirt were unbuttoned and turned casually back revealing tanned forearms. He made her trim kitchen seem cramped, Ashley thought resentfully as she unwillingly took a seat at the small breakfast bar.

'Here.' He poured coffee into a mug and pushed it across the worktop to her.

'Thank you,' she acknowledged stiffly.

'And three bags full to you.' He gave her a long look. 'Unless you relax your attitude, lady, and fast, we're going to get nowhere.'

'Well, that suits me down to the ground,' said Ashley coldly. 'As I haven't the slightest wish to make any kind of progress with you.'

'So, hurt pride and resentment still rule, O.K.

You aren't prepared to swallow either or both for the sake of Landons?'

'I'd give whatever I had to in order to save the company,' Ashley retorted. 'I've already given the last couple of years of my life. Apparently for some of the board, this isn't enough. I don't know what more they want—blood, presumably.'

'No,' he said, 'I think they want the assurance that Landons will continue to be the dynamic, thrusting concern that Silas made it.'

'You seem very well informed,' said Ashley coldly, gritting her teeth, as she complied with his signal to start on her grapefruit. 'Perhaps you're also aware that Landons had a record profit last year.'

'That's true,' he admitted. 'But accrued from the projects that Silas set up. You've kept the company ticking over, and you've delivered the goods, as no one could wish to deny. But your forward planning is lousy. There've been a number of tenders you should have gone for—and got—but haven't. Silas went out and sold Landons in the market place. He was the arch-instigator of all time. Those new civic buildings in town were a case in point. The council never thought on that scale until Silas sold them the idea. Now no one can imagine how they ever did without them. And you can repeat that story over and over again up and down the length of the country.'

'We have plenty of work,' Ashley protested indignantly.

'For the time being—but how much of it is new? How many of your present contracts have you fought for and won?' He shook his head. 'This is what concerns the majority of the board, Ashley, and in their place, I'd probably share that concern.'

Ashley bit her lip, looking with disfavour at the plate he was setting in front of her. 'I can't possibly eat all that,' she protested.

'You'll eat it if I have to hold your nose and force-feed you,' Jago told her forthrightly. 'You're going to need all your strength, lady, and besides, we have other more important issues to argue about than food.' He took his place beside her and began to eat with relish as she registered with annoyance. His presence in her flat, his intrusion into her life was an outrage, but he seemed unconscious of the fact.

'So why are you interfering?' she asked sulkily, cutting into her bacon, and noting crossly that it was done to a crisp, just as she liked it. 'I suppose you've come here to give me some good advice. Well, let me tell you, I don't need ...'

'Mere advice won't get you out of the hole you're in.' He reached for a piece of toast. 'I think the situation calls for rather more drastic action.'

'And you, of course, know exactly how to cope with the crisis,' she said derisively.

'I could get rid of Marshalls for starters.' Jago bit into his toast.

'How?' His confidence needled her.

He sighed. 'By persuading the board to reject their offer.'

Ashley put down her knife and fork. 'But why should they do any such thing, particularly on your say-so?' she demanded heatedly. 'My God, you're not even a member of the Landons board!'

'But I could be.' The hazel eyes looked coolly and directly into hers. 'In fact I could be chairman— if you and I were married.'

CHAPTER THREE

In a voice she hardly recognised as her own, Ashley gasped 'That—has to be the most insane idea I've ever heard!'

'On the contrary, it makes a lot of sense.' He even had the gall to go on eating, she realised dazedly. 'Think about it, and try using your head, instead of your hormones. It was what Silas always intended, after all.'

'I'm only too well aware of that,' she said rigidly. 'It was a very nice, businesslike arrangement for you both, until you allowed your other—proclivities to get in the way.'

'Ah,' Jago said softly, 'I thought we wouldn't get far before that thorny subject was dragged kicking and screaming into the light of day. You never gave me a chance to explain at the time. Perhaps now you might allow me a few words.'

'The fewer the better.' Suddenly she was hurting again, every image from that terrible night etched on to her memory in agonising detail. 'Although I fail to see what possible explanation you can come up with for your conduct.' She paused theatrically. 'Ah, I know. The lady was your long-lost sister—or your maiden aunt twice removed seeking shelter for the night. Is that how it was?'

'No,' he said, his mouth curling. 'The situation was exactly as you read it. And before you ask— no, she wasn't an old flame, either. I'd picked her up in a bar earlier in the evening. Satisfied?'

'Please spare me the sordid details,' Ashley said scornfully. 'I don't want to hear them.'

'What did you want to hear, I wonder?' he asked cynically. 'Some cosy lie, designed to make you feel better, and whitewash the whole incident? Not a chance. I offered an explanation for what it's worth, but no excuses.'

'There is no possible excuse for what you did,' she said bitterly. 'And you have no right to walk back into my life, and—proposition me in this insulting way.'

'The word is proposal,' Jago interrupted sardonically. 'A proposition has a totally different connotation, although you wouldn't know anything about that, my little Puritan. You froze me off so many times during our brief but eventful engagement that it was a miracle I didn't die from frostbite.'

'Oh, I see,' exclaimed Ashley, heavily sarcastic. 'Then it's all my fault. I should have allowed you to seduce me when you wanted to—and then this little local difficulty would never have happened.'

Jago pushed his plate away. 'Seduction,' he said levelly, 'was never what I had in mind. All I wanted from you, Ash, was a little human warmth—a sign, however fleeting, that when we were married, you'd welcome my arms round you—enjoy going to bed with me. All I got was one terrified hysterical rebuff after another. Is it any real wonder that my courage failed at the prospect of a bride who turned to stone every time I came near her?'

'And human warmth was presumably what the lady in the bar had to offer,' said Ashley, her heart beating harshly and discordantly.

His smile was twisted. 'No, it was slightly more than that. In fact, she made it quite clear that she fancied me rotten, and that was balm to my soul after having you fight me off night after night as if I was the Mad Rapist. I don't go in for one-night stands as a rule, but she caught me at a weak moment, and I was more than ready to enjoy what she was offering.' He paused. 'Now you know everything.'

'What a pity all I had to offer was Landons.' Ashley drank some coffee. 'And what a pity you wanted not just the cake, but the icing too. Getting control of the company eventually wasn't enough for you—you wanted passion as well. It never occurred to you that I might not feel particularly passionate towards a man who was using me only as a stepping stone to being chairman of the board.'

There was a silence. He said at last, 'Frankly, no, it never occurred to me.'

'You were clearly too used to finding your attractions irresistible,' she said savagely. 'And I was young and naïve, and easily conned, or so you thought. But I soon realised what the score was.'

'My congratulations on your perspicacity,' he said ironically. 'But if you expect me to bow my head and creep away in shame, you can think again. It alters nothing as far as I'm concerned. In fact, it almost makes things easier. You came to terms once with being married for Landons. Why not again? After all, you said only five minutes ago you'd give all you had to save Landons. Well, all I'm asking is our joint names on a marriage certificate—nothing more.'

Ashley laughed. 'You expect me to believe that?'

'Believe what you please,' he said curtly. 'But my little experiment at the Country Club last night told me loud and clear that nothing's changed between us, that you wouldn't countenance me as a lover at any price. Well, I can accept that. Three years ago

I tried to woo you into becoming my wife in the fullest sense of the word, and failed. So at least now we know where we stand. And didn't Silas always say his motto was "The end justifies the means"?'

'Yes,' she said huskily. 'He always used to say that. But I don't believe that any result could justify what you're proposing. Why are you doing this?'

'I've told you—I liked Silas, and I respected him and everything he was trying to do. If you hadn't turned up at the flat that night, we'd have got married and struggled along somehow for the sake of Landons. In fact, if I'd been around to take some of the pressure off him, Silas would probably still be here now, and don't think I haven't blamed myself for that. Perhaps this is my way of trying to make reparation.'

'But everyone will know why we're getting married …' Even in her own ears, the protest sounded stock and feeble.

'What will they know?' he asked. 'They'll know that we had some kind of rift three years ago, and parted. And now, older and wiser, we're together again.' He gave her a wintry smile. 'Our tender embrace at the Country Club won't have gone unremarked, you can bet. Anyone remotely interested in our private affairs will take it for granted that our reconciliation began there and then.' He paused. 'When's the next board meeting?'

'On Thursday,' she said helplessly. 'But …'

'Well, that gives us enough time if we apply for a special licence. We need to present the board with a *fait accompli*.'

'Wait,' Ashley said desperately. 'You're talking as if everything was settled—agreed between us, and it isn't.'

'But it will be,' he said. 'Think of it as a means to an end, Ash. You may not be able to stomach the thought of me as a husband, but I swear I'll give you nothing to complain of as a business partner.' He held out his hand. 'Shall we shake hands on a deal?'

Slowly and reluctantly, Ashley complied. 'There must be some other way,' she said, half to herself.

'If you're thinking of presenting them with Witham in my place, then forget it. He may be a wow in court, but he'd be out of his depth with Landons, and with you.'

She looked at him, her jaw dropping in shock as she registered his words, and realised that she had never even given Martin a second thought.

Instantly she rallied her defences. 'How easily you dismiss my personal happiness,' she began.

'Is it centred on Witham? You amaze me, darling. There must be more to him than meets the eye, if he's found the way to melt your icy little heart.'

'Because you failed,' she lashed back, 'it hardly means that no other man is capable of success. Even you can't be arrogant enough to believe that!'

Jago inclined his head politely. 'So it's only my touch that you find abhorrent. Well, we live and learn.' He glanced around him. 'This is a pretty flat. You should make a handsome profit when you sell it.'

'I have no intention of selling it.'

'Then you'd better form such an intention,' he said pleasantly. 'Your home will be with me at the Manor.'

'No!' she said hoarsely. 'I won't live with you ...'

'Now you're being absurd,' Jago said shortly. 'Our private arrangements are our own affair, but as far as the rest of the world is concerned, this is a normal marriage. And in normal marriages husbands and wives share the same roof. We are not going to be the exception. Do I make myself clear?'

'As crystal.' Ashley glared at him. 'Has it occurred to you that there'll be a third party sharing our roof as well, and that she may not welcome me at the Manor in any capacity?'

He shrugged. 'That's a bridge we'll cross when we come to it. Anyway, I don't anticipate that Erica will be at the Manor all that much. Giles left her comfortably provided for, and she's always had a yen to travel which he didn't share. There'll be nothing to stop her now.'

Ashley remembered the possessive hand clamped to his arm, and thought—nothing, except the fact she wants you for herself.

Aloud, she said, 'Erica and I have never been the best of friends. Perhaps I should mention that.'

He smiled faintly. 'No one's asking you to fall into each other's arms. I imagine you can manage being civil to each other for limited periods.'

'That,' Ashley said tautly, 'might depend on how limited the periods were.'

Jago frowned impatiently. 'Why look for snags?' he asked. 'Erica is my concern. I'll handle her.'

'Of course,' she said. 'And that will make everything all right.'

He sighed. 'Let's agree this isn't a situation either of us would choose,' he said. 'But the prime concern is to stop Landons being swallowed up by those sharks from Marshalls. Do you want to see your family's name used to dignify the kind of jerrybuilding they go in for?'

'No,' Ashley admitted in a low voice. 'But this— marriage you're foisting on us isn't going to be easy.'

He said flatly, 'Very little is in today's world. Don't worry, Ashley. If it becomes totally impossible, then we'll take the quickest way out. You're not being sentenced to life imprisonment with me.'

'I'm grateful for the reassurance,' she said tonelessly. But she didn't feel grateful as she began to gather the used crockery together. She felt frightened, and defeated, and out of her depth. The last three years of slowly and painfully becoming her own woman, of battling to control Landons, might never have happened. In Jago's presence, she seemed to revert to the bewildered girl, just out of childhood, and torn apart by her emotions.

Oh, it's not fair! she thought desperately, as she fumbled with a handful of cutlery. Why couldn't she practise the indifference to him she professed? And why, after all this time, was she still hurting, and hating him for what he'd done to her?

She ran hot water into the sink, and added detergent. Jago came to stand behind her. His nearness was disturbing, she thought, her body rigid as she registered the warmth of his breath on the back of her neck.

'So I'll make the necessary arrangements. We'll be married on Thursday morning, first thing, before the board meeting.'

'And divorced in the afternoon, after it,' she wanted to say. Instead she heard herself saying quietly, 'That would probably be best.'

She could still hardly believe what was happening. She was selling her life for the sake of Landons with no more emotion than if she'd been making a dental appointment.

'I'll be in touch,' he said. There was a pause, and she tensed, terrified that he was going to touch her—put his hands on her shoulders, and turn her to face him.

She couldn't face him. She was afraid he would read the confusion in her eyes, and she could afford no evidence of frailty where Jago was concerned.

After what seemed an eternity, she felt him move away, and a moment later she heard the decisive closing of the front door as he left.

Ashley found she was gripping the edge of the sink unit, her knuckles white with the strain. Slowly she unclenched her hands, making herself move away from the sink, and out of the kitchen into the living room, where she collapsed on the sofa, her body suddenly boneless.

She looked around at the pleasant room. Her home—her environment—her world, slowly and painfully put together from the pieces of the old one. Soon to be hers no longer.

She said aloud with fierce desperation. 'There must be some other way. There must be!'

Henry Brett's house was a pleasant red-brick villa with gardens sloping down to the bank of the river. As Ashley parked on the gravel sweep in front of the house, Shelagh Brett, who was bedding out plants in one of the borders, straightened and gave her a cheerful wave.

'Ashley dear, how nice!' she exclaimed, coming over to the car. 'Have you come for lunch?'

Ashley shook her head with a rueful smile. 'I don't think so, thanks, Shelagh. I don't seem to have much of an appetite.'

'Oh, this business with Marshalls,' Shelagh said with immediate sympathy. 'Such a worry for you! Henry was so sorry to interrupt your holiday, but he felt it was the only thing to do.'

'Henry was right.' Ashley looked about her. 'Is

he around? Could I have a quick word?'

'When last seen, he was tinkering with the mower,' Shelagh admitted with a wry grin. 'That thing spends more time in pieces than it ever does cutting the grass! But I suppose that's the nature of the beast.'

Henry was in the far garage, wielding a spanner, looking flushed and cross. 'Damned thing,' he was muttering.

'Darling,' his wife said, 'why don't you admit defeat and invest in a new one? Or would you miss these weekly battles?'

Henry got to his feet, wiping his hands on his ancient and disreputable trousers. 'Absolute nonsense,' he said flatly. 'The thing is perfectly good. I'll have it running properly in no time.'

Shelagh laughed. 'He's getting incredibly mean in his old age,' she teased. 'Do you think he's paid enough, Ashley?'

'Don't be ridiculous,' Henry said shortly. 'Let's have some coffee on the terrace.'

While Shelagh poured the coffee, Ashley made small talk, asking about their elder child Jeanne, now at university, and young Colin who was due to take A levels soon. She was genuinely interested. She'd always liked the Bretts. After her gipsy-like existence with Silas, their home had often seemed like a sanctuary to her, a place of total security. Shelagh was a serene and smiling woman, whose openly admitted priorities were her husband and children.

How nice, Ashley thought, as she sipped her coffee, to know such stability.

After a while the telephone rang, and Shelagh excused herself, saying it was probably a message for her about a forthcoming jumble sale.

Left alone with Henry, Ashley felt an awkward silence pressing down on her. She made a few commonplace remarks about the garden, while she searched for a suitable opening.

'What is it, my dear?' asked Henry at last. 'Has something happened?'

Ashley moistened her lips. 'You could say that,' she agreed carefully. 'I may have found a way of avoiding the Marshalls takeover.'

'Have you indeed?' said Henry, after a pause. 'Am I to know what it is?'

'Everyone's going to know eventually,' Ashley shrugged. 'It isn't the kind of thing you can keep secret.' She took a deep breath, 'Henry, I'm going to marry Jago Marrick.'

Henry sat up with a jerk, spilling some coffee. 'Damnation!' He mopped at the cushion on his chair. 'Ashley, this is no joking matter ...'

'I'm perfectly serious.' Ashley stared past him to the flicker of water beyond the smooth lawns. 'He—he came to see me this morning, quite early, and we—we talked the whole thing through. And I began to see it was the only way. As you said yourself, he's what the board want—a strong man at the top. If anyone can talk them round from recommending the Marshalls offer to the shareholders, then it has to be Jago.'

Henry looked in deep shock. 'Ashley,' he said faintly, 'you don't know what you're saying. People don't do things like this ...'

'Not in the normal course of events.' Ashley stared down at her hands, trying to imagine a gold ring on her wedding finger, and failing utterly. 'But saving Landons is the kind of situation which calls for extreme measures. I thought you'd understand.'

'Understand?' Henry almost exploded. 'For God's

sake, girl, you hate the man! I've seen your reaction each time his name has been mentioned. I don't know what he did to you—heaven knows I don't want to pry, but it was obvious to anyone that you'd finished with him for good. Why, even yesterday ...'

'I know, I know.' Ashley bit her lip. 'But at least this time I have no illusions to shatter. Our marriage is going to be—a means to an end. Nothing more.'

Henry was staring at her as if she'd just grown a second head. 'Child, no company on earth is worth that sort of sacrifice.' He made a clumsy gesture. 'We'll sort something out with Marshalls—insist on retaining some kind of control ...'

'No,' Ashley said steadily. 'Over my dead body. Jago and I have reached an agreement, and that will stand.'

Shelagh returned at that moment. 'Such a fuss about hiring a hall for a few hours!' She paused. 'Why is Henry spluttering? Has his coffee gone down the wrong way?'

Ashley shook her head. 'I've given him some unwelcome news.'

'You've made him redundant,' Shelagh said amiably. 'Perhaps we can get a new mower with the golden handshake.'

Ashley bit back an unwilling laugh. 'No, it's nothing like that. I simply came to tell him I was getting married, and he doesn't approve.'

Shelagh frowned at her husband. 'That's rather presumptuous of you, darling.' She turned to Ashley, her face anxious. 'Who's the lucky man, my dear? That young solicitor, I suppose.'

'If only it were!' Henry broke in thunderously. 'She's going to marry Jago Marrick.'

Shelagh's eyes widened. She said softly, 'Oh,

Ashley,' and took her hand in both of hers.

'Don't encourage her!' Henry almost howled. 'It's madness—sheer madness! Why, they haven't even spoken to each other for three years.'

Shaken, Ashley looked at him. 'I never thought you'd react like this,' she said. She tried to smile. 'Why, I even thought it might be you who'd given him my address and phone number. He must have got them from somewhere.'

'Not from me,' Henry said bleakly.

As Ashley put her coffee cup back on the tray, she caught sight of Shelagh's face, a mixture of guilt and embarrassment. She caught her breath.

'Shelagh, it was you, wasn't it?'

Henry sat bolt upright, staring at his wife. 'You?' He groaned in disbelief. 'Whatever possessed you to do such a thing?'

Shelagh sighed. 'Because he asked me, I suppose,' she said quietly. 'I wasn't going to tell you, Henry, because I knew you wouldn't approve. But I've never forgotten, Ashley, how much in love with him you were once. When you parted, and he went away, it was as if someone had switched off a light inside you.' She paused. 'Engagements are such difficult, edgy times. Sometimes people quarrel over quite trivial things, and each of them is too proud to make the first move. I never knew what had gone wrong between you, but when Jago telephoned me and asked how he could get in touch with you, it seemed like a new beginning for you both.' She squeezed Ashley's hand. 'And I was right, it seems. I'm so happy for you.'

'You had no damned right to interfere!' Henry almost roared, his faced flushed and furious. 'Why the hell did that fellow have to come back here now? I was afraid you'd do something idiotic—

that's why I was so reluctant to send for you.'

Ashley stared at him in bewilderment. She'd never seen Henry so upset before, and certainly never heard him shout at Shelagh.

'I'm sorry,' she said miserably. 'I didn't expect you to be delighted, but it seems all I've done is ruin your day. I'd better go.'

'I need a drink,' muttered Henry, and strode indoors.

Shelagh tried to smile. 'I apologise, Ashley. I don't know what's the matter with him. Worry, I suppose. I'll calm him down. He's been short with all of us recently.'

'I didn't realise he disliked Jago so much,' Ashley confessed.

'Neither did I.' Shelagh bit her lip. 'I'm sure he doesn't, Ashley. He was all in favour when you were engaged to him before. I think he's probably just concerned for you, that you're being hasty. He'll come round.'

'I hope so,' Ashley said quietly. She got to her feet. 'I'll see him at the office on Monday.' She paused. 'I'd like him to keep the news to himself for the time being.'

'Of course,' Shelagh acceded immediately, but her face still looked anxious as she waved Ashley off down the drive.

Ashley felt frankly disturbed as she drove back towards the town. She hadn't expected Henry's wholehearted approval for her decision, but she hadn't been prepared for such outright condemnation either. And yet she'd believed that Henry was as committed to the salvation of Landons as she was herself. That he would be as willing to grasp at any straw.

But his reaction had jolted her into a fuller

comprehension of what she was doing.

After Jago's departure, she had been almost in a daze, moving restlessly between one trivial chore and the next, until at last the once beloved flat seemed too claustrophobic to endure. The need to share her incredible secret with someone had been an impelling one. Now she wished she had said nothing.

She parked at the side of the road, and sat hugging herself, trying not to tremble, as she realised what she had committed herself to. How could she so easily have allowed herself to be talked into a fatal step like marriage, and to a man like Jago who had already demonstrated he was incapable of fidelity, or any decent feelings, for that matter? she reminded herself bitterly. And what hope could there be for any relationship based on sheer necessity on the one hand, and cold-blooded ambition on the other?

Jago enjoyed power. It was something she had recognised in him from the first, but it was familiar to her, because it was a quality he shared with Silas.

By agreeing to marry him, she had offered him absolute power, not merely over Landons, but over herself. He'd offered himself as her business partner, nothing more, but could it really be as simple as that? she asked herself desperately.

Could she bear to go on living under the same roof as Jago, day after lonely day, and night after sterile night, with nothing to look forward to except the possible, painful amputation of divorce to end the bleakness of their life together?

'No,' she breathed aloud. 'No, I can't. I can't!'

If her marriage was the only way to save Landons, then there was another candidate. Jago might have dismissed Martin, but he was a successful man in his own field. Why shouldn't the board find him acceptable? He might be new to the world of property development, but he could learn, as she'd done. And if she belonged to Martin, she would be safe from Jago for ever, she thought feverishly.

Exactly what it would mean to belong to Martin, she would not allow herself to dwell on too deeply. She liked him, and enjoyed his company, and wasn't that altogether a better basis for a permanent relationship than the delirium of joy and pain she'd known with Jago?

Martin's home was one of a small terrace of late Georgian red-brick houses. His car was parked outside, instead of in the lock-up garage he normally used, indicating that he was about to go out. Probably to see her, Ashley thought, bracing herself resolutely. He was a good man, trustworthy and reliable. The kind of husband most women would dream of, even if his first marriage had foundered. In one of his scant references to its failure, he had once said that his wife had found him dull, and resented the hours he'd spent trying to establish his career as a newly qualified solicitor.

As she stopped the car, the front door opened and Martin came down the steps to the pavement, carrying a small suitcase. He looked preoccupied, and Ashley called to him twice before attracting his attention. He came over to the car, forcing a smile.

'Ashley, I tried to ring, but there was no reply. I planned to write you a note. I have to go away for a few days—perhaps longer.'

Her heart sank. She got out of the car. 'Is something wrong?'

He said quietly, 'My—ex-wife telephoned. It's Claire, our little girl. She's been ill—measles, and there are complications. Apparently she's been asking for me.'

'I'm so sorry.' Ashley put a hand on his arm. 'Of course, you must go at once.'

'Yes,' he acknowledged unhappily. He roused himself and looked at her. 'I'm sorry, darling. I had all sorts of plans for this weekend, but I knew you'd understand. And it's nice to see you,' he added. 'You don't often come round here. Was there something special you wanted?'

'No.' She shook her head. 'I just—happened to be in the area, that's all.'

Martin kissed her briefly, his mind obviously elsewhere. 'I'll be in touch as soon as I get back,' he promised, and went over to his own car.

Ashley didn't wait to see him leave. Fate had taken a hand in her affairs, it seemed. Martin was no longer an escape route, but a harassed man driven by ties and responsibilities from the past. It was unfair and selfish even to attempt to burden him further.

She too had ties from the past, she could neither evade nor forget. Jago had come back, and she was in his hand, as helpless as a pawn.

But, between them, they could save Landons.

'That,' she told herself, 'is all that matters.' And wished with all her heart that she could believe it.

CHAPTER FOUR

IT was not, by any stretch of the imagination, the wedding Ashley had ever envisaged for herself.

They'd done their best with the room, Ashley thought detachedly, looking at the banked flowers, and the velvet-covered chairs in front of the registrar's desk, but it remained an office—a suitable place, she decided, for the enactment of the business agreement she had with Jago. She would have hated the hypocrisy of vows made in church.

There were flowers in her hands too, a charming arrangement of tiny orchids and white rosebuds which Jago had presented to her with an ironic glance at the beige suit which had been the first thing she'd taken from the wardrobe that morning.

What had he expected her to wear? The wild silk and organza in which she'd dreamed of enchanting him three years before?

She might not look like a bride, but she didn't feel like one either. She hadn't given herself time to think about what she was doing. She had gone to the office each day, dealt with correspondence, refused to issue any statement on the Marshalls takeover bid to the Press, and listened to Henry's daily pleas to her to think again.

'Disaster,' he'd said, running a hand through his hair, and making it stand up in unruly spikes. 'Sheer disaster, Ashley, I beg of you ...'

And she'd replied each time, from some frozen place deep within her, 'It's the only way. It's what

Silas would have wanted.'

She had seen Jago only fleetingly, to make the necessary arrangements for obtaining the licence. The rest of the time, she went to ground at the flat, which no longer seemed to belong to her. It was already on an agent's books, and potential buyers seemed to be lining up.

The furniture she had chosen with such loving care would be going to a saleroom. There was no place for it at the Manor. There was no place for her either, but she wouldn't allow herself to think about that.

She tried not to flinch when Jago took her hand and put his ring on her finger. The registrar was saying the final words, looking at them expectantly, waiting, she supposed, for Jago to kiss her. He bent his head, and she lifted her face obediently, feeling the brush of his lips like ice on her own.

She stole a glance at her husband, as he got into the car beside her for the drive to the board meeting, wondering at the cool confidence he exuded. This marriage was, after all, only the beginning. Now they had to win over the hard-headed businessmen waiting at Landons, persuade them to reject the Marshalls offer. The possibility of failure didn't seem to occur to him. She was the only one who was afraid, she realised, and not just of failure.

He looked magnificent, she was forced to acknowledge. His dark grey suit was superbly tailored, the silk shirt and discreetly sober tie equally immaculate. By contrast, she felt drab, but hadn't that been her intention?

The security guard's expression was curious when they arrived.

'Good morning, miss. The other board members

are here.'

She said a quiet, 'Thank you,' and walked to the lift, Jago at her shoulder. She did not look at him or speak as they rode up to the sixth floor.

As they walked down the corridor, Ashley could hear the murmur of voices from the boardroom, and squared her shoulders.

As they reached the doorway, Jago said softly, 'I think this is appropriate,' and took her hand in his, so that they entered together, united.

It was a long room, dominated by the portrait of Silas Landon which hung over an ornate fireplace. The fire was unlit, but the room felt close and oppressive as Ashley walked with Jago to the head of the table. She glimpsed the expressions on the faces of the other directors as they passed. She saw amazement, disbelief, the beginnings of comprehension, and in Henry's case, a kind of resigned despair.

She had prepared a little speech, and she delivered it with strained composure, telling them that Jago and she were married, and that she was resigning as chairman of the board in his favour.

An incredulous silence followed her words, then Clive Farnsworth spoke, offering a few stilted words of congratulation, in which the others joined more or less reluctantly. They were all clearly stunned, except Henry, who seemed sunk in gloom.

Jago was speaking now, his voice clear and incisive, but Ashley couldn't concentrate on what he was saying. Her gaze kept wandering to the massive portrait of her father.

She thought, I've done what you wanted, Daddy, but do you know the cost? Do I even know it myself?

It seemed to her that the harsh mouth was set in

lines of approbation. It was a scene Silas would have appreciated, she thought bitterly—the son-in-law he'd always wanted taking over the reins from the daughter he'd doubted. A wave of sudden desolation swept over her. She had made Landons her life. What did she have to take its place?

She was aware of a silence, and came out of her reverie with a slight start.

'Dreaming,' someone said with a chuckle.

They had always been wary of her in the past, but now there was a new indulgence in the air.

Clive Farnsworth said, 'We were just saying—er—Mrs Marrick— that you'll obviously have other matters than board meetings to occupy you today. There's not the slightest need for you to stay. No doubt there's going to be some hard talking.'

They were all standing, she realised, and someone was politely holding open the door. They wanted her to leave, she thought, stunned.

She said, 'But I'm still a member of the board.'

'No need to worry yourself about that today,' Angus Brent told her with heavy paternalism. 'I'm sure we'll all be happy to excuse you from any further part in the day's business. You can leave your proxy vote with your husband, naturally.'

'Naturally,' Ashley repeated with heavy irony. Inwardly, she was shaking with rage. She'd only stood down as chairman. That didn't reduce her to a cipher—someone of no account. She was still Silas' daughter.

She said icily, 'I prefer to remain and cast my own vote.'

There was an awkward murmur, silenced by Jago saying smoothly, 'Perhaps we could have a brief adjournment, gentlemen. Five minutes while I have a private word with my wife.'

Ashley watched them file out of the room. When the door had closed behind them, she turned on Jago furiously.

'What the hell's going on?'

He said calmly, 'You're an embarrassment, darling. Your presence inhibits them, and their wish to speak freely about the Marshalls offer. They'll find it easier to be honest—to say what's on their minds, if you leave.'

'You mean they want to criticise me—the way I've been running things since Silas died.' She was very pale.

Jago shrugged. 'I'm not a clairvoyant,' he said shortly. 'But it's possible.'

'I can take it.' Ashley lifted her chin proudly.

'I'm sure you could,' he said drily. 'But could they?'

She exclaimed passionately, 'You can't treat me like this! My God, Henry said they were hidebound, but I never thought …'

'Henry was right.' He looked faintly amused. 'Don't take it so personally, sweetheart. This is your wedding day, after all. They can hardly be expected to know you'd rather spend it here, arguing about the company's future, than at home planning all the ways you're going to make me happy. They're trying to spare your blushes, Ash,' he added sardonically. 'Why don't you spare theirs, and go quietly?'

Her hand swept up involuntarily to strike at him, but he caught her wrist before any blow could land.

'You don't do that,' he said gently. 'Not now— not ever. Not unless you want me to reciprocate, and with interest. And I hardly think spanking you comes within the parameters we've set ourselves for our future relationship. Now stop being a damned nuisance, and let's play this particular meeting their way. When we've won, we can start re-thinking what role you're going to play in the set-up. But unless I do win, we may both end up out in the cold, and you won't help by alienating half the board by insisting on your rights as of now. Do I make myself clear?'

'You knew this would happen!' she accused, her voice trembling.

'I guessed it might,' he said coolly. 'As you'd have done, if you'd been as much on the ball as you like to think. In the same way, I'd probably have spotted the first signs of discontent long before Marshalls made their offer.'

'So wise, so all-seeing,' she snapped angrily. 'You know everything, don't you?'

He smiled a little. 'No. For example, I wouldn't have put any money on the certainty of you turning up at the registrar's office this morning.'

'What choice did I have?' Ashley shrugged, her green eyes sparking at him. 'After all, nothing matters except Landons.'

His mouth curled. 'If that's so, then why not allow me a free rein to save it? Well, are you going or staying? We can't keep them waiting much longer.'

She said, 'I'll go. But I won't forget this.'

'No,' said Jago, a muscle flickering in his jaw. 'Forgetting isn't much in your line, is it, sweetheart? Or forgiving either.' He took his car keys from his pocket and tossed them to her. 'I'll see you later at the Manor.'

'Where I wait, I suppose, like a dutiful wife,' she said bitterly.

'Yes,' he said. 'No matter how little appeal it may have for you.' He walked over to the door, and opened it, waiting with cold civility as she walked past him into the corridor.

The adjoining room was loud with talk, and thick with cigar smoke. Ashley walked past it without a second glance, aware of a sudden embarrassed lull in the conversation as she did so.

As she reached the lift, a voice, over-jovial and pitched slightly louder than the others, said, 'Sent her home to warm the bed, Jago?'

She didn't catch Jago's reply, but the burst of concerted laughter which greeted it made her smart all over as the lift gates closed on her, and it descended rapidly to the ground.

She was still hot with resentment when she drove up the Manor's curving drive. She parked in front of the house and got out of the car, looking uncertainly up at the imposing façade. Odd to think how she had once dreamed of living here. Now, every instinct she possessed screamed at her to take Jago's powerful car and drive it anywhere until the petrol and her nerve gave out.

But she couldn't do that. For the sake of Landons, she had to endure living here, somehow.

The front door opened, and the spare figure of Mrs Bolton, the housekeeper, appeared at the top of the shallow flight of steps, suggesting she was expected.

'Good morning, madam.' The woman's smile was vinegary. 'Mrs Marrick is waiting in the drawing room.'

'My cases——' Ashley began, but Mrs Bolton held out a hand for the car keys.

'That will be attended to, madam.' Her eyes slid sideways to give Ashley a swift head-to-toe scrutiny. She went on, 'I hope the arrangements are to your satisfaction. You'll appreciate that the notice Mr

Marrick gave us was extremely short.'

'I'm sure everything will be fine,' Ashley said neutrally. She had never cared for Mrs Bolton on her former visits to the Manor. She had been Erica's choice, she recalled, employed when Giles Marrick's old housekeeper finally retired.

As she walked down the hall towards the drawing room, the years seemed to fall away, and she was the nervous, uneasy girl she had been then, desperately seeking Jago and reassurance. It took all the courage she possessed to walk into the drawing room. She half expected to see Erica engaged on her everlasting needlework, but instead she was standing at the french windows, staring out at the gardens, and smoking with rapid, almost nervous movements.

She swung round as Ashley entered. She looked incredibly beautiful in an exquisitely cut grey skirt, and a matching silk shirt, her blonde hair swept with casual chic into a gleaming topknot. Her eyes, as they met Ashley's, were venomous.

She said, 'The happy bride.' She gave a small harsh laugh. 'My God, when Jago told me the news, I thought it was an extraordinary joke!' She stubbed the butt of her cigarette viciously into an ash tray. 'Are you quite mad? Didn't you learn your lesson three years ago?'

Ashley said, with a composure she was far from feeling, 'I learned everything I needed to know three years ago.'

'And you've still been fool enough to marry him!' Erica shook her head in disbelief. 'I wouldn't have credited you with a taste for blood sports. Or did you think Jago had forgiven or forgotten the way you threw him over last time? Because I can promise you that he hasn't. I could almost feel sorry for you.'

Ashley bit her lip. 'I prefer not to discuss my marriage ...'

'Marriage?' Erica interrupted stridently. 'What marriage? This time he isn't even pretending he cares a damn about you. He's got Landons, just as he always wanted, and he's had to take you with it. But when he's wrung the company dry, he'll throw it on the scrap heap, and you, Ashley dear, will be there with it. He's a cold-blooded, single-minded bastard, and he wants his revenge for being jilted so thoroughly three years ago. I don't envy you one little bit. Or did you think you were going to live happily ever after?'

She walked over to the sofa and picked up a jacket which matched her skirt, thrusting her arms into the sleeves. 'And now I'll be on my way, and leave you to enjoy your honeymoon in privacy—if enjoy is really the word I'm looking for.'

'You're going somewhere?' Ashley hid her relief.

'For a day or two. For the sake of appearances.' Erica's smile was catlike, calculating. 'But I'll be back. This is my home, after all. And believe me, dear, it's going to stay mine. No one wants you here. To Jago, you're just a necessary evil, so if you were hoping for anything else, you're due for a disappointment.'

'I'm not hoping for anything.' Ashley didn't even realise she had spoken the words aloud until she saw Erica's smile widen.

'How very wise! Keep remembering that, and you might just get out of this affair without too many broken bones. Although I expect Jago will keep you around for what's termed "a decent interval" at least.' She picked up her bag. 'We've waited for each other for a long time,' she added almost

casually. 'A little more patience won't hurt either
of us.' She walked to the door, then looked back.
'If you need some light reading for your wedding
night, I should just check through the grounds for
annulment. It's always best to be prepared, after
all.'

Ashley listened to the fading click of her heels
down the hall, heard her call something, presumably
to Mrs Bolton, then registered the slamming of the
door.

She groped her way forward as if she was
struggling through fog, and sank down on the sofa,
her legs shaking. She hadn't expected Erica to make
her welcome, but she hadn't anticipated quite
such blatant animosity either. So she hadn't
misinterpreted the air of possession she'd noticed
Erica exhibit towards Jago that night at the Country
Club. Erica's tone of voice, her smile, had said
louder than any words that she and Jago had been
lovers while Giles Marrick was still alive, and it was
only some mechanical observance of convention
which was keeping them apart now.

She didn't even know why she should be surprised,
but she was. In fact, she felt sick with shock, and
an uncontrollable shiver ran through her.

'Your cases have been taken up, madam.' Mrs
Bolton appeared in the doorway. 'Perhaps you'd
like to see your room now. Lunch will be served at
one. I hope you don't object to a cold collation.'

Ashley felt chilly enough. She rose to her feet,
squaring her slender shoulders. 'I'm afraid I do
object,' she said evenly. 'I've had nothing to eat
this morning, and I'd prefer a hot meal of some
kind—ham and eggs would be fine—served in about
twenty minutes. And perhaps someone would light
the fire in here.'

Mrs Bolton looked totally affronted. 'At this time of year, madam, the fire is never lit until the evening.'

'Never until now.' Ashley met the older woman's glance. 'Find me some matches, and I'll do it myself.'

Mrs Bolton's lips tightened until they almost disappeared. 'That won't be necessary, madam. I'll give the necessary instructions—and about luncheon.' She paused. 'May I suggest that you discuss any permanent changes you may be contemplating in the running of this house with Mrs Marrick—Mrs Marrick senior, that is. I mention it because—your husband gave orders that everything was to proceed as usual.'

'Perhaps it's a little premature to be talking about permanent changes,' Ashley said quietly. 'But when I do decide on something, you'll be the first to know.'

She saw shock in the other woman's face. 'And now perhaps you'll show me my room,' she added.

She'd never been upstairs at the Manor before. As she walked up the stairs behind Mrs Bolton, portraits of past generations of Marricks looked down on her—the interloper—with blank indifference.

The housekeeper opened a door, halfway along a corridor. 'Mr Marrick gave orders that this room should be prepared for you, madam.' She stood back, letting Ashley see the prim single bed. 'Perhaps you would confirm that his instructions were correct.'

It was her turn to triumph, Ashley thought, swallowing. 'Perfectly correct,' she responded coolly. 'I presume the door in the corner leads to a bathroom.'

'Yes, madam.' Mrs Bolton turned away. 'If you'll excuse me, I'll go and speak to Cook. Please ring the bell if you require anything.'

Left alone, Ashley looked wryly round her. It was like every other room she had occupied since childhood—well furnished, even luxurious, but strictly for sole occupation only.

Jago, she thought, had meant what he said, and it should have been relief, yet somehow it only served to heighten her sense of isolation. Erica's words rang in her ears: *'This time he isn't even pretending that he cares ...'* The muscles of her throat felt taut suddenly, and there was a burning sensation behind her eyelids. She fought the weakness back savagely. It had been an emotionally charged day, and it was bound to get to her sometime. But she wasn't going to cry. She hadn't allowed herself to shed a single tear on Jago Marrick's behalf since that night three years ago. She wasn't going to start now.

The afternoon passed with agonising slowness. Her meal, Ashley found, didn't help at all, but sat like a concrete wedge somewhere in her abdomen.

She sat in the drawing room, listening to the crackling of the burning logs in the hearth, and straining her ears for the sound of a returning car, or the telephone.

She was tempted more than once to call the office herself and see if anyone knew what was happening in the boardroom, but she thrust the temptation aside. Whether the news was good or bad, she would know soon enough. When Jago returned ...

She bit her lip, trying to quell her inner disquiet, as Erica's words came sidling back to torment her. But she had known what to expect, she told herself vehemently, trying to rally her spirits. The prospect of sharing a roof with Jago might be a daunting one, but it was no marriage she'd put her name and hand to that day. It was a business arrangement, no more, and when it had served its purpose, it would end, and she would be free again, to live her life on her own terms.

Free, she thought restlessly, adding another log to the fire. Have I ever been that? First there was Father, and then there was Landons. I've been alone, but never really free.

She looked blankly down at the glint of the ring on her otherwise bare hand. And now she was more bound than ever.

When Mrs Bolton came to ask her rather ostentatiously about her plans for dinner, she opted for a tray in her bedroom. The housekeeper's face showed no surprise at her choice. Clearly the woman hadn't expected her to suggest an intimate meal for two, to be served when her bridegroom returned.

There was a selection of books in a small revolving bookcase: classics, mixed with magazines and periodicals on sporting matters and estate management, and a smattering of current bestsellers in paperback, which were presumably Erica's choice.

Ashley picked out *Jane Eyre*. There was no madwoman hidden in the attics at the Manor, but its unfriendly atmosphere seemed to blend well with the dour goings-on at Thornfield Hall. And Miss Eyre's practical approach to her troubles suited her mood.

She watched the early evening news on television, then tried to take some interest in a wild-life documentary, but found herself unable to concentrate. The evening stretched bleakly ahead of her.

I might as well go to bed, she thought.

Accordingly, when Mrs Bolton brought her dinner tray to her room, Ashley was already bathed, and in her nightdress and robe curled up in the one easy chair the room boasted, beside the small electric fire.

'Will there be anything else, madam?' Mrs Bolton drew up a table and set the tray upon it.

'No, thank you.' Ashley hesitated. 'That is—has Mr Marrick telephoned?'

Mrs Bolton's smile was edged with something that could have been malice. 'There has been no message at all, madam. Goodnight.'

Her solitary meal of soup, followed by lamb cutlets, completed, Ashley leaned back in the chair, allowing her feeling of quiet repletion to comfort her. Although why she should be in need of comfort, she wasn't too sure. She'd gone into this situation with her eyes upon, after all. The terms of the bargain were quite clear.

It was just that she hadn't expected to feel so—alone.

She'd never felt like it before, not even on that night three years before when she had wrenched Jago out of her heart, and, she had thought, her life for ever. Not even, heaven help her, when Silas died.

Tomorrow, she thought. Everything will be different tomorrow.

She shifted restlessly on her cushions, staring at the single glowing bar of the electric fire. But first there was this evening to get through, and this interminable waiting for the phone to ring, or the sound of the front door to tell her Jago had come back. She tried to read, but her attention, all her senses were attuned to his return, and she couldn't concentrate on the printed words which, after a while, began to swim in front of her eyes. Sighing irritably, she let the book drop to the floor and put her head back, closing her eyes. She was tired, she realised suddenly, worn out from the emotional turmoil and tension of the past week. And it wasn't over yet ...

She awoke suddenly to darkness. She sat up slowly, stretching cramped limbs, and swearing mildly under her breath. She'd only meant to rest, not actually fall asleep. The fire was still burning, providing the room's sole illumination. She pressed the switch of the lamp she had been using, but nothing happened. The bulb must have failed.

Wondering what the time was, she got to her feet and padded over to the door. Her hand on the other light switch, she hesitated for a moment, then turned the handle quietly and looked out into the silent corridor. Darkness there too, except for a thread of light showing under the door at the far end. Mrs Bolton had not described the layout of the house, but Ashley assumed it was the master bedroom.

And presumably, the master had returned.

Her feet made no sound on the thick carpet, as she moved towards the betraying light as if it was a beacon. Her knock on the door panels sounded startlingly loud in the quiet house.

There was no immediate response, and she was just about to turn away defeated, when the door was flung open and Jago confronted her. He had clearly been taking a shower, because he was wearing a robe, and towelling the excess moisture from his hair. His brows drew together when he saw her.

He said coolly, 'Is something the matter? It's late.'

'I know that.' Ashley swallowed. 'The—meeting must have gone on a long time.'

'Yes, it did.' The hooded hazel eyes, the enigmatic face gave nothing away. 'Perhaps we could discuss it tomorrow.'

'I want to discuss it now,' Ashley said sharply. 'Didn't it occur to you that I'd be waiting to hear?'

'It occurred to me.' His mouth curled. 'As the sole object of your concern, Landons must be very dear to you.'

'It is,' she said stonily. 'As I wasn't allowed to attend the meeting as I wished, the least you could have done is tell me what happened as soon as you got back.'

He lifted a shoulder. 'Your room was in darkness. If you'd woken and found me in your room, my motive might have been open to misinterpretation.'

'Not by me,' she said tersely. 'For God's sake tell me. Did they turn down the Marshalls offer?'

'Eventually,' he said. 'And—just. It was a bloody near thing.'

'Oh, thank heaven!' she whispered.

'I suppose that's a suitably abstract target for your gratitude,' Jago said harshly. 'A word of thanks to me would be to much to ask.'

She said stiffly, 'Naturally, I'm grateful.'

He smiled, not pleasantly. 'There's nothing natural about it, my sweet. But the fact remains, that however little you may relish it, you are beholden to me. I had to fight damned hard all along the line, and it's not over yet.'

'But you said they'd refused ...' Ashley began.

'So they did,' Jago agreed levelly. 'But I know Paul Hollings who's just taken over as Marshalls' managing director. We were at university together.

He's not a guy to give up the campaign, simply because he's lost the first battle. I suspect he has other weapons.'

'I don't understand.' She stared at him, biting her lip.

'Nor do I—completely.' He draped the damp towel round his shoulders, and gave her a look compounded from patience and boredom. 'However, I'd find comprehension easier, I'm sure, after a night's sleep.' He leaned towards her suddenly, the hazel eyes mocking and predatory. 'Unless you insist on staying and offering me some other form of relaxation.'

She jumped away like a scalded cat, and heard him laugh.

'I thought not.'

Ashley stared at him. 'You've been drinking,' she accused.

'Some of the board, anxious to assure me that they'd been against the Marshalls offer from the first, took me out for a small celebration, yes.'

'I see.' She gave a wild little laugh. 'I was here— shut up in this damned mausoleum, worrying myself sick—with never a word from you, and you were out—carousing!'

'Now that's a sweet old-fashioned word,' Jago said lightly, but his eyes had narrowed. 'But it was rather more inhibited than that my sweet. They were far too anxious to see me restored to the arms of my loving bride to turn it into a full-scale session. After providing me with a little Dutch courage first,' he added jeeringly. 'I think they felt I'd need it. How well they've got to know you!'

There was a sudden flare of colour in her face. She said angrily, 'They don't know me at all, and neither do you.' She turned, stumbling over the hem of her robe a little, and went back to her room.

She shut the door, and leaned against it for a moment, trying to control her rapid breathing.

They'd won. This soulless bargain she'd made with Jago had been justified after all. She should have been jubilant. So why, suddenly, did she feel so desolate?

I'm tired, she told herself quickly, that's all. She untied the sash of her robe and slipped out of the bulky thing, dropping if across a chair as she made her way to the bed. The mattress was soft enough, she discovered, as she slid under the covers, but the sheets felt chill and unwelcoming, and she grimaced slightly as she gingerly stretched out a foot, sending a longing thought towards her electric blanket left behind at the flat. She would fetch it tomorrow, she thought. If she had to live in this house, she would at least be comfortable in it.

But you don't have to live here, a small inner voice reminded her. The company's safe. And your marriage was an expedient which can now be dispensed with.

Ashley twisted on her pillow, forcing it to submission with a vicious thump of her fist. What was it Erica Marrick had said—something about the annulment? Prompted, she supposed, by the sleeping arrangements Jago had ordered—the separate room, this horrid, narrow little bed.

She sat up furiously, pushing her hair back from her face.

I'm never going to sleep, she thought.

And, as if in response to her thought, the room flooded with light.

For a moment she was dazzled, blinking involuntarily against the unexpected glare. Then, out of the dazzle, came Jago, carrying, Ashley saw incredulously, a bottle and two glasses.

Open-mouthed, she stared at him. 'What—what are you doing?'

He seated himself on the edge of the bed. 'The fact that you'd been left out of the celebration seemed to upset you,' he said, almost casually. 'So I thought some champagne might be appropriate—particularly as this is our wedding night—nominally, at least.'

'I don't want any champagne,' she protested. She knew an overwhelming urge to grab the edge of the sheet and haul it up to her chin. He was too close, she thought frantically, aware that the hazel eyes were studying with open appreciation her slender shoulders, bare except for the straps of her nightgown, and moving downwards.

'Of course you do,' he said briskly. 'It's the best remedy in the world for the kind of incipient nervous breakdown you've been having this evening.' He smiled at her. 'Besides, you like champagne, Ash, or you always did.'

She was trembling inside. She remembered with an awful clarity the first time she'd drunk champagne with him. It was the night they had become engaged. Her father had produced the bottle, noisily insisting they drank a toast. Jago had lifted his glass in salute, his eyes smiling at her, and she'd thought her heart would burst with joy.

It was hammering now, but with a very different emotion.

'Perhaps I've changed,' she said curtly. 'Now, please get out of my room.'

'The room belongs to me,' he said. 'Like everything else in this house. My home, Ashley— not a mausoleum. Now, drink your wine.'

Silently she took the glass he handed to her, suppressing an urge to throw it at him. Silently she sipped at the pale, bubbling liquid, feeling its golden warmth caress her throat.

'That's better,' Jago approved, and topped up her glass.

'No more!' There was panic in her voice, and she hoped he hadn't heard it. It wasn't just the wine she was refusing, although it held an insidious danger all its own, but the whole situation with its enforced, unwelcome intimacy. It wasn't a large room, but the walls seemed to be narrowing, closing in on her, making her acutely aware of his physical nearness, oppressed by it. She wanted to move her legs, but knew, somehow, it was safer to keep perfectly still.

'Relax,' Jago advised mockingly, but his glance was searching. 'You're so tense you're about to fall apart!'

She said between her teeth, 'Is it really any wonder?'

'Bridal nerves?'

'Hardly,' snapped Ashley. She took another hasty swallow of champagne. Oh, why the hell hadn't she locked her door? she raged at herself. Or, better still, why hadn't she waited it out downstairs, where at least any encounter would have been conducted with them both fully dressed—where she would have been able to keep him at a safe distance.

'You don't feel like a bride?' he questioned silkily. 'But you should, Ashley. It's supposed to be a once-in-a-lifetime sensation, after all.'

'Not necessarily,' she returned sharply. 'When the company's problems have been finally settled, I intend to make a life for myself. It could include marriage.'

'You're already married, sweetheart—to me.' His voice was still smooth, but there was a note in it that triggered her defence mechanisms, warning her to tread carefully.

'Yes—well,' she said lamely, 'there's no real reason, all the same, for us to feel—tied in any way.'

'Why, darling,' his drawl was exaggerated, 'are you telling me there was no need for me to rush home to your side tonight?'

'None at all,' Ashley retorted, stung. 'You should have stayed in whatever bar you were drinking in. Who knows, you might have found yourself another willing lady.'

She saw a betraying muscle flicker in his jaw as her barb went home. 'Instead of which I came back to my unwilling wife,' he said quietly. 'Shall we talk about my reasons?'

'No.' Her mouth was dry. 'Jago, I'd like you to go—please,' she added with a trace of desperation.

'You told me you'd changed.' His face was an enigma. 'I'm intrigued. You certainly sound the same, Ashley—still as reluctant to have me anywhere near you.'

'I thought we'd already established that,' she said bitingly. 'Leave well alone, Jago. God knows, you've got what you wanted ...'

She stopped abruptly, the words choking in her throat as she absorbed the heated glitter in his eyes.

'How do you know what I want?' His voice was sombre, almost harsh. 'That's something I could never make you understand, but God help me, it hasn't stopped me wanting to try!'

He took the glass from her hand, spilling some of its contents on the quilt.

'No!' She sounded like a child, frightened and pleading, when she needed, more than ever, to sound like a woman in control of herself, and her destiny. But that control was splintering as Jago bent towards her, his face fierce with desire. Her little apprehensive cry was stifled at birth as his mouth took possession of hers.

There was no tenderness in him, she realised, just a raging hunger that demanded satisfaction. A satisfaction which her own physical starvation yearned to yield, to share. When he'd kissed her while they were dancing at the Club, she'd had to fight not to respond. Now, the temptation had doubled. The cool, clean smell of him seemed to be all she could breathe. The realisation that they were both next door to naked, the remembered weight of his body against hers, pressing her down into the bed—all these things were conspiring against her, undermining the sheer necessity of her resistance to him.

And the first wildness of that ravaging kiss was altering too, gentling almost magically, its violence being superseded by a warm and perilous subtlety. She could have gathered her forces to fight the anger in him, perhaps, but now it was an agony to remain passive as his lips and tongue caressed hers, coaxing a response with silken urgency.

Her hands hungered to lift to his shoulders, to hold him to her. She could have withstood anything but this slow ravishment of her senses, she thought dazedly.

When he lifted his head and looked down at her, she stared back at him, unable to speak, to voice her resistance. And perhaps something of her inner bewilderment showed in the wide green eyes, because for a moment his finger stroked the curve of her cheek in a gesture that was almost like reassurance.

There was no mistaking the expression in his own eyes. His gaze was burningly intense, heavy with need. The silence between them seemed to quiver, as Jago slid his thumbs under the fragile straps of her nightdress and slid them from her shoulders.

'I need to see you.' His husky voice was barely a whisper.

Ashley was trembling suddenly, remembering. This was one of the intimacies she had always shied from—his desire to look at her, to uncover her body for his intimate regard. No matter what persuasions Jago had used, what assurances he'd offered, she had invariably backed away as if she'd suddenly found herself teetering on the edge of some precipice. She knew, of course, that Jago was trying to coax her out of the shallows of passion into its deeper waters, yet it had never seemed possible to tell him she was already out of her depth and drowning in her feelings for him.

Now she was aware of all the old tensions, her hands lifting to cover her bare breasts, but this time he was too quick for her, capturing her wrists in his hands and anchoring them to the pillow on either side of her head.

Heated colour rose in her face, and she closed her eyes, her head threshing from side to side.

'Let go of me!'

'No,' he said quietly. 'Not this time, Ash.'

Her heart was hammering so hard, it felt bruised. Hammering so loudly, she could hear it.

Then, suddenly, she was free. Shocked, her eyes flew open, her lips parting on a little startled gasp as she clawed at the sheet, pulling it protectively across her nakedness.

And then she heard the hammering again. No physical manifestation on her part, but merely someone knocking at the bedroom door, she realised with a sense of utter absurdity.

Jago turned towards the door, his expression a mingling of impatience and disbelief.

'Yes?' His tone was not encouraging.

'It's the telephone, sir.' Mrs Bolton's voice was pitched a little higher than usual, but it was totally expressionless. 'Mrs Marrick—or Mrs Erica, I should say. She apologises for disturbing you but says it's important.'

Jago swore under his breath, pushing his dishevelled hair back from his forehead. He got up from the bed, tightening the sash of his robe.

'I'd better go,' he said half to himself, then glanced at Ashley, a wry smile curling his mouth. 'The lady picks her moments!'

Yes, Ashley thought. And she always will.

Aloud, she said, 'Please don't keep her waiting on my account.'

That checked him. He gave her a guarded look. 'Ash, listen to me ...'

'No,' Ashley managed, although her throat was strangling with pain. Only a moment ago, she thought dazedly, a moment ago he'd undermined her defences with his kisses so that she'd wanted to give him everything he could ask of her. But all Erica had to do , it seemed, was call ...

Humiliation burned in her. Hadn't she learned anything from that sharp, bitter lesson of three years ago?

She said, 'I've heard enough. I've asked you to leave. Perhaps now you'll go, and have the grace to stay out of this room in future.' She paused. 'I may be obliged to live under this roof, but it doesn't mean I have to put up with being—mauled by you!'

For a moment his face darkened, and she was terrified that she'd gone too far, then his mouth twisted sardonically.

'How inconsiderate of me to trespass on your maidenly preserves,' he said mockingly. 'I'd hoped the passage of time might have softened you, that under the ice and the resentment there might be a warm, living woman. How wrong can anyone be,' he added with a shrug.

Ashley lay watching, as he crossed the room and went out without a backward glance. As he'd walked away before, she reminded herself, then turned on to her face and lay like a stone.

CHAPTER FIVE

ASHLEY woke the next day with a headache—a sure sign that she hadn't slept properly, she told herself as she lifted herself up to one elbow to survey the morning. Although, in view of what had transpired the night before, it was a miracle she had slept at all.

Sunlight was spilling through a slight gap in the curtains, and frowning a little, she glanced at her watch. Then with a muffled yelp, she pushed away the covers.

It was late—terribly late, at least an hour and a half after her normal rising time. She'd neglected, she thought crossly, to tell Mrs Bolton what time she should be called, but surely the woman's common sense should have told her what office hours were like.

By the time she had showered and dressed, she was feeling slightly more human. The house was already busy when she arrived downstairs, and she returned the greeting of a woman in an overall polishing the furniture in the hall.

The dining room was empty, although the big table was set for one. Ashley checked, her brows snapping together. She turned and came face to face with Mrs Bolton, who had materialised silently from somewhere. Like some Demon Queen through a trapdoor, Ashley thought, stifling the annoyance that the woman seemed to provoke in her.

'Good morning, madam. May I get you

something?'

Ashley gestured at the table. 'I'd like some breakfast,' she said quietly. 'If you'd be good enough to lay another place.'

Mrs Bolton inclined her head. 'Certainly. You are expecting a guest?'

'Why, no.' Ashley was taken aback. 'I thought Mr Marrick would be having breakfast and ...'

Mrs Bolton permitted herself another of her vinegary smiles. 'Goodness me, no, madam! Mr Marrick had his breakfast and left for the day some time ago. He gave orders that you were to be allowed to sleep on.'

'I see,' Ashley managed, her hands curling into fists in the folds of her flared grey skirt.

And she did see, she thought furiously. It was bad enough being excluded from the board meeting yesterday in that high-handed way. God only knew what kind of a march he was stealing on her this morning. But certainly his decision to leave her resting hadn't been motivated by the simple milk of human kindness.

She said with all the calmness she could conjure up, 'Then perhaps I could have some toast and coffee. And make sure in future that I'm called at the same time as Mr Marrick,' she added. She glanced at her watch. 'I have a busy day ahead, I can't really afford such a late start.'

Mrs Bolton bowed her head in acquiescence, but her smile had a derisive tinge as she left the room, and Ashley had the feeling she hadn't been fooled for a minute.

She walked to the window and stood looking out at the sun-washed garden, her fingers drumming restlessly on the pane. I'm a cipher, she thought angrily. Jago has taken over my company, and

Erica still owns this house. I belong nowhere.

It was uncanny, but even Landons felt different. She was conscious of it as soon as she arrived. Conscious too of the stares and whispers that proclaimed her hasty marriage was the talk of the place. Or were they merely surprised to see the bride on the first morning of what was, ostensibly, her honeymoon? she wondered ironically.

She was glad to gain the sanctuary of the big office suite which Silas had always used, and she had inherited. She sank down into the high-backed padded leather chair behind the desk and closed her eyes for a minute. She had to forget about the events of the past twenty-four hours, she told herself, and revert to being Ashley Landon, girl executive. She had dictated letters before she left on Wednesday evening, and there had been no time to sign them since. She would do that first, then make a start on the figures the costing department had supplied for the Craigmore project.

She pressed the buzzer on her intercom. 'Bring in the letter file, please, Katie. I'll sign them while you dig out the Craigmore file for me.'

'Yes, Miss Land—I mean Mrs Marrick.' Katie's correction sounded flurried.

Ashley was tempted to say, 'Don't worry, it was an even bigger shock to me,' but she refrained.

When Katie came in with the letters, she looked uneasy, her usually bright smile muted. She stood watching nervously as Ashley skimmed through the neatly typed sheets, appending her signature to each in turn. And if she thought it was odd that she was still using her maiden name, she made no comment.

When Ashley had finished, she blurted out, 'Mrs Marrick, the Craigmore file—it's gone!'

'Gone?' Ashley replaced the cap on her fountain pen. 'Gone where?'

'To Mr Marrick's office, with the rest of the files. He had the security men up to move everything this morning. It was done before I arrived.' Katie shifted from one foot to another. 'I thought you knew.'

'I'd forgotten,' Ashley said calmly, after a pause. She even managed a smile. 'I've had rather a lot on my mind.' Her pulses were drumming madly. 'Which room did Mr Marrick decide to use in the end?'

'The empty one at the end of the passage,' Katie supplied eagerly. 'The one that used to be a store room. And he's got Sue Burton from the typing pool working for him.' She paused uncertainly. 'It's not a very nice office for him. Just a couple of desks and chairs, and the filing cabinets.' She hesitated again. 'I think Mr Farnsworth suggested he should use this room, but Mr Marrick said he didn't want to inconvenience you.'

Big of him! Ashley thought furiously.

She stood up. 'Fine, Katie. That will be all for now.'

When she was alone, she took a long incredulous look around her. The chairman's office, she thought, with its thick carpet and panelled walls, and enormous curving desk. All the trappings of power reduced in one stroke to a façade, a sham. Jago had taken control, and left her to rot in this big empty room.

'Over my dead body,' Ashley said grimly, and aloud. She got to her feet, thrusting her shaking hands into the pockets of her jacket, then marched out of her office and along the corridor. The door was shut, but she could hear the murmur of voices inside, and she opened the door and went in. Jago looked up from behind his desk with a thunderous frown.

'I thought I gave orders——' he began, then stopped. 'Ah, Ashley,' he said, getting to his feet with cool civility. 'I wasn't expecting to see you here today.'

'Weren't you?' Her smile was a brilliant, but her eyes sparked at him. 'Now where else should a working girl be but at work? Hullo, Sue.' She nodded at the secretary, who was obviously bewildered, notebook and pencil poised for further dictation.

Jago glanced at her. 'We'll resume presently, Sue,' he told her pleasantly. 'Perhaps you could rustle up some coffee for us.' When the door had closed behind the girl, he added drily, 'Sit down, Ashley, before you explode.'

'Don't tell me what to do, you bastard,' she said rapidly. 'What the hell do you mean by removing all the files from my suite?'

'Familiarising myself,' he said. 'With the company's current and future projects.'

'It didn't occur to you to ask me?'

'Frankly, no.' His voice was dry. 'I felt I'd probably had as much co-operation from you as I could expect—as last night proved.' The hazel eyes watched sardonically the faint tinge of colour that rose in her cheeks.

'That still doesn't justify your totally high-handed ...'

'Oh, spare me the moral splutterings,' he said wearily. 'There was no easy way of doing it, Ashley, and Landons' problems are too pressing for me to tiptoe round your sensibilities any more than I have to. Yesterday you resigned as chairman, and I took your place. It wasn't a nominal appointment, and I intend to fulfil each and every one of my responsibilities.'

'Implying that I didn't?' Her voice shook.

'Implying nothing,' Jago said flatly. 'We've had this out already, Ashley. You did your best, but you were out of your depth from the start. Silas hadn't time, unfortunately, to teach you half the things you needed to know.'

'Such as?' she flung at him.

'Such as the kinds of things you can't find between the covers of a file.' Jago resumed his seat. He was in shirt sleeves, she'd already noticed, and now he put up a hand to tug irritably at the knot of his tie, dragging it loose. 'To know who, when and how to trust, for example.'

'Silas wasn't such a genius at that,' Ashley flashed. 'After all, he trusted you.'

Jago leaned back in his chair, looking at her speculatively. 'So he did,' he drawled. 'I suppose it's useless for me to suggest you do the same.'

'I discovered all over again last night how much I can trust you,' she said bitterly. 'You promised me that any marriage would only be a business arrangement.'

He inclined his head slightly. 'That's true—but did no one tell you, my sweet, that you can sometimes mix business with pleasure?'

'No pleasure for me, I assure you!'

'Unnecessary. You made your thoughts on the subject perfectly clear at the time.' His mouth twisted a little. 'However, it was our wedding night, and it would have been very unchivalrous for me not to have—tried, at least.'

She shrugged. 'If you have any other chivalrous impulses,' she said sarcastically, 'kindly strangle them at birth. And now I want my files back.'

He shook his head. 'No, Ashley. The files are

staying here. One of the reasons I chose this room was because it contains a very large safe—unused. You knew that? I thought not. A locksmith is coming this afternoon to change the combination. From today the files, especially those concerned with tenders, and projects still in the planning stage, will be stored in there.'

'My God,' she said slowly, 'the new broom really does intend to sweep clean.'

He smiled grimly. 'You'd better believe it. And from now on all files taken from this office will be signed for in a register which Sue will keep.'

'Oh—Sue,' she said derisively. 'May I congratulate you on your choice of secretary? If she wasn't blonde with good legs, she might still be in the typing pool.'

There was a silence, then Jago said wearily, 'Some of your remarks are beneath contempt, Ashley. I didn't "choose" Susan Burton in any sense. I simply asked the Personnel Manager to send up whichever girl was next in line for promotion. It turned out to be her, and I'm damned if I'm getting rid of her just to silence your waspish remarks.'

Ashley said sweetly, 'I'm sorry if I'm wronging you, Jago, but with your track record ...' She shrugged. 'And now if you'll show me this register, I'd like to sign out the Craigmore file.'

'I'm afraid not,' he said briefly. 'I'm using that myself.'

'But I was working on that!' She stared at him, aghast.

'You were,' he agreed. 'But it's a tender we badly need to win, Ashley, and I'm not at all happy with some of the figures.'

'My own thoughts exactly,' she said tautly, her

nails digging into the softness of her palms. 'And I'm quite capable of handling it.'

He opened a drawer in his desk and produced a sheaf of papers. 'Then perhaps you'd like to have a close look at these.'

She flicked through the sheets he handed her, her brows lifting. 'But these are finished with. They're all past tenders ...'

'Did Landons get the work?'

'No,' she admitted. 'But ...'

'But nothing.' His voice held finality. 'Look through them, Ashley, and find out why Landons lost. I'd like a written report.'

The silence between them stretched, quivering with tension. At last she said savagely, 'Yes—sir,' and lifted her hand in a parody of a salute. She looked round her. 'You seem rather cramped here, for someone of your ambitions. Are you quite sure you wouldn't prefer to take over the main suite, along with everything else?'

He gave her a level look. 'Thanks—but no, thanks. It may have suited Silas, but I find all that panelling rather oppressive—not my style.'

'I see,' she said wonderingly. 'And what exactly is your style, Jago?'

'You, my sweet, will be the first to find out.' He reached out and picked up the file in front of him. 'Now, if you wish to continue this cosy domestic chat, may I suggest you join me for lunch. Because now I'd like to get on with some work.'

Ashley was in the corridor, almost without realising she'd been dismissed.

Sue Burton was coming towards her, carrying a tray. 'Oh, Mrs Marrick, you're leaving.' She gestured at the cups she was carrying. 'I'm sorry I've been such a long time over the coffee. I'm still finding my way around on this floor.'

Ashley took hold of herself with an effort. 'It's all right,' she said. 'I—I'm not thirsty.' Not for coffee, anyway, she added silently. Blood, perhaps.

She went back to her office, shut the door, buzzed Katie and told her she was not to be disturbed for any reason, then burst into tears. She wept silently, her head bowed, and the tears scalding her pale face. Henry had warned her, but she hadn't listened. Erica had taunted her, but it had been too late. Jago, it seemed, had the reins in his hands and was bent on driving her down. Landons had the strong man at the top the company had wanted—but what place was there for her? He'd taken everying, and left her with nothing—treated her as if she was some junior clerk, as if the past two years counted for nothing.

But then they didn't, she thought. Jago's memory went back further than that. It hadn't pleased him to be jilted, and now he was taking his revenge by humiliating her in every possible way.

Her buzzer sounded, and she started. 'Er—yes?' At least her voice sounded steady enough.

'It's Mr Brett,' said Katie. 'I gave him your message but he wants to see you anyway.'

There was a pause, then Ashley said dully, 'Send him in.'

She had no secrets from Henry, she thought, as she dried her eyes. Or at least, not many.

He came in looking glum, an expression that sharpened to concern when he saw her.

'My dear child, what's happened?'

'Everything,' she said tightly. 'Go on, Henry. Say "I told you so". You're entitled.' She looked down at her hands, clenched together in her lap. 'I was too naïve to realise that when I resigned as chairman, I was also relinquishing every scrap of control I possessed in the company. I now know better.' She marshalled a smile. 'And I suppose it's the habit of new régimes to pile all the blame on to the old ones. Accordingly, I'm doing penance for my sins of omission with an office girl's job. Perhaps, if I'm very lucky, he may let me choose the next lot of plants for the reception area.'

Henry said heavily, 'I don't think anything will ever be the same again.' He paused. 'That was a marvellous performance he gave yesterday. You missed a treat. He's got the board eating out of his hand.'

She thought, And last night, he nearly had me … Bitterly she said, 'Perhaps they'll turn on him in the end too.'

'Not if he comes up with the goods, they won't.' Henry roused himself. 'And that's what it's all about.'

'Yes,' she said tonelessly, 'I suppose it is.' She bit her lip. 'Did you want to talk to me about something special? If it's company business, perhaps you should go down the corridor.'

He smiled at her. 'It's social. Shelagh would like to invite you—and your husband—to dinner next week. She hoped Friday would be a suitable evening.'

'It's fine for me. I have nothing planned.' Ashley ran a finger along the graining of her desk. 'I'll mention it to Jago tonight at—the Manor.' She couldn't bring herself to say 'at home'.

'And there's one other thing.' Henry's face was rueful. 'I've been asked to mastermind your presence and his in the boardroom this afternoon at four.' He coughed. 'A couple of presentations. Wedding gifts from the board, and the office staff.'

Her face showed her dismay. 'Must I?'

'Oh, yes.' Henry nodded his head vigorously. 'In the eyes of the world, my dear, you're man and wife, whatever the private difficulties you may be undergoing.'

'Yes.' She swallowed. 'And he has put Marshalls to flight—as we wanted.'

'I suppose so.' He frowned a little.

You think they'll try again?' She remembered that Jago had hinted the same thing.

Henry hesitated. 'I don't think they're altogether prepared to take "no" for an answer,' he said guardedly. 'As a matter of fact, I was in Jago's office earlier this morning when the switchboard put a call through to him. It was from Paul Hollings, that new managing director at Marshalls that I was telling you about. Apparently, he and your husband know each other quite well.'

'So Jago told me,' Ashley confirmed.

'Did he?' Henry looked startled. 'Well, I suppose he has a great many business contacts, but I must say that this particular one—surprised me a little.'

Ashley smiled faintly. 'Oh, Jago is full of surprises,' she said with irony. Not all of them welcome, she added silently.

When Henry had gone, she pulled the sheaf of papers towards her with a grimace, and began to read through them. She remembered the first project very well. Landons had been invited to tender for the building of a new leisure centre and sports complex in a depressed inner city area. It was a prestige development, and the kind of scheme they were noted for, and they had been confident their tender would be accepted. Ashley frowned as she recalled the shock wave that had gone through the company when another firm had got the job, and the continuing tremors when it had been discovered to be a subsidiary of Marshalls.

In fact, all the tenders Jago had given her to study had been lost to Marshalls, she realised, and by a gallingly slender margin each time.

We didn't lose by much, she thought defensively. No one can win all the time. We offered a reasonable price, but Marshalls pipped us at the post. These things happen.

She bit her lip. Yes, she argued silently, but when the favourite for the race keeps coming second, maybe there should be an enquiry. Perhaps I should have called one—looked into the estimates department, tried to find out where we were going wrong.

With a sigh, she pulled a notepad towards her and began to jot figures.

In spite of herself, she found she was becoming interested in her tiresome task. When Sue Burton phoned to say Jago was going to lunch and had asked if she would join him, she refused quietly, saying she way busy, and intended to grab a sandwich at her desk.

Although she was not very hungry, she thought, digging the point of her pencil into the paper. But even if she had been, the sheer impersonality of Jago's invitation would have robbed her of any appetite she had.

As the time for the presentation approached, she went into the small private washroom adjoining her office and carefully and methodically removed all signs of strain and grief. She kept a make-up kit there as a standby, and she applied cosmetics carefully, glad for once that they existed to hide behind.

A nice mask, she decided judiciously when she'd

finished. And if her eyes were rather too bright, and if the smile on her lips had been painted there, she doubted whether anyone would notice.

Jago was waiting for her as she walked down the corridor towards the boardroom.

'Another act in the farce,' he observed sardonically, as he took her hand. 'Try and look as if the radiance was more than skin deep, Ashley.'

She glared at him, then schooled her features to pleasant anticipation as they entered the boardroom together to an outburst of applause.

Accepting the gifts was less of an ordeal than she expected. Ashley was able to unwrap the heavy silver tray from the members of the board, and the pretty china coffee service from the office staff, and exclaim with genuine pleasure while Jago made a speech of thanks, brief but humorous and drawing peals of delighted laughter from their audience.

'That was—kind of everyone,' Ashley said stiltedly when they were alone.

'And quick off the mark,' Jago agreed. He picked up the tray and studied it with a slight frown. 'Although, of course, this isn't the kind of thing you can pick up in a day.' He sent her a sardonic look. 'I imagine this has been waiting in a strongroom somewhere for just this auspicious occasion—probably for the last three years.'

She could think of nothing to say to that but, 'Oh.'

'I'll see these things get safely back to the house,' he went on. 'But I shan't be joining you for dinner tonight, although in the circumstances that's probably a relief. In fact, I shall be away most of the weekend.'

She stared at him. 'I see. May I know where you're going?'

'I think that's my business, don't you?' he asked pleasantly. 'Although I'm flattered by your interest, naturally.'

She wanted to say, 'Are you going to be with Erica?' but she forced the words back. She would not degrade herself by asking, she thought painfully.

She said quietly, 'You're free to go where you please, of course. But won't people think it—odd, if we don't even make a pretence of spending some time together.'

His brows lifted. 'My dear Ashley, I wouldn't dream of asking you for such a sacrifice. And what people are you talking about, anyway? Mrs Bolton and the servants? I think they've probably drawn their own conclusions already.'

'Undoubtedly,' Ashley said grittily. 'But that doesn't mean I want to be dumped at the Manor, like another unwanted gift,' she added, stabbing a finger at the silver tray.

'And an unwrapped one at that,' Jago jeered softly, and colour washed her face.

'Don't,' she said unevenly. 'This—marriage was your idea, not mine, and I won't have it used to humiliate me.'

'Wouldn't it be more humiliating to have to play the part of the devoted wife all weekend?' he enquired satirically. 'I can't say I've been impressed by your acting powers so far.'

'I do my best,' she said coldly. 'But I won't spend the weekend alone in that hateful house.'

Jago's face darkened. 'There was a time when you loved the Manor,' he reminded her. 'You thought it the most beautiful house on earth, and you couldn't wait to live there.'

'I was a naïve child then, Jago. I didn't look below the surface and see things as they really were.' She lifted her chin. 'Not a mistake I intend to make again.'

'I'll go along with that,' he said coolly. 'Talking of looking below the surface, how did you get on with those tenders?'

I haven't finished going through them yet,' she said defensively.

'I didn't expect you would have,' he said. 'But you must have formed some kind of impression.'

She shrugged slightly. 'All right—I'd have said the figures we arrived at were the right ones.'

'So would I,' he agreed. 'Interesting, isn't it?'

'Frustrating,' Ashley said shortly. 'As we didn't win.'

'A temporary situation,' Jago said quietly. 'As I intend to ensure. I like to win, Ashley, and don't you ever forget it.'

'I'm not likely to,' she said tightly. She glanced at her watch. 'Well, I suppose I may as well go back to the house. There's nothing else to keep me here.'

He was silent for a moment, his glance almost wary as he looked at her. 'If the thought of your own company tonight is so intolerable, how do you fancy playing hostess?'

'Hostess?'

He said, 'I'm having dinner with Paul Hollings tonight. I'd planned to take him out somewhere, but I can always change my plans.'

'Paul Hollings,' she said slowly. 'The managing director of Marshalls?'

'The very same.' He watched her. 'It occurred to me that he might be the last man on earth you would ever want to meet. So when he suggested a rendezvous, I opted for neutral territory.'

'No need,' said Ashley. After her conviction that

Jago was spending the evening with Erica, Paul Hollings seemed very much the lesser of two evils. 'Invite him, by all means. After all, Silas always used to say it was as well to know one's enemy.'

'How true,' he said. 'As long as you know who your enemy is. I'll leave the arrangements for the evening to you, then. But bear in mind, darling, that you're a radiant bride. No shapeless suits or sludge colours tonight, please. Put on that dress you wore at the Country Club.'

She gasped in outrage. 'Are you implying that I don't know how to dress?'

'I think it's an instinct you prefer to suppress most of the time,' he said, the hazel eyes flicking wryly over her. 'No one looking at you today, for instance, would guess what a lovely body you're hiding under all that dull grey wool.'

She was blushing, she realised angrily. She said sharply, 'A compliment from an expert? Please don't expect me to be flattered.'

'I don't,' Jago said mildly. 'It wasn't really much of a compliment.' Amusement glinted under his eyelids. 'But then I haven't been allowed to look too closely, have I, my sweet?'

Ashley bit her lip. 'I can't believe that's a genuine hardship,' she said coolly. 'Be content with your other conquests, Jago. You won't add me to them.'

'Even though I've just warned you I like to win?' His voice was light, but it held an undernote which shivered across her nerve-endings. 'I lost out with you once, Ash. I don't intend it to happen again.' He paused tauntingly. 'Still want me around this weekend?'

Her mouth was dry, and she was trembling inside. He said he'd lost out, she thought wildly, but hadn't she lost too? Lost all the warmth, love and laughter her girlhood had promised—the anguish of his betrayal turning her to stone. Only stone could crumble, as she'd discovered to her cost the previous night.

Wasn't it safer, as common sense and reason were screaming at her, to back down and spend the weekend virtually alone?

She flung her head back and saw him watching her, his derisive smile anticipating her flustered retreat.

She heard herself say, 'I'm not worried,' and wished with all her heart that it was the truth.

CHAPTER SIX

She had plenty of time to panic as she got ready that evening. She had expected to be too busy to think too deeply, but the preparations for the dinner party were completely out of her hands. Unexpected guests at the last minute, she was given to understand, were no novelty at the Manor, and would be coped with.

Ashley was grateful to Mrs Bolton, but she wished all the same that all that grim efficiency could be swapped occasionally for a little human warmth.

After much heart-searching, she had decided to wear the emerald dress. She had little else that was suitable, she thought, reviewing her wardrobe, and if there were to be many dinner parties, she would have to buy some more clothes.

But at future dinner parties, she thought, Erica would have returned, and would expect to act as hostess. Ashley bit her lip. She would not be spending money on playing second fiddle.

But tonight she took her time, making sure her make-up was faultless, and her hair swinging in dark glossy wings almost to her shoulders. When her dress was on, she stood looking at herself in the mirror, composing herself, drawing her self-command about her like a cloak.

Jago was waiting in the drawing room when she went down, his foot tapping in restless impatience. The formality of his evening clothes added an edge to his already potent attraction, which took her by the throat, startling her. She threw her head back defensively, daring him to guess at the strange, secret flare of excitement, as his narrowed gaze travelled over her appraisingly. He gave a brusque nod.

'Thank you.' His voice was expressionless. There was a pause, then he said, 'Would you like a drink?'

'A dry sherry, please.' She sat down, smoothing the folds of her skirt. As he handed her the small glass, she asked, 'What's this Paul Hollings like?'

'When we were at university together, he had the reputation of being a go-getter. He's certainly come a long way in a short time.'

'You clearly have a great deal in common.' Ashley said acidly, as she sipped her drink.

Jago looked at her levelly. 'Perhaps. I thought it might be valuable to discover how much. Hence the invitation when he rang to say there were no hard feelings.'

'Do you believe that?'

'Hardly. I know what I'd feel in his place.' Jago drank some of his own whisky. 'It should make for an interesting evening.'

'And he's coming alone,' Ashley mused aloud. 'Isn't he married?'

'Divorced,' Jago said succinctly. 'I don't think settled domesticity was his scene.'

'He's hardly unique in that point of view.'

'Is that a dig?' He sat down beside her, making her acutely conscious of the proximity of his long muscular thigh to the silky green folds of her skirt. She had to restrain an impulse to shy away. 'What could be more domestic than this—my wife and I enjoying a drink together while waiting for our guest to arrive?'

She could think of all kinds of things, but she

compromised by remaining silent, and taking another sip of sherry. It occurred to her that Jago could sense her inner discomfort, and was amused by it.

It was almost a relief to hear the sound of the front doorbell, signalling Paul Hollings' arrival. Jago got to his feet in one slow, lithe movement, then reached down for Ashley's hand and pulled her up too, so that for one pulsating, tingling movement she was caught against him, breast to breast. Then, as suddenly, he let her go, and moved towards the opening drawing room door.

'So this is the enemy camp!' Paul Hollings was smiling wryly as he came in. He was a tall man, and very fair with the kind of good looks Ashley had always associated with Robert Redford. His hand gripped Jago's. 'It's been a long time, and after that stroke you pulled yesterday, I could wish it had been longer.' He turned to Ashley, his smile widening. 'Mrs Marrick, thank you for asking me to your home. Our companies may be rivals, but we, I hope, can be friends.'

'I hope so,' Ashley said politely, letting her hand remain neutrally within his firm grasp.

'I always knew it would take an exceptional girl to tempt Jago away from bachelorhood,' Paul Hollings went on, just as if he thought their hasty marriage had taken place for romantic reasons rather than expediency. 'Perhaps you could work the same kind of miracle for me, and find a woman who'd be prepared to put up with me. They all tell me it's time I tried again.'

'How brave of them,' Ashley said coolly, taking back her hand. He was as charming as all get out, but she wasn't fooled. He hadn't got to the top of a concern like Marshalls by exercising his charm. It fitted him as well as his elegant dinner jacket, but could, she thought, be as easily discarded. But she could do a line in charm herself, if required, and she smiled back at him now, turning on both batteries. 'I'll certainly see what I can do. Do you prefer blondes or brunettes?'

His expression didn't waver by a fraction, but she knew she'd disconcerted him. 'I'd say brunettes if Jago hadn't snapped up the most attractive one around. He seems to have all the luck these days. But mine may change,' he added casually.

'Perhaps,' Jago broke in levelly. 'Is it still whisky with ice?'

'Of course.' Paul watched Jago move away to fetch the drink, and turned back to Ashley. 'What a pity,' he said softly, 'that I didn't come to Landons myself to conduct the negotiations. You see, no one told me just how lovely you were.'

Ashley smiled at him, veiling her eyes demurely with her lashes. 'Do you really think it would have made any difference?'

'It might.' He looked at her mouth, then let his gaze travel deliberately downwards to the thrust of her breasts. 'You won't believe this, but my information was that you and Jago were yesterday's news.' He gave her a rueful look. 'I should have seen for myself, instead of letting him steal a march on me like this.' He shrugged. 'But it's only a temporary setback.'

It would have pleased her to fling the remaining sherry in her glass straight in his face, but she kept smiling. 'That we shall have to wait and see,' she said lightly. 'Here's your drink.'

The conversation changed to general topics, the two men swapping stories of mutual friends, but the little confrontation had unnerved Ashley. Paul Hollings must be very sure of his ground to show his hand so clearly, she thought uneasily.

Dinner was excellent, with sole fillets in a light creamy sauce following avocado vinaigrette, and preceding succulent duckling cooked in the English style with green peas and apple sauce. A pineapple shortcake completed the meal, and Paul Hollings laughingly declined cheese. It should have been a totally pleasant meal, but Ashley was unable to relax or enjoy her food. At this rate, she was due to emerge from her marriage with chronic indigestion, she thought with unwilling humour.

She excused herself from the table and went off to the drawing room, leaving the men alone to enjoy some port. She switched on the television, and flicked through the channels with the remote control device, trying to find something to catch her interest, and failing. She wondered what they were talking about. If it was business, perhaps she should have remained to hear what was being said. Jago might have moved her sideways in the company, but she would show him she was still a force to be reckoned with.

'You seem to be having grim thoughts,' Paul Hollings accused laughingly as he walked into the room. 'I hope they're not directed at me. It's just occurred to me that I'm intruding unforgivably on your honeymoon.'

'Well, please don't worry about it.' Ashley rose gracefully, and rang for coffee.

'Oh, but I do.' He sat down, giving her a long speculative look. 'If you were my bride, I wouldn't be sharing your company with anyone else.'

'Please don't play games,' Ashley said coldly. 'Don't pretend you don't know why Jago and I got married.'

He grinned. 'You're your father's own daughter,

Ashley Landon! I'm told he believed in plain speaking too.'

'That was certainly the impression he liked to give,' Ashley agreed coolly.

'Meaning I should look beneath the surface?' His brows rose questioningly. 'Is there any real need? I'd much rather have you as a colleague, Ashley, than an adversary.'

'I'm afraid that's too much to hope for.' She sent a restless glance towards the door. 'Where is my husband?'

'Making some kind of urgent phone call. He sent me to ensure you weren't feeling neglected.'

Or to make sure I wouldn't interrupt the phone call, Ashley thought with a hollow feeling.

She lifted one shoulder in a slight shrug. 'He's always so busy.'

'I shall have to see if I can't devise a way of giving him more leisure.' Paul Hollings' eyes glinted.

'I don't think he'd take very kindly to that,' she returned.

'Perhaps he wouldn't have a choice in the matter,' he came back at her smoothly. 'After all, your board is just delaying the inevitable, and our next offer won't be nearly so generous, believe me.'

She shrugged again. 'But as it's going to be refused, I hardly see that matters.'

'I wouldn't be too sure.' His voice sharpened, the velvet touch slipping a little. 'A company facing possible liquidation seeks any port in a storm.'

Ashley's heart missed a beat, but she laughed lightly. 'But Landons is nowhere near liquidation.'

'Not yet, perhaps, but these are early days.' The ruthlessness was overt now. 'How much work can you afford to lose to us, my dear? I know, even if you don't. Just think back on all the projects we've squeezed you out of lately, and we haven't even been trying.' He paused. 'I know, for instance, you're after the Craigmore contract. So are we, and we're going to get it. And that's just for starters.'

'So—war is declared.' She was glad to hear she sounded detached, and even faintly amused.

'It doesn't have to be war,' he said intently. 'We could call a truce right here and now. We could renew our offer, and you could recommend acceptance to your board. I'd see that neither you nor Jago would suffer financially. Isn't that a better proposition than watching your markets disappear from under your nose until Landons is worth peanuts? After all, we both know if you don't get the Craigmore development, you're going to have to start laying off some of your workforce. And that will be the beginning of the end.'

Ashley kept smiling, but her heart was hammering violently now. It was galling to know that Paul Hollings had a point. If Landons lost the Craigmore project, it would be a blow they could not afford.

She said, 'And just how long do you think you can go on undercutting us? It must be costing you too.'

'The margins aren't that great,' he reminded her. 'We regard it as an investment. Why don't you sell, Ashley, while you still have a commodity worth the name? Because I should warn you that you can't count on Jago's everlasting support, even if you are married to him. We go way back, Jago and I, and he likes to get his financial irons out of the fire in plenty of time. When he realises Landons is finished, you won't see him for dust. He gets bored very easily, especially with failure. If he can't win, he looks round for fresh pastures—but I'm sure this can't be any real secret to you.'

Her eyes flew to his, 'What do you mean?'

He looked faintly surprised. 'You were engaged to him once, weren't you? You must have discovered a few things about him.'

'A few,' said Ashley, recovering her cool with an effort. 'Of course, Jago doesn't allow anyone to know everything.'

Paul Hollings laughed. 'He must be a very complicated bridegroom!' He paused. 'Now, if you belonged to me, I'd want to share everything with you.'

She smiled gracefully, 'Perhaps I'm complicated too,' she said, as the door opened to admit Mrs Bolton with the coffee tray.

She was thankful to see Jago walk in behind her, but less than pleased to hear him say, as the housekeeper set down the tray, and turned to leave, 'Mrs Erica has left her ear-rings behind. Perhaps you could dig them out for me.'

So it had been Erica he'd been calling, she realised, pain striking at her. She reached hurriedly for the coffee pot, busying herself with the cups to cover the moment.

She had half expected Paul Hollings to raise the subject of the Marshalls takeover again, but to her surprise it was never mentioned. It was social chit-chat, touching lightly on economics and the political situation, without so much as a hint at the rivalry between the two companies.

Ashley contributed little to the conversation. Anger was uncoiling slowly inside her, tightening the muscles of her throat, curling her fingers into claws. And it had nothing to do with the fact that Jago was clearly planning to meet Erica during the next couple of days, she told herself vehemently. How could she possibly be disturbed by the confirmation of something she already knew? No, it was Paul Hollings' jibes that Jago might be prepared to sell out Landon's, if the price was right, and run which were setting her on edge. That was the important issue—not some passing sexual infidelity.

Her mouth felt dry as she remembered that Erica had levelled the same kind of contemptuous taunt. Jago wanted his revenge, she'd said. '*But when he's wrung the company dry, he'll throw it on the scrapheap* ...' The words echoed and re-echoed in her mind. Could this be what had prompted Henry's warning too? Did they all know something of which she remained in naïve ignorance?

If it was true—oh God, if it was true ... Her fingers curled round the delicate porcelain cup as if she wanted to crush it to powder.

The pretty mantel clock struck the hour, and Paul Hollings got to his feet, smooth phrases of regret on his lips.

'I'm convinced I've thoroughly outstayed my welcome as it is,' he said, refusing Ashley's tight-lipped offer of a nightcap. He took her cold hand and lifted it to his lips. '*Au revoir*,' he added lightly. 'I'm sure we shall be meeting again very soon.'

Jago accompanied him out to his car. Ashley stood by the fireplace, drumming her fingers on the mantelshelf.

'May I clear the coffee things, madam?' Mrs Bolton had made one of her ghostlike appearances.

'Yes,' Ashley said abruptly, her mouth compressed, her eyes stormy.

The housekeeper sent her a sidelong glance. 'I hope everything was satisfactory, madam. Cook does prefer more notice if there are to be guests, of course.'

'I'll try and remember,' Ashley was aware of the curiosity in the other woman's eyes, and strove for a normal tone.

'Then if there's nothing else, I'll say goodnight.' Mrs Bolton's departure was as quiet as her arrival.

I suppose that's one of the things I don't like about her, Ashley thought. The way she seems to glide about the place, so that you never hear her coming. She'd make a wonderful spy.

She heard the front door slam and Jago's swift stride coming down the hall. He walked into the drawing room and closed the door behind him, his eyes speculative as he watched her.

He said softly, 'So—what's been burning you up for the past hour, or is it a secret?'

Her voice shook slightly. 'I don't like your friend.'

Jago shrugged. 'I didn't make it a requirement.' His eyes narrowed. 'What has he been saying to you?'

'Not very veiled threats of starving us of work until we're bankrupt, among other things.'

'Hm.' Jago came forward, putting up a hand to tug his black tie loose. 'I get the impression it's these "other things" which are really bothering you.'

She said, 'Can he do what he's threatening?'

If it was a plea for reassurance, it fell on stony ground. Jago's mouth twisted.

'It's possible. You know the way things have been going, or you do now I've alerted you to the fact,' he added with a trace of grimness.

'He's competing against us for the Craigmore tender.'

'Naturally,' Jago retorted crisply. 'I hope you didn't fall apart when he told you as you seem to be doing now.'

'I am not falling apart,' Ashley said between her teeth. 'Aren't you even a little bit disturbed by what I'm telling you?'

'It's hardly news.' His voice was clipped. 'Did he have anything else to say? I can't believe what you've been telling me could have provoked such a strong reaction from you.'

She moistened her lips with the tip of her tongue. 'He—he said if Landons went broke you'd walk away. Was he right about that?'

The look he sent her was compounded from irony and derision. 'Going down with a sinking ship may be very gallant, darling, but it makes no business sense at all. Does that answer your question?'

'Only too well.' She felt deathly tired suddenly. 'So much for your loyalty to Silas' memory which you said so much about!'

'But I'm also a realist.' The hazel eyes were hard and watchful as they rested on her pale face. 'However, the real trick is to prevent the ship from sinking in the first place. That's what we need to concentrate on. Or don't you agree?'

'You know my feelings,' she said sharply. 'Why else do you think I sold myself into this mockery of a marriage? I thought I'd bought your loyalty to Landons with the chairmanship of the board.' She gave a little harsh laugh. 'I'd forgotten, you see, that if you were for sale once, you could be so again.'

'Ah,' he said softly. There was a silence. 'Did Paul mention a figure?' he asked almost casually.

'He suggested the terms could be generous, for both of us.'

He smiled reflectively. 'He doesn't know you—does he, darling?'

'But he knows you,' she said. 'He said you "go

way back". Presumably he could be expected to know what you'd regard as your personal equivalent of thirty pieces of silver.'

His smile widened. 'He may have done, once, but my price has risen considerably since then. Well, aren't you going to ask me, darling? The million-dollar question?'

'If you don't really care about what happens to Landons,' she said slowly, 'why did you marry me?'

'To get you into bed,' he drawled insolently. 'Don't pretend you don't know. You've been as aware of it as you were three years ago, when you were driving me crazy with your touch-me-not tactics. I was prepared to be patient then, Ash, prepared to give you time to come to terms with your own sexuality, but I failed. You never turned to me, my sweet, never offered anything of your own accord. But you will, Ashley—that is if you want me to go on fighting for Landons for you. Because you won't win on your own—you know that. But I'm no knight in shining armour, darling. I'm a mercenary. If I'm to go on winning your battles, I want payment in kind.'

'You said it would just be an agreement,' she said hoarsely. 'My name on a marriage certifi-cate …'

He shrugged. 'I know what I said. I also mentioned something about the end justifying the means. Didn't it occur to you that can be interpreted in all kinds of ways?'

Ashley began desperately, 'Jago, I trusted you …'

He shook his head, his mouth curling. 'I don't think so. You weren't really surprised when I showed up in your room last night. If we hadn't been interrupted, all the arguments would have been settled by now. Well, tonight no one's going to interrupt us, and you're going to start learning about what it means to be a woman—my woman.'

'I don't believe this!' Her dark hair swung violently as she flung back her head in defiance. 'You can't mean what you're saying!'

'I've never been more serious.'

In spite of her brave words, she knew he was speaking the truth. There was a cold purpose in the lean incisive face which terrified her.

She said huskily, 'And what about Erica? How will she feel, if she finds out? You don't really want me. You have a future with her. Are you going to jeopardise that?'

Jago shrugged. 'But she's not here, darling. And I certainly won't tell her—will you? Not that it would matter,' he added cynically. 'I'm sure, in her way, Erica has even fewer illusions about me than you. And if you're about to appeal to my sense of decency, forget it, because it doesn't exist.'

Her lips felt numb. 'Do I have no choice in this?'

'Certainly,' Jago said mockingly. 'Would you prefer to make love here on the floor or in bed?'

Ashley stared at him. 'You disgust me,' she whispered.

'Tell me something I don't already know.' He sounded almost bored. 'You're prevaricating, sweetheart, and I'm getting impatient. Well, shall it be here or ...'

'Upstairs.' Her voice was barely audible.

'Very well.' He walked to the door and opened it. He was smiling, but his hazel eyes were inexorable as they rested on her pale face and quivering lips. 'Shall we go up, then—darling?'

CHAPTER SEVEN

She went up the stairs ahead of him, her head held high, moving carefully so that she would not stumble. That, in some ridiculous way, was important.

When they reached her door she hesitated, but Jago put a hand under her arm and led her down the corridor to his own room.

The lamps on either side of the massive bed had been lit as though in invitation, she thought bitterly.

Jago said softly, 'Alone at last.'

'I hate you,' she burst out, and he nodded slowly.

'It's possible. My God, you must have had some motive for putting me through the torture of the damned three years ago! You left me with an ache in my guts, and now, willing or unwilling, you're going to ease that ache for me. You can start by taking that dress off—slowly.'

Ashley wrapped her arms round her body. 'You actually expect me to degrade myself ...'

'With Landons at stake?' he broke in softly. 'This is the price you have to pay, darling. You start learning to please me, and you start now. Unless you'd prefer me to undress you?' he added casually.

'No.' Her voice cracked.

'Then don't keep me waiting any longer,' he advised coolly, but with faint amusement dawning in his face. 'Don't look so stricken, Ashley. A lot of women make a good living taking their clothes off in front of complete strangers every day of their lives. They survive, and so will you. Or doesn't

114

Landons mean that much to you after all?' He paused. 'Shall I ring Paul tomorrow, and tell him that we've decided to recommend acceptance of his next offer to the board?'

'I'll see you in hell before that happens,' she said thickly. She reached for her zip, jerking it downwards, dragging with shaking hands at the fragile folds of her dress until it lay in a shimmering heap at her feet. She kicked it contemptuously away and faced him. 'Satisfied?'

'Far from it,' Jago returned drily. He beckoned. 'Come here.'

Her moment of rebellion was over. She went to him on reluctant feet.

She said huskily, not meeting his eyes, 'You've—humiliated me. Isn't that enough?'

It isn't even the beginning,' he told her flatly. 'I know all about humiliation, Ashley. Remember how you made me crawl on my knees to you?' His voice deepened in savage self-mimicry. 'Ashley darling, let me touch you. I won't hurt you, I swear. I won't do anything you don't want.' He laughed harshly. 'But it never made any difference, did it, you cruel little bitch? You enjoyed hearing me plead, loved turning the knife. Only now it's my turn. Before I'm through with you, I'm going to make you want me every bit as bloody badly as I ever wanted you, my reluctant wife.'

As he reached for her, she closed her eyes, shutting him out, but he ignored the tacit rejection, the long supple fingers stroking along the vulnerable line of her shoulders, and down to her taut, naked breasts.

Ashley stifled a gasp in her throat as his hands cupped her, the thumbs stroking in insolent torment across her nipples. She was rent by a sensation of pleasure so powerful it almost resembled pain, and it terrified her, demonstrating in one succinct lesson what she was capable of feeling, and more. And proving, she realised, that the wild, sensual cravings which had always so alarmed her were not dead, as she'd believed, but merely dormant, waiting for Jago's caress, as an early flower waits for spring sunlight.

Her whole body shivered, but in delight now as he touched her, and she had to sink her teeth into the inner softness of her lower lip to stop a little moan of acceptance and surrender rising in her throat.

The cool, clever hands slid down her body in a lingering voyage of exploration which seemed to miss no tumultuous pulse point, no clamouring nerve ending, hardly even checking as her last remaining covering joined her dress on the floor. Then the caressing fingers were on her spine, urging her towards him, making her aware with a shock of shamed excitement that he was still fully dressed, the brush of his clothing tauntingly abrasive against her total nakedness.

Slave girl mentality! she lashed herself in self-contempt. She flung her head back and looked into his face, her eyes sparking.

'Damn you,' she muttered out of her aching throat, and Jago laughed softly, and bent and put his lips against the jerking pulse below the smooth line of her jaw.

Against her skin, he said huskily, 'You take my breath away, Ashley. Now it's my turn to take ...'

He pulled back the covers on the bed, then lifted her fully into his arms and put her down on the yielding mattress, his eyes travelling with open hunger over every line and curve, from her rose-tipped breasts down to the shadowed mystery of her thighs.

As he turned away to shrug off his dinner jacket, Ashley flung herself on to her side, dragging her arm across her eyes, trying to shut out, along with the sight of him, the reality of what was happening to her.

She could always fight—make him take her by force, but a little shudder of recoil pulled her back from that particular brink. Besides, from the very first time Jago had ever taken her in his arms, she had been aware of the lean whipcord strength of his body, and the obvious restraint he had always practised towards her. Like a lion in a cage, she had thought then—only, now, the lion was free, and the risk of his anger was more than she dared kindle.

It was with her mind she had to oppose him, and her turbulent senses, with their traitorous clamour for fulfilment. When, at last, she felt the slight shift of the mattress under his weight, as he came to lie beside her, her mind dizzied into blankness and her nails clenched painfully into the palms of her hands.

He touched her bare shoulder, his questing fingers recognising the sheer rigidity of the delicate bones and muscles, and Ashley heard him sigh faintly.

He said quite gently. 'It seems you have another choice. You can either meet me halfway, or you can carry on being the virgin sacrifice. But I should warn you now, Ash, that I want you very badly, and I'm going to have you, whatever you choose to do.'

His grip tightened, making her turn towards him, forcing her to read the stark purpose in his unsmiling eyes. He took her hands in his, uncurling the taut fingers, his brows snapping together as he saw the little crimson weals scored into the soft flesh. He drew a breath, then raised her hands, so that he could touch the angry marks with his lips.

His voice husky, he said, 'Oh God, darling, let go. Don't fight me. Don't make it be like this.'

'And how else can it be?' She hardly recognised her own voice. 'You've broken faith with me, Jago, over and over again. You can hardly expect me to fall into your arms. Do what the hell you want—I can't stop you. But for God's sake, get it over with.'

He smiled slowly into her eyes. 'Is that what you'd prefer? I'm sorry to have to disappoint you, Ashley. I've waited a long time for this, and I intend to enjoy every minute of it. You, of course, must do as you please.'

He bent his head and put his mouth against hers very lightly, his tongue stroking the soft outline of her lips with tantalising gentleness. His hands were gentle too, but very sure as he caressed her skin. He knew exactly how and where to touch, to arouse, to inflame to breathless longing, reminding Ashley bitterly exactly how he had learned his undoubted expertise.

It added steel to her resistance, turning dull passivity to determination. She had endured his betrayal and loss. Now, she would endure his possession of her, somehow, combating her reeling senses, and the wild urging of her awakening flesh.

But it was unfair, she screamed silently at the warm, swirling universe of pleasure that threatened to overwhelm her. It was unjust that she should be so vulnerable, so totally at the mercy of her responses. It would have been so much easier to hate him if he'd been casual and uncaring—even brutal. But, of course, Jago was none of these things. As he'd made clear, first in words, and now in this infinitely, exquisitely drawn out savouring of every quivering inch of her body with his mouth and hands, he wanted her entire capitulation, and nothing else would do.

Gradually, painfully, she retreated from him down some dark, emotional tunnel to a cold, secret place inside herself, where she existed in chill isolation. She made herself think—think about Paul Hollings and his threats—about the pages of facts and figures she'd studied earlier that day—about anything or anyone but the man in bed with her.

She succeeded well enough to achieve a kind of numb acceptance when, at last, Jago's body invaded hers in the ultimate intimacy. She had expected him to hurt her, had in a perverse way wanted pain so that she could turn the shrinking of her flesh back on him in guilt, but it didn't happen. He was too clever for that, too patient and too subtle.

Ashley knew a discomfort so fleeting it was over before she could clutch at it. She heard the soft, triumphant sound he made in his throat, felt his hands slide under her body, lifting her, locking her against him. He kissed her, his lips parting hers in passionate mastery, the thrust of his tongue against hers mirroring the increasing forceful demand of his loins.

He wasn't gentle any more. He was out of control at last, driven by a need so dark and desperate that all she could do was allow herself to be carried along by the storm of his desire for her. The culmination, when it came, was violent, his face wrenched, almost defenceless as he cried out, his body shuddering in release.

Then the taut body slumped against hers, his

relaxed weight pressing her down into the bed. He was the vulnerable one now, and it would be easy to push him away. But she didn't want to. In fact, all her instincts were clamouring at her to take the opposite course, to hold him close to her breasts, to smooth back the dishevelled sweat-dampened hair from his forehead, and touch his face with her lips. It was a reaction that startled her, horrified her, and it had to be dealt with.

She said icily, 'If you've finished with me, I'd like to go to the bathroom. I want a wash.'

She felt sudden tension grip him, and braced herself for his anger, but when he lifted his head and looked down at her there was nothing in his face but a faint, lazy amusement.

'To scour the taste and touch of me off you—out of you?' he asked mockingly. 'I wonder if it's as simple as that. As it is, the question's purely academic, because I haven't finished with you, my darling. Not by a long way.' His voice slowed to a drawl. 'If your lacklustre performance just now was supposed to turn me off, I'm afraid it hasn't worked. The night is young, and I have three sterile years to make up for.' His hand shaped her breast, stroking the delicate nipple until it peaked proudly under his caress.

He added softly, 'Starting now ...' and began to kiss her again.

Ashley awoke slowly and reluctantly, forcing her grudging eyelids to admit the instrusion of daylight.

For a moment she stared dazedly round, bewildered by the unfamiliar room, then memory came flooding back, and she sat up abruptly, eyes drowsy no longer, but alert and apprehensive.

But she was, it seemed, alone. She occupied the

rumpled bed in solitary splendour. She bit her lip until she tasted blood as the events of the past night came crowding back to torment her. In a series of devastating lessons, Jago had taught her that he had meant exactly what he'd said. He had made no further attempt to woo her, but instead had used her as if she was some instrument designed slowly for his pleasure, and his enjoyment of her had been unequivocal and totally uninhibited, she remembered, a warm wave of colour washing over her body.

And when, at last, he had fallen asleep, one arm flung carelessly across her body, she had been left to lie awake, shattered, aching with physical frustration in every fibre of her being.

The victor with his spoils, she had thought stormily, trying to fan the flames of her angry resentment when all she really wanted to do was burst into weary tears. But she had held them rigidly back. The last thing she wanted was for him to wake and find her crying.

She had won in her way. She had never by word or gesture indicated that she found his lovemaking anything more than a matter of total indifference to her, crushing down her starving body's need for appeasement. Yet now she felt utterly defeated.

She knew exactly what she could expect from now on at her husband's hands. The question still to be answered was—how could she bear it?

She pushed the covers away and swung her feet to the floor, a glance at her watch showing her that it was already mid-morning. She collected her scattered clothes from the floor, then opened the door cautiously, peeping round to make sure there was no one in sight before running like a hare for the seclusion of her own room.

As she waited for her bath to fill, she took stock of herself in the big mirror. She had escaped relatively unscathed. She had a few unfamiliar aches and pains, and some reddened patches on her breasts and thighs where the faint stubble on his jaw had grazed her, but apart from that she looked much the same, she told herself—if she didn't look too closely.

She bathed quickly, an apprehensive ear tuned all the time for sounds of movement in the bedroom which might signal Jago's return, then dressed, dragging on a pair of slim-fitting white cotton jeans, which she topped with a scarlet cotton T-shirt. She disguised the telltale fullness of her mouth with lipstick, but there was little she could do about the shadows under her eyes. But then it would probably give Jago's ego a fillip to have her going downstairs looking as if she'd taken part in some sexual marathon, she thought bitterly.

She took some of her anger out on her hair, brushing it until it shone, then started off downstairs.

There seemed to be no one about, although she could hear the whine of a vacuum cleaner in the distance. She hesitated at the foot of the stairs, wondering restlessly where Jago was. She must have been heavily asleep when he left the bed, because she hadn't been conscious of his departure. And if she was honest, she acknowledged, her face warming a little, she hadn't expected to find herself alone when she woke. He had awoken her more than once during that long night, his mouth warm and sensually insistent. Why hadn't he told her it was morning in the same way?

'Good morning, madam. Do you require breakfast now?'

Ashley spun round with a startled yelp, to find

Mrs Bolton had done her materialisation act yet again, and was standing at her shoulder, an unpleasantly avid look in her narrow eyes.

'Just some coffee please,' Ashley said, grabbing at her poise. 'And could you tell Mr Marrick I'd like to speak to him.'

She was allowed a glimpse of the vinegary smile. 'I'm afraid Mr Marrick has already left for the day, madam. He went immediately after breakfast. Did he not mention it to you?'

Ashley was very still suddenly. 'Oh, yes,' she said, after a pause. 'I—I'd forgotten.' She hesitated again. 'Did he remember to take those ear-rings with him?'

Oh, yes, madam.' The tone was respectful enough, but there was a covert, malicious glee peeping at Ashley from somewhere which was somehow more disturbing than open insolence would have been. 'I found them for him last night, as the matter seemed so urgent. Would you like me to bring your coffee to the drawing room for you?'

'Thank you,' Ashley managed as she turned away. Somehow, she found herself in the drawing room, stumbling across the thick carpet towards the french windows, flinging them open and drawing deep breaths of the cool spring air. It was a grey morning with a hint of rain in the air, and the dampness settled on her cheeks like soft tears.

She had not realised, she thought dazedly, that it was possible to suffer so much. She had promised herself she had wept for Jago for the last time. Now, suddenly, a whole new era of heartbreak had opened up in front of her.

Oh, no! she moaned silently, as pain tore into her, wrenching her apart. How could this be happening? How could Jago, the faithless, the opportunist, still have the power to hurt her like this?

And she heard the desperate truth ringing through her heart, soul and mind.

'Because I love him, God help me. I still love him.'

She stood for what seemed like an eternity, staring across the windless garden with eyes that saw nothing.

She wondered how she could have been such a fool not to recognise the conflict inside her for what it was—and thought what irony it was that recognition should have come at this moment, when it had just been brought home to her, yet again, that she had nothing to hope for in any relationship with him. Last night he had possessed her body, claiming that last remaining asset Landons had brought him, she thought bitterly, and that was all it had meant to him. His cynical absence this morning proved that.

Pride told her that she should be glad she had resisted the potent sensual magic of his lovemaking, giving nothing in return, making him take. Because if she had surrendered, given way to the urgency within her, it would have made no difference. She would still have woken—alone.

She couldn't even be jealous of Erica, because she knew that Jago would never truly belong to her either, no matter how passionate their affair. He had his own priorities, and any woman in his life would have to accustom herself to occupying a place somewhere down on the list. Even Erica.

For herself, she was thankful Jago couldn't know, and wouldn't ever know about the bruised, vulnerable confusion inside her. Loving him was her grief, and had to remain her secret.

Shivering, she turned back into the drawing room, as Mrs Bolton arrived with the coffee tray.

Ashley said, 'I see the fire hasn't been lit again.'

'Mrs Marrick's orders, madam, are ...'

'I am Mrs Marrick.' Ashley's voice was cool and sharp. 'And while this cool weather continues, I require the drawing room fire to be lit each morning. Do I make myself clear?'

'Perfectly clear.' Mrs Bolton's meagre bosom swelled. 'But I am used to taking my orders from Mrs Erica. And I should point out—madam, that she will not be pleased to find her instructions being countermanded.'

'And nor am I,' Ashley said quietly. 'I think you and I are going to have to come to terms, Mrs Bolton, or else a parting of the ways.'

A mottled flush appeared on Mrs Bolton's face and neck. 'You have no right ...'

'I think you'll find I have.' Ashley poured herself some coffee. 'Shall we say a month's notice?'

'You can say what you please!' The older woman was making no effort to conceal her contempt now. 'It will make no difference, as you'll find out. We'll just see which of us is the one who's leaving!'

The drawing room closed behind her with a slam.

Phew! thought Ashley, leaning back in her chair. The confrontation seemed to have blown up out of nowhere, but it had been inevitable. She remembered her first shy visits to the Manor as Jago's fiancée three years before, and how gauche and schoolgirlish Mrs Bolton had managed to make her feel. But not again, she told herself grimly. Mrs Bolton was a born bully, homing in on weakness wherever she saw it, but Ashley was no longer the child she had been. Her mouth twisted. If nothing else, Jago had seen to that.

And for a while, for better or worse, the Manor was to be her home.

She gave her surroundings a wry look. They might be elegant, but they were far from homelike. The drawing room alone looked like an illustration from an upmarket furnishing magazine, but it was not cosy in any way. The only really comfortable room, she recalled, had been Giles Marrick's study, which he had kept jealously to himself, and which Jago now used. Perhaps she too would adopt a room, and make it her own.

Because there was no denying the Manor lacked heart. She supposed that was what happened to a house like this when it lacked the children, and the pets, and the sprawling family life it had been originally intended for.

Ashley swallowed past a painful lump her throat. Well, there was nothing she could do about that, but she could organise her own room. She knew where to go too.

There was a small morning room at the rear of the house, overlooking the shrubbery. It was dark, and rather cramped, and probably for that reason it had escaped the glossy patina which Erica had imposed on the rest of the house.

The furniture was heavy and old-fashioned, and needed relegating to an attic, she decided critically. She could easily replace it with some of the favourite pieces from her flat. She would keep the faded charm of the silk wallpaper, however, but add lighter curtains. And she would start now.

Taking a deep breath, she summoned Mrs Bolton and told her quietly that she wanted the room cleared. She had expected further protests, but apart from the inevitable tightening of the lips, Mrs Bolton showed no sign of dissent.

She probably thinks a small back room is the best place for me, Ashley decided with faint amusement.

She drove into town. The estate agent was not altogether pleased when she told him she had changed her mind about selling all her furniture, although he admitted reluctantly that he hadn't cleared the flat yet.

And he was pardonably annoyed when she said she was no longer interested in selling the flat, but letting it part furnished instead. It seemed he had two clients involved in a contract race already.

Ashley shrugged. 'Ask if they're interested in a short-term lease instead.'

'They won't be,' he said mournfully. 'May I know why you've changed your mind? Mr Marrick was quite positive that you wanted to sell.'

She caught a speculative gleam in his eye, and smiled nonchalantly. 'We talked it over, and decided a *pied-à-terre* near the office might not be such a bad thing to hang on to.'

It was odd, letting herself back into the flat again. It had only been a few days since she had left it, yet it seemed like a lifetime. And it was a desirable property, she thought as she wandered through the rooms. It was no wonder it had been so easy to dispose of. What she hadn't bargained for was feeling a stranger in her own home, and she didn't like it.

'Hey!' she said aloud, looking around her. 'I haven't been away that long. And I'm going to need you to come back to, so don't you reject me.'

She decided on the furniture she would have at the Manor, and tagged and labelled it. The agent had given her the phone number of a reliable firm which did small removals, and she was dialling them when she heard someone at the front door. Another interested client, she thought, as she opened it.

'Martin!' She couldn't have been more taken aback.

He looked in a state of shock himself. 'Someone said the flat was up for sale and then they told me ...' He stopped abruptly. 'Ashley, it can't be true! You're not—married?'

Mutely, she extended her left hand.

'Good God!' He leaned weakly against the door jamb. 'You don't waste any time, do you? I mean, when I went away, I thought—I intended ...' He stopped again. 'You must have known.'

She felt sorry to her soul. But there was no way she could tell him that, in spite of his intentions, their relationship would always have been fruitless. Because, in her secret heart, she had always been waiting for Jago to come back. She couldn't damage Martin's pride by even hinting at that.

She said awkwardly, 'Would you like a drink? There's still some here. I can't offer you coffee because the power's turned off.'

'I could do with something,' he muttered.

Ashley let him in reluctantly, and busied herself finding the remains of the whisky, and two glasses. She poured him a measure of Scotch, and filled her own glass with bitter lemon.

She said too brightly, 'How's your little girl? Better?'

'Yes—oh, yes. Children shake these things off so quickly. And my—Susan was always prone to panic rather.' There was a wistfulness in his voice. Martin missed being married, she thought sadly. He missed being masterful and reassuring. Only those weren't the qualities she'd been looking for. Unknown to herself, she liked living dangerously, she thought wretchedly.

He said, 'Of course, I wondered when I saw you and Marrick together at the Country Club. But you were so positive that it was all over. I thought I could trust you.'

His tone irritated her. She said, 'I didn't think we'd reached that degree of exclusivity. I'm sorry.'

Martin stirred restively. 'There are all kinds of rumours flying around. I suppose you know that.'

She shrugged, and sipped her drink. 'Inevitable, I suppose. Under the circumstances.'

'What are the circumstances?' The note of injury was more pronounced. 'I think I have a right to ask.'

'And I have an equal right to keep silent,' she said gently. 'Martin, don't push.'

There was a lengthy silence, then he sighed. 'I'm sorry. But you might have let me know what the situation was, instead of letting me come back here, thinking that everything between us was fine. That we'd be taking up where we left off.'

'It was thoughtless,' she agreed. 'Let's just say Jago—swept me off my feet, and leave it at that, shall we?'

'Perhaps I should have tried that,' he said ruefully. He finished his whisky and got to this feet. 'Well, no hard feelings, Ashley. Am I allowed to kiss you goodbye?'

The short answer to that was 'No', but she didn't want to injure his feelings any further, so when he took her arms and drew her towards him, she went passively, lifting closed lips to his touch. Only Martin didn't see it that way at all. His mouth fastened on hers greedily, sucking and tugging, while his tongue tried insistently to force an entry. Her hands came up and pushed at his chest with sufficient force to let him know this wasn't mere coyness. But he was in no hurry to let go, she realised with mingled dismay and annoyance. He was set on proving his point, making his mark—showing her that it could have worked for them. And all she could feel in return was a muted remorse.

As his hands slid down her arms to touch her breasts, Ashley stiffened. The situation was getting out of control, and it was going to take one shrewd, upward jerk of her knee to bring him to his senses.

And as she nerved herself to do it, a voice from the doorway said with a bite like an arctic wind, 'I seem to have arrived at a bad moment.'

It was Jago.

CHAPTER EIGHT

MARTIN let her go so suddenly, she nearly fell over. His face was so nonplussed as to be almost comic. He'd clearly remembered that this was an important client's wife he'd just been caught embracing. Ashley could have burst into hysterical laughter, only it wasn't funny. It wasn't funny at all.

He said, stumbling over his words, 'I—I ought to explain …'

The sardonic expression on Jago's face riled Ashley. What right had he to put Martin through any kind of hoop, she asked herself stormily. Or did he think there was one law for him, and a different one for everyone else?

She said swiftly, 'There's no need, Martin. Goodbye, and good luck.'

'Good luck, indeed,' Jago said silkily, as Martin sidled past him. 'I presume you can find your own way out.'

Husband and wife waited in silence for the sound of the front door closing behind him, then Jago said, 'I suppose I should apologise for my intrusion. But I'm not going to.' The hazel eyes were harsh. 'I wondered what the hell was going on when Jack Macauley phoned, bleating about you taking this place off the market. I didn't realise you were planning to turn it into a love nest.'

'I'm not,' Ashley said tightly. 'Martin was just— saying goodbye.'

'Oh, really?' There was an insolent challenge in

131

his voice. 'It looked more like hello to me.'

The colour in her face deepened hectically. 'Don't be sarcastic!' she snapped.

Jago shrugged. 'Didn't last night warn you what to expect?'

She didn't know what to say in answer to that, so she picked up the used glasses and took them to the kitchen, rinsing them under the cold tap.

Jago followed her. She was all too conscious of him watching her as she busied herself at the sink.

She said resentfully, 'How did you know I'd be here?'

'Your car was outside,' he said. 'You're not very good at the assignation game, are you, Ash? You should park several streets away, and walk if you don't want to be caught.'

'Thanks for the expert advice. I'll try and remember.' She tried to match the satire in his voice.

'So why have you decided to let instead of sell? And why are the gardeners at the Manor indoors, heaving furniture all over the place?'

It was Ashley's turn to shrug. 'I decided to take over the morning room for my own use. No one seems to want it, and I would like some privacy, and my own things about me.' She paused. 'I hope you don't object.'

'In the daytime, you can do as you please,' Jago said. 'But the nights are different, and I've given some orders of my own about those. Your clothes and belongings are being moved to my bedroom.'

'Oh.' She could feel herself flushing again, and kept her back rigidly turned. 'Was that necessary?'

'Yes,' he said. 'Or did you think last night was all there was to it?'

'I've tried not to think about it at all.'

He gave a short laugh. 'I can believe that.' He paused. 'So—why are you keeping a stake in this place?'

'So that I'll have somewhere to go,' she said evenly. 'When you get tired of all these little power games of yours, and decide to let me go, that is.'

'Is that what I'm planning?' He sounded amused.

'God knows,' she said shortly. 'But I'm not letting the flat go. If Macauleys can't find me any short-term tenants, then the place can stay empty. I presume I'm still going to be paid some kind of salary from Landons, so that I can keep the mortgage payments going.'

'Of course. As long as you don't make a habit of using the place to entertain other men.'

She turned then, to face him, angry and at bay. 'You hypocrite! Do you think for one moment I don't know where you've been this morning?'

'I imagine you do. I didn't intend to make a secret of it.'

'An open marriage, in other words. Please don't forget that can work both ways.'

'I shan't,' said Jago, after a pause. 'Although your reaction last night didn't prompt me to suppose you were planning to fling yourself headlong into the sexual deeps.'

Ashley jerked a shoulder. She said clearly, 'Just because you don't turn me on ...'

Her voice trailed away into a charged silence. 'I see,' Jago said at last. 'So it's—anyone's kisses but mine. Is that it?'

'Perhaps,' she said. She didn't look at him. 'Now, I'd better phone that removal firm.'

'Later,' Jago said too gently. 'After all, they might remove the bed, and I have a use for it.'

As he moved towards her, Ashley read the

purpose in his eyes with real alarm. She would have retreated, but she was pinned against the sink, with nowhere to go.

She said shakily, 'You're being ridiculous ...'

'Probably,' he said. 'But what the hell! After all, I spoiled your little rendezvous with Witham, so the least I can do is make it up to you for that.'

'I hadn't planned to meet him,' she protested. 'He'd been away. He came round to see me because he'd just heard the news ...'

'Of course he did.' He took her by the shoulders, drawing her towards him, the hazel eyes hard and mocking as they studied her flushed, pleading face. 'And then I turned up and spoiled it all.' He shook his head. 'With my record, I can hardly object to you having a life of your own, Ashley. And I won't stop you using this place either. But whoever you bring here, you're going to remember I had you here first.'

'You're disgusting!' His nearness was affecting her profoundly. Inwardly, she was trembling, starting to ache ...

'I'm sure you think so.' Jago picked her up in his arms and carried her back into the living room, depositing her full length on the big sheepskin rug in front of the empty fireplace. She struggled up on to an elbow.

'What are you doing?'

'Your memory can't be that poor,' he jibed, peeling the thin wool sweater he was wearing over his head and tossing it to one side. 'What I did last night, darling, with a few variations on the central theme, perhaps.' He dropped to one knee beside her, his hand moving with heart-stopping intimacy over her jean-clad thighs. She gasped and tried to twist away, but he was too quick for her, straddling her struggling body with one lithe movement.

'Some animation at last,' he commented. 'Last night I thought I was in bed with a marble statue.'

'Let go of me!' she spat at him. 'Get away from me, damn you!'

'Not a chance.' He had captured both her wrists in one hand, rendering her virtually powerless. Now he slid his hand under the midriff of the scarlet T-shirt, easing it upwards. His fingers found the fragile clip which fastened her bra in the delicate valley between her breasts, and twisted it open, so that the lace cups fell away, baring her. He bent, and she felt his mouth, warm and sensuous against her flesh, his tongue teasing one hardening nipple with deliberate eroticism. His lips paid tribute to her other breast, then drifted downward over her ribcage, and the flat plane of her stomach to the waistband of her jeans.

He lifted his head. His eyes, intent, slumbrous with desire, held hers making it impossible to look away.

He said huskily, 'You taste like heaven.'

He let go of her wrists so that he could free her completely from the tangle of her T-shirt, and she made no effort to fight him. Her skin was tingling, unbearably sensitised by the leisurely brush of his mouth.

Last night she had denied herself the pleasure he offered, her fear of the unknown bolstering her resistance. But she could no longer use her sexual ignorance as a barricade. Her senses were reminding her with compelling urgency just how Jago had felt inside her.

He kissed her mouth, parting her lips without haste, and with a little sob, she responded, shyly at first, then with increasing confidence as the kiss deepened, and demanded.

She twined her arms round his neck, holdi·.g him against her, enjoying the sensation of the hard wall of his chest against the softness of her breasts.

Jago took his lips from hers and began to plant tiny kisses on her face, tracing her hairline, her cheekbones, her closed eyes. She found she was revelling in the swift, sensuous caresses, her head turning restlessly. When his mouth covered hers again, she didn't shrink from its urgent mastery, but answered fire with breathless fire.

He lifted himself away from her and she felt his hand at the waistband of her jeans, and the downward rasp of her zip. She twined her arms round his neck as he eased her slenderness free of the clinging material, her body burning, melting as his fingers cupped her intimately before deftly disposing of the few inches of lace which still covered her.

She was quivering in every fibre of her being, eagerly awaiting his caress, but she was totally unprepared for the warmth of his mouth against her, exploring every sweet secret of her womanhood.

'No!' Ashley reared up in outrage and sheer panic.

'Hush,' he said. And, gently, 'It's all right.'

His hands stroked her trembling body, offering the physical reassurance of his touch, as if she was some small, frightened animal whom he was soothing to acceptance. As the shocked rigidity seeped out of her, he whispered, 'There's a journey into pleasure ahead of us, Ashley. This time I don't intend to travel alone.'

His lips touched her breasts, moving in insidious beguilement from the heated rosy peaks to the scented valley between, then laid a warm trail downwards over her abdomen. The lazy brush of his mouth tantalised and beckoned, drawing her from the shelter of her remaining inhibitions, so that when he regained his goal she was incapable of further resistance. Her head fell back on the softness of the rug, a little helpless sigh rising in her throat as she surrendered to the ripples of sensation spreading through her tingling body.

The ripples became waves, small fierce storms of delight driving her relentlessly towards some peak of pleasure as yet undreamed of.

There was a pulse beating within her, deep and savage as the universe. Nothing else existed, or ever had. The pulsation deepened unbearably, drew her down into some vortex, consumed her, then flung her out into a vast shimmering void.

Jago said, 'Now,' and took her.

Locked with him in the harsh, driving rhythm of his possession, new spasms convulsed her. She heard herself cry out, gasping for breath, torn apart by ecstasy—felt the great shudder of final consummation engulf him too.

Reality returned slowly. Ashley was aware of his weight on her, the unheated air of the flat striking a chill against her perspiring skin. Jago moved abruptly, lifting himself away from her, pushing his sweat-dampened hair back from his face.

Ashley lay still, watching him under her lashes. She wanted to tell him how much she loved him, but shyness paralysed her, making it impossible to speak. After all, he knew everything about her now. She had no secrets left, nor did she want to have. But the hangover of her old fears and reticences was still there, and she needed reassurance.

But the harsh, brooding expression on his face

offered her no comfort at all. Had she shocked him? she wondered. Had the wildness of her response confirmed that she was, in some way, abnormal?

She swallowed, trying to relax the taut muscles in her throat. She had to speak—to ask.

As if aware of her trembling regard, Jago turned his head slightly and looked at her, the hazel eyes expressionless as they brushed over her nakedness.

'So much for your Miss Frigidity act!' The firm mouth twisted as he reached for his clothes. 'So— who did you pretend I was? Witham, or one of the future dream lovers you plan to entertain here?'

The edge of contempt in his voice stung like a blow. With shaking hands, Ashley reached for her own scatter of garments, letting her dark hair swing forward to conceal her flushed, downbent face.

'A dream lover,' she said.

It was no more than the truth. Jago had always filled any dream of love she had ever possessed. It was her tragedy that he was the only man she had ever wanted, or ever would want, and she was going to have to live with that.

'My congratulations,' he said mockingly. 'I had no idea you had such a vivid imagination.'

He got to his feet and walked over to the window, staring out, his back turned to her, while Ashley huddled into her clothes. He said brusquely, 'Do you want me to drive you back to the Manor?'

'No, I'll use my own car.' She paused. 'I still have some things to see to here in town.'

She could hardly believe what was happening. Only a short while before, they had been united in a passionate intimacy she had never dreamed could exist. Now it was over, and they were back in the mundane world, as separate as they had ever been, talking banalities.

Jago shrugged. 'As you wish,' he said curtly. 'I'll see you at the house later.'

The door closed behind him, shutting her into the empty room, reminding her with bitter emphasis of all those other empty rooms which would face her one day—when their marriage was over.

She took her time over her errands, deliberately delaying the moment when she would have to return to the Manor, and all the problems which awaited her there. She tried to fill her mind with her plans for the morning room, poring over carpet samples and curtain fabrics, but she couldn't banish Jago from her brain, or the heated recollection of the passion they had shared from her memory. She had given him everything, and now she had to come to terms with the reality of how little her gift had been valued. After all, she told herself wretchedly, Jago was an expert lover, virile and exciting. To him, her capitulation would have been no more than his due. But it changed nothing between them.

Eventually she chose some ready-made curtains in an attractive shade of old rose, added cushion covers to match, and drove slowly back to the house through the lanes.

She took her purchases straight to the morning room. Emptied of its furniture, it already looked larger and lighter, she decided critically.

She fetched a chair from the dining room, and stood on it to take the old curtains down. It was a stretch, and the weight of the fabric made her arms ache, but she persevered. Her task achieved, it was comparatively easy to transfer the hooks to the new curtains, then she gathered up the folds of material and clambered back on her perch. But re-attaching the hooks to the waiting curtain rings was more difficult than she had anticipated. It was a fiddly task, and the chair began to feel more and more precarious as she struggled.

Ashley gritted her teeth, rising on tiptoe to secure the last hook. As she did so, the chair rocked alarmingly, and she gave a startled cry, lunging at the window frame to regain her balance.

From behind her Jago demanded glacially, 'What the hell do you think you're doing?'

His hands clamped round her waist, steadying her, and lifting her inexorably to the floor.

'Hanging curtains.' Mutinously, Ashley pulled herself free, her face flushing.

'I thought perhaps you were trying to hang yourself,' he said caustically. 'But I should warn you that fooling around on old chairs leads more often to a broken ankle than a broken neck. Why didn't you get Mrs Bolton to help you?'

'Because I don't like her.' Ashley bent and retrieved an errant hook from the carpet. 'As a matter of fact ...' She paused.

'Yes?'

She lifted her head defiantly. 'As a matter of fact,' she repeated, 'I've given her a month's notice.'

'Have you indeed?' Jago's brows snapped together in a frown. 'Don't you think that's something you should have discussed with me first?'

'You weren't there to ask,' she said coolly.

'Then you should have waited until I was,' he said grimly.

'I don't see why,' Ashley protested. 'There are other housekeepers in the world. She isn't indispensable.'

'Erica thinks she is,' he said quietly. 'So I'm afraid Mrs Bolton will have to be reinstated.'

'You can't be serious,' Ashley said, after a pause.

'Never more so.' His mouth twisted. 'I can't say Mrs Bolton is my flavour of the month either, but to fire her unceremoniously could cause all kinds of problems, which I'd prefer to avoid if possible.'

'You mean it would upset Erica?'

'You could say that.'

'And that, of course, must be avoided at all costs?' Ashley used sarcasm to mask the hurt.

'Yes.' The hazel eyes met hers directly. 'Ashley, there's something you have to understand ...'

'Oh, but I do understand—believe me, I do. In fact, the only thing that baffles me is why you married me, instead of waiting for her to finish her period of mourning, if that's what it is. In fact, there was very little need to wait at all.'

He shrugged, 'Oh, I think the conventions should be preserved—sometimes.'

'You surprise me.' Her voice sharpened. 'So— why did you marry me?' She stopped. 'Oh, but of course, there was Landons.'

'Exactly,' Jago said softly. 'Above and beyond all personal considerations, there was Landons.'

She twisted the hook in her fingers, bending it out of shape. 'So Mrs Bolton stays. Will you tell her, or am I expected to?'

'I'll speak to her myself.'

'Good.' Ashley bit her lip. 'And during the course of conversation, perhaps you could arrange for my things to be put back in the guest bedroom. After all, if Erica's feelings are so important to you, you can hardly upset her by sleeping with another woman.'

He shrugged again. 'I think she's more of a realist than you give her credit for,' he said. 'But your consideration for her amazes me, Ashley. I'm not sure she'd treat you quite so delicately, if she were in your place.'

'Perhaps.' She dragged a ghost of a smile from somewhere. 'I'll have to—wait and see, won't I? But in the meantime, I'd rather sleep alone.'

'I'm sure you would,' he said pleasantly. 'But I'm afraid I'm not prepared to gratify your whim. I've married you, Ashley, and I want you in my bed, physically at least, even if your heart and mind are elsewhere. But that doesn't mean you can repeat your ice-maiden act, however,' he added, with a touch of grimness. 'You proved very satisfactorily a few hours ago that you're subject to the same urges and lusts which drive ordinary mortals, so I won't settle for anything less in future.' He took her chin in his hand and looked down into her eyes. 'Try and freeze me away again, sweetheart, and you'll regret it.' His mouth twisted, and he gave the bare room around them a swift, comprehensive look. 'Meanwhile—enjoy your sanctuary.'

'I haven't one,' she said. She took a step forward. 'Jago, I know I made you angry when I broke off our engagement. Perhaps you expected me to be sophisticated enough to—take our relationship for what it was, and turn a blind eye to your other amusements. But haven't you had your revenge? How long do you expect me to go on—like this?'

He said levelly, 'Until I decide it's time to stop. I'll let you know when that is.'

Ashley moistened her lips with the tip of her tongue. 'When you're tired of me? Or when Erica comes back?'

'Now that would be telling,' he mocked her. 'But I'd say a little of both, wouldn't you?'

'Haven't you any mercy?' Her voice shook.

Jago shook his head slowly. 'I seem to be fresh

out of that particular commodity, especially when it involves spending my nights alone.' He laughed. 'But cheer up, my sweet. Look at your life with me like a balance sheet. Weigh the credit of keeping Landons inviolate against the debit of having to lend yourself to my unspeakable passions, once in a while. I'm sure you'll see where the profit lies.' He ran a caressing finger down the curve of her cheek. 'You always did, after all.'

'Thank you for reminding me,' she said quietly. 'That makes it all worth while, naturally.'

His eyes narrowed. 'I thought it might.' He bent and kissed her. It was only a breath of a caress, the merest brush of his mouth across hers, but it burned her like a brand.

He walked to the door and went out, without even a backward glance.

As, she supposed, he would, one day, walk away from her.

She sank down on to the shabby carpet, hugging her arms protectively across her breasts.

Oh, God, she thought achingly. What am I going to do?

CHAPTER NINE

'AND we look forward to meeting you on site to discuss your requirements in more detail. Yours, etc.' Ashley switched off her dictating machine and leaned back in her chair.

Another bread-and-butter reply successfully completed, she thought morosely. And very dull when used, as she was, to the real cut and thrust of decision-making.

She got up restlessly and went over to the window.

A week, she thought broodingly, since she had undertaken that reckless marriage. But they had proved seven of the most eventful days of her life. Although not, she was forced to concede, as far as her working life went. Jago was still keeping her, quite deliberately, on the fringe of things at the office. She was given routine tasks, but even these, she was aware, were scrutinised thoroughly.

For instance, she knew that this was the day when the final figure on the Craigmore tender would be decided, but that was the extent of her information. She had attended no meetings, nor received any memos on the subject, and in view of its importance to Landons' future, this was a ludicrous situation. Jago had imposed a tight new security régime on the whole building. There was a sense of urgency and purpose in the corridors these days that Ashley had to admit had not always been present over the past months, but that did not excuse the fact that she was excluded from the top-level decisions that were being taken about the company's future.

And when she had protested to Jago, insisting that she should be allowed to safeguard her interests, he had merely raised his eyebrows and drawled, 'Your interests are mine, darling. Don't you trust me to protect them?'

And had waited, mockingly, as the silence between them lengthened ...

There had been many such silences over the past week, Ashley thought unhappily. Silence when Mrs Bolton came to tell him that Mrs Marrick was on the phone and wished to speak to him—something which happened with monotonous regularity each evening, so that, almost unconsciously, Ashley was waiting for the shrill of the telephone bell.

Silence, when Jago vanished, sometimes for hours at a time, and returned volunteering no explanation.

And the most breathless silence of all when she awoke beside him in the morning to find him propped up on one elbow, watching her, the faint sardonic smile playing about his mouth reminding her more potently than any words could have done of the passion he had made her share the previous night.

She was allowed no respite. He made love to her with an erotic artistry which made her writhe in helpless shame when she recalled in daylight's sanity the depth of response he had drawn from her.

And she knew it must amuse him to contrast the cool self-contained image she maintained during working hours with the wild girl, sobbing with abandonment, whom he held in his arms each night. He took, she thought, an almost clinical pleasure in wringing every last ounce of sensation from her, leaving her drained and boneless on some barren shore of loneliness and need.

It was moments like these which made her want to turn to him; to beg words of love from him, even if they were only a pretence. It was moments like these which made her grateful for the silences which forbade any such disastrous impulse.

There had been other difficulties too, one of them Mrs Bolton's quiet but barely concealed triumph at the withdrawal of her notice. She had never actually said 'I told you so', but her attitude had implied it at every turn.

The only place where Ashley felt free of her encroaching presence was the morning room. Her furniture had arrived, and had been arranged to her satisfaction, so that part of the Manor felt like home at least. But it was a very small part. In the rest of the house, she still felt like an unwanted guest, and what it would be like when Erica returned she could only guess at and dread.

She had asked Jago tentatively whether she could have a dog, only to have the suggestion vetoed. Jago had been quite blunt about it. Erica, it seemed, couldn't stand dogs and hadn't allowed Giles to have his elderly retriever in the house, in case Polly did some unnamed damage to the expensive furnishings.

'I see.' Ashley had lifted her chin.

'I don't think you do,' Jago had returned wearily. 'But, for the time being, I'd be grateful if you'd respect her wishes. Believe me, it would make things very much easier.'

'I believe you.' Ashley turned away, icily masking her hurt and disappointment. 'God forbid that I should do anything to upset your cosy little applecart!'

'Amen to that.' Jago's voice followed her crisply. 'Just for once, Ashley, will you credit me with knowing what I'm doing?'

A bitter smile touched the corners of her mouth. 'I've always credited you with that, Jago. I'm sure you plan every move you make. I just wish I could have avoided being involved in your machinations.'

'And so do I.' His voice bit. 'But at the moment, it's a situation we're stuck with, so kindly make the best of it, as I'm doing.'

It had been a sharp little confrontation, and it had shaken Ashley to realise that, in spite of his unconcealed enjoyment of her body, Jago was also ill at ease in their taut relationship. It had depressed her too, and she shivered a little now as she stared unseeingly down at the sunlit street below.

A brief tap at her door made her start, and she turned quickly, forcing a smile as Henry Brett came in.

'Sorry to interrupt if you're busy,' he said. 'But Shelagh wanted me to remind you that you're coming to dinner tonight.'

'I hadn't forgotten.' Ashley walked back to her desk and sat down. 'We're both looking forward to it.'

Which was not strictly true, she thought ruefully. When she had mentioned the invitation to Jago he had lapsed into frowning silence for a while, then asked abruptly if they could make some excuse.

'No.' She had shaken her head vehemently. 'Henry and Shelagh are old friends of mine. He's looked after me like an uncle ever since my father died, and they'd be hurt if we turned them down. I'll go on my own, if you prefer,' she had added defiantly.

His frown had deepened. 'There's no need for

that,' he said. 'If you've already accepted for both of us, then of course we'll go.'

And the matter had been left there.

'You look pale,' Henry said, frowning a little. 'I hope you're not overworking.'

'Far from it.' Ashley waved a hand at the paperwork in front of her with a semblance of gaiety. 'As a matter of fact, I've already filled today's quota. It doesn't take a great deal of effort, I promise you. In fact a properly programmed robot could do it.'

Henry's face grew thunderous. 'It's a disgrace!' he muttered. 'Ashley, my dear, I'm so sorry, but ...'

'But you did warn me,' she completed for him with a faint grimace. 'Only I can't say I expected to be relegated to the Second Division quite so fast!'

'If it's any consolation, you're not the only one,' Henry said sourly. 'Your husband has instructed me to re-examine the financial and working structure of the entire company, and report on how they could be updated and improved. And he wants it yesterday.'

Ashley looked at him with compunction. Henry looked tired, she thought, and harassed. If she could get Shelagh on her own tonight, she would suggest they went away for a holiday. He looked as if he was in desperate need of a complete break. Immersed in her own troubles, she had forgotten what a fraught time this had been for him too. He'd had to bear the brunt of the early pressure from Marshalls, and she must not forget it.

She asked tentatively, 'Do you need extra help? We could get you a temp, or more than one. It's what we've always done in the past.'

Henry shook his head. '"Past" is the operative

word, my dear. Jago has already made it clear that
he regards this particular project as being fully
within the present capabilities of my department—
and I quote.' He gave an irritable sigh, pushing a
hand through his thinning hair. 'I suppose he feels
if I'm drowning in a sea of paperwork and statistics,
I won't have a chance to throw a spanner in any of
his works.'

'Why should he think you want to do that?' asked
Ashley, frowning a little in her turn.

He shrugged. 'God knows—except that I'm one
of the leftovers from your father's era and therefore
can't be expected to approve of the changes
he's making to Landons. Silas believed in open
management. Your husband, in contrast, holds his
cards so close to his chest, it's difficult to know
whether he's even worked out their value himself.'
He snorted. 'All this secrecy! What's he afraid of?'

She said slowly, 'Jago thinks we've been losing
too many contracts lately.'

'And what, precisely, does he blame for that?'
Henry demanded sharply.

'I don't know.' Ashley began to play with the cap
of her pen. 'But perhaps he's right, Henry. Perhaps
our security has been lax—I don't know.' She
sighed. 'And maybe he blames me for it, perhaps
that's why ...' She stopped.

'What were you going to say?'

She spread her hands helplessly. 'Perhaps that's
why he makes sure I don't get access to anything
important these days.'

'Haven't you asked him?'

Ashley shifted some of the papers on her desk,
her movements restless and jerky. 'Not in so many
words,' she said, after a pause. 'It isn't as easy as
that.'

'I can believe that,' said Henry with a snap. 'Surely he doesn't suspect you of—industrial espionage?'

She smiled drearily. 'I doubt it. I think he regards me as simply inefficient, which in some ways is worse.'

'My dear girl!' he sounded shocked. 'Nothing could be further from the truth. You mustn't allow Jago to treat you like a cipher. You need to—stand up for your rights. You were Silas' daughter before you were his wife, after all.'

'Provoking mutiny, Henry?' She smiled with an effort. 'You surprise me.'

'I don't see why.' He shook his head. 'I was against this ill-advised marriage from the first, as you know. I feel you allowed yourself to be rushed into it without giving the consequences sufficient thought.' He paused. 'I can see you're not happy—indeed how could you be?—and it worries me.'

'Don't be worried.' She gave him an affectionate but searching glance. 'All marriages have their—teething troubles, I suppose, but you mustn't be concerned. As it is, you look as if you haven't been sleeping properly for weeks. I hope that isn't on my account.'

'No—no.' Henry shook his head vaguely as if his thoughts were elsewhere. 'It's just all this extra work. I think I must be getting old.' His lips pursed. 'And Jago requires a daily report on my progress.'

She said quietly, 'It doesn't sound as if relations are very good anywhere along the line. Perhaps this dinner party will—restore things a little. After all, we're working for a common cause.'

'Are we?' he asked heavily. 'Sometimes I get the impression—forgive me, Ashley—that your husband is working for himself alone. But perhaps tonight will promote a better atmosphere. I certainly hope so.'

As he reached the door, Ashley said casually, 'Henry, have you seen the final tender figure for the Craigmore project?'

He turned abruptly. 'No—no, I haven't. Why do you ask?'

There was an edge to his voice that bewildered her. 'Because I haven't seen it either, that's all. And both of us would normally have done so.'

He gave a short laugh. 'Tenders are tantamount to classified documents these days. Haven't you been reading your memos? I don't think either of us are on Jago's "need to know" list.'

'But that's quite ridiculous!' Ashley stood up with resolution. 'I'm going to speak to him about it now. After all, both of us were in on that project from the first.'

'So we were,' he said. 'But times have changed. It's been made clear to me that I'm no longer involved in that side of things. But don't let me stop you trying,' he added drily. 'Do you know the combination of that safe of Jago's?'

She flushed. 'No—but he has to let me see the tender. He must.'

'I hope he will,' said Henry. 'But I wouldn't count on it, my dear. And there's no point in tackling him about it at once, because he's not there. When I rang his office just now, his girl said he'd already left for an early lunch appointment. And he's pretty tied up this afternoon, it seems. I'm to leave my report on his desk.' He patted the folder under his arm.

'I'll take it,' said Ashley, putting out her hand. 'And I'll tell Sue to fit me in between the other appointments, if that's what it takes.'

But when she reached Jago's office, it was to find

it deserted. Ashley stood looking round her in slight perplexity. It was unusual not to find Sue at her post. In the short time she had been working for Jago, she had established herself as an excellent dragon, and the office was rarely unoccupied.

Ashley wrote a brief note, requesting a few minutes of Jago's time when he got back from lunch, and propped it in Sue's typewriter. Then she glanced across at Jago's desk. It was strewn with papers, which, again, was unusual, as he preferred to work without clutter. And lying on top of the papers was one of the distinctive blue and gold folders in which Landons sent out their tenders.

Ashley's brows drew together. She went over and picked it up, skimming through the contents. Sure enough, it was the Craigmore tender, she realised in total bewilderment. But in view of Jago's strictness about security, what on earth was it doing here where anyone could see it?

Determinedly she picked it up, dropping Henry's report in its place, and turned towards the door. That would be something else she would take up with Jago when he came back from lunch.

As she went back towards her own room, she spotted Henry talking to the Chief Accountant. She gave him a small wave, drew his attention to the folder she was carrying, and gave him a small, triumphant thumbs up signal.

She sat down at her desk and began to go through the figures. They were competently and concisely put together, she thought, but the actual result wasn't so different from her own tentative figure.

No wonder he didn't want to show it to me, she thought rather bitterly. I might have said 'I told you so'.

She sighed, closing the folder, and buried her

face in her hands for a moment. Wasn't it bad enough that she and Jago were at odds in their private life? Did the fight have to carry over into the business world as well? Somehow she would have to convince him that she still had a contribution to make at Landons.

The buzz of her telephone made her jump. Katie said, 'There's a Mr Hollings on the line for you, Mrs Marrick. Shall I put him through?'

Ashley's brows lifted incredulously. After a pause, she queried, 'Are you sure the switchboard got the name right, Katie?'

'Yes.' Katie hesitated. 'Is it someone you'd rather not speak to?'

A thousand times, yes, Ashley thought wryly. Aloud, she said, 'It's all right, I'll speak to him.'

'You're guarded well,' was Paul Hollings' greeting. He sounded frankly amused.

'I think sometimes I need to be,' she said shortly. 'What can I do for you, Mr Hollings?'

'Always so formal,' he said mournfully. 'Can't you bring yourself to call me Paul?'

'I doubt it,' she said. 'And I'm rather too busy for social chit-chat, so if you don't mind ...'

'Of course,' he said. 'This is a big day for both of us. The deadline for the Craigmore tender, no less. I hope you're prepared to accept defeat gracefully, Ashley.'

'I'm not prepared to accept it at all,' she snapped.

He laughed. 'I can believe that! Let's call a truce, and have lunch together.'

'Why should I do any such thing?'

'Because I happen to be in the neighbourhood, and because you, presumably, need to eat.' He paused. 'Unless you're otherwise engaged, of course. Won't Jago let you off the leash for once, darling?'

'Jago's not here,' she said, and could have bitten her tongue out.

'Better and better,' he said softly. 'That's how I like inconvenient husbands—absent. So will you take pity on me, and grace my lonely lunch table?'

Ashley nibbled at her thumbnail, torn between a desire to slam the phone down and the need to know what he was up to. Curiosity won.

'Where shall I meet you?' she asked.

'There's rather a good roadhouse out towards Ashbrook, I'm told.'

'There is indeed,' Ashley said lightly. 'We built it.'

'Then I'm sure it can be trusted not to come crashing round our ears while we eat,' he said. 'Shall we say—half an hour?'

She agreed, and heard the click as his line disconnected.

She replaced her own receiver slowly. Paul Hollings had sent flowers with a polite note to thank her for her hospitality, but there had been nothing to suggest that he intended any further social contact between them. Yet—now this.

She went into the washroom and renewed her lipstick, looking at herself critically. She was wearing one of her discreet, anonymous office suits today, in navy. He would find her a very different proposition from the exotic creature in emerald green he'd met the previous week, she thought, her mouth curling in faint amusement as she combed her hair.

The car park at the roadhouse was filling up when she arrived, but she managed to wangle her car into a space near the front door. An enquiry at the reception desk in the foyer told her that Mr Hollings was waiting for her in the cocktail bar.

He got to his feet, and came to meet her smiling. 'I daren't tell you that you look as lovely as ever,' he said, as he ordered her the glass of white wine she requested. 'I'm sure you have some dagger-like reply all prepared.'

His quizzical look forced a laugh from her. 'You're learning!'

'I try.' Paul lifted his glass to her. 'Here's to a closer relationship—in every way.'

She lifted an eyebrow. 'I think I'll drink to your health,' she said. 'It sounds safer.'

'Always so cautious,' he sighed. 'How can I make you trust me? Get you to see that being taken over by my company isn't the worst thing that could happen?'

Ashley took a composed sip of her wine. 'You can't,' she said succinctly.

'You're really determined, aren't you?' he said softly. 'But so am I. Don't you think we should be looking for some kind of compromise?'

'I don't think so.' Ashley kept her voice level. 'You see, Mr Hollings, your company fails to meet any of the standards my father fought all his life to maintain. I refuse to stand back and allow you to take over his company, and use its reputation for your own ends.'

'You don't pull your punches,' he said wryly. 'But I like that. I admire a lady who doesn't know when she's beaten.'

'Is that what I am?'

'I'm afraid so. The Craigmore tender is as good as ours, and without it Landons will be in trouble. You can't deny that.' She remained silent, and he went on, 'Now I'm prepared to renew our earlier offer for Landons' shares on the understanding you call an emergency board meeting and recommend urgent acceptance of our offer.' He shrugged. 'I'd say that was an offer you couldn't refuse.'

'I wouldn't be too sure.' She set her glass back on the table. 'You're beginning to annoy me, Mr Hollings. I think I'll forgo lunch and go back to my crumbling business.'

'I'm sorry.' His tone altered, and he put a hand on her arm. 'If I swear not to raise the subject again, will you stay?'

Ashley sighed. 'I don't know why you should want me to,' she pointed out.

'Because when your marriage to Jago breaks up, I want to be around to pick up the pieces,' Paul Hollings said calmly, and signalled to the waiter to take their order.

Dazedly, Ashley opted for pâté, followed by poached salmon with a side salad, and heard her companion order the same.

When the waiter had moved away, she said, 'I think you must be out of your mind!'

He shook his head. 'On the contrary. You're a beautiful girl, Ashley Landon, and you're not happy. But then how could you be? On your own admission, your marriage was a put up job to pacify your board of directors. You deserve better than that.'

'From you?' she raised a caustic eyebrow.

'Why not? I've made my matrimonial mistake and paid for it. I won't be trapped into the same error again. I didn't enjoy divorce, but it taught me quite a lot.' He gave her a straight look. 'You have to learn to turn your back on failure, Ashley, whether in business or in your private life.'

'I don't regard my marriage as a failure,' she said steadily. 'It was—a means to an end, that's all, and it's worked.'

'Loyal but misguided,' Paul Hollings said mockingly, and began to study the wine list.

Ashley had never felt less hungry in her life, but it was almost a relief when the head waiter arrived to conduct them to their table in the green and gilt dining room.

As she'd noticed on her few earlier visits, the male presence predominated in the dining room, and she was aware of frankly curious stares as she was escorted to her table.

Aware, with a prickle of sensitivity, of something more than curiosity in the atmosphere. As the waiter shook out her napkin and began to pour the wine, she glanced casually round—and froze.

From a table intimately secluded in a corner, Jago looked back at her, his eyes cold with angry conjecture. She saw his companion, and the way she was leaning towards him, her face wreathed in smiles, saw the champagne bottle nestling in ice beside their table.

Ashley felt her nails curling into claws beneath the shelter of the tablecloth. Her reaction was savage, primitive, shocking. Pain was striking at her, and she wanted to inflict pain in turn—smash that celebratory bottle over Erica's smooth blonde head, scratch the triumph from her face.

Mark them both, she thought in agony, as they've marked me!

With a jolt, she pulled herself together. Paul Hollings, luckily, was sitting with his back turned to that corner, and hadn't, she would swear, noticed its occupants. Or at least she prayed he hadn't. She would have to make sure that his attention stayed riveted—on her.

'It all looks delicious,' she said lightly. 'Perhaps we should forget our irreconcilable differences for the next hour, and simply enjoy ourselves?' She made it sound like an invitation, inwardly despising herself.

He smiled back, letting his eyes linger with undisguised appreciation on her lips and breasts. Oh God, he thought he was so damned irresistible!

He said softly, 'I ask for nothing more—at the moment.' He raised his glass. 'I say again—here's to our closer relationship.'

She lowered her lashes demurely. 'In every way,' she agreed, deliberately echoing his own words, noting the gleam in his eyes as he registered the fact.

She tasted her pâté, making appreciative noises, watching him relax and bask in her approval. A basking shark, she thought detachedly. Because she didn't believe one of the reasons he'd formulated for inviting her to lunch. She didn't doubt he still wanted to acquire Landons, and would be prepared to go to any lengths to do so, but his renewed offer made no sense. Why pay a high price for a company he intended to drive into the ground? As for his other proposition, she supposed that as a young wife trapped in a marriage of convenience she was intended to be grateful for his sexual interest in her, and flattered by it.

She would have, she thought, to find some way of convincing him once and for all that she wasn't interested in any offer he might make, either personal or professional.

The salmon arrived, and hollandaise sauce was offered.

Paul Hollings was talking, making conversation, and doing it well, canvassing her views on music, the theatre and current affairs. Trying to establish common ground, Ashley thought idly, and if she'd been as naïve as he thought, or even halfway interested in him, this lunch could have been one big thrill from start to finish.

As it was, each mouthful was a profound effort, even though the food was good, and the wine like silk against the taut dryness of her throat.

Looking past him, she saw that Jago was preparing to leave, signing the bill, and helping Erica into her jacket. She watched them walk towards the door, Jago's head bent attentively towards his companion, who was chatting vivaciously, clearly revelling in the glances she was attracting. He did not even spare Ashley a glance. As they disappeared through the arched doorway, Ashley sank back in her chair, aware she was trembling violently.

'Is something the matter?' Paul Hollings had stopped in mid-eulogy of the Royal Shakespeare Company and was studying her with bewilderment.

'Everything's wonderful,' she said. 'It was a lovely meal. You must forgive me if I tear myself away.'

If he hadn't practised so hard at being suave, his jaw would have dropped. He made a good recovery. 'Surely you don't have to go yet? There's dessert—and coffee. Besides—' he gave her a smile designed to melt her bones, 'I had—plans for this afternoon.'

'I'm sorry.' Ashley got to her feet, shaking her head. 'I'm going to be busy this afternoon. And so are you. You have a visit to the dry cleaners to fit in, for one thing.'

This time he looked really blank. 'I don't follow you ...'

'Good,' said Ashley. 'Let's keep it that way.' She reached for the sauce boat and poured the remains of the hollandaise sauce all over him.

And in the most profound silence since the beginning of the world, she walked out of the restaurant.

CHAPTER TEN

SHE was still shaking inside when she got back to the office. She buzzed Jago immediately, but it was Sue who replied, informing her that he hadn't returned from lunch yet.

Ashley said with an assumption of calm, 'Please let me know as soon as he returns.'

Each time her buzzer sounded, she tensed, but it was never the message she was waiting for. Incredulously, she realised that almost two hours had passed. She could only suppose that as she'd caught Jago with Erica publicly, he saw no reason to maintain any kind of subterfuge.

She paced up and down, dry-eyed, trying to close her mind against insidious images of Jago in bed with Erica, their bodies moulded together in passion. Unbearable, hateful images scalding against her closed eyelids.

She said aloud, 'I can't go on like this.' And at that moment, the buzzer sounded, and Sue's voice said, 'Mrs Marrick? Is it convenient for you to come along, please?'

She was vanishing discreetly as Ashley arrived. Jago's face was like a mask, but he could not disguise the angry glitter in his eyes as he rose to greet her.

He said icily, 'I hope you had a pleasant lunch.'

'It had its moments.' She was determined to play it cool. She wanted to scream accusations, burst into tears, stamp and throw things, but this was not the time or the place.

'I'm sure it did.' His mouth was tight-lipped. His voice would have cut chips from granite. 'You don't care to explain what you were doing there with him?'

Ashley shrugged. 'I'm astonished you should want to know. Especially when I could ask you the same thing—about her.'

'Ask,' he grated. 'I'm perfectly willing to tell you.'

'You clearly regard frankness about your affairs as some sort of virtue,' Ashley said quietly. 'It's a view I don't happen to share. I don't want to know, Jago. You're a free agent, you can have lunch with whomever you please. But I have the same right too.' She put the Craigmore file down on the desk in front of him. 'I didn't come here to cross-examine you. I came to return this.'

His brows snapped together. 'Where the hell did you get this?' he almost snarled.

'It was lying about on your desk,' she said. 'Obviously you were in too much of a hurry to get to your lunch engagement to bother with your usual security precautions.'

Oh hell! she thought furiously. That last remark had all the elements of a jealous whine.

But Jago seemed oblivious to its implications. He cursed savagely and slapped the folder with a clenched fist. Then he looked up at her. 'And may I know where it's been since you—acquired it?'

'I put it in my desk drawer. I think it was as safe there as it was here.'

'Hmm.' His expression was abstracted. 'Did anyone know you had it? Did you discuss it with anyone?'

'With Paul Hollings, for instance?' she asked.

'You know better than that.'

His glance was loaded. 'I'm not sure I know anything any more. But O.K., I acquit you of Hollings. However I really need to know whether you discussed the contents of this file with anyone in this building.'

'No,' she said shortly. 'Is that what you wanted to hear?'

Jago sighed. 'Not particularly,' he returned curtly. 'It's just an extra complication which I didn't need.'

'I haven't the vaguest idea what you're talking about.'

'I don't suppose you have.' His mouth curled. 'And that's just how I wanted it. You on the outside, uninvolved.'

'And what about my own wishes?' Ashley demanded. 'I'm sick of being treated like an office junior!'

'Is that how you see yourself?' he asked flatly. 'I don't think office juniors get wined and dined by our main business rivals, but I could be wrong.' He paused. 'Did he mention the Craigmore project to you while you were playing footsie over the prawn cocktails?'

'We had other more important things to discuss.'

'Like the fact that he fancies you?' Jago asked contemptuously. 'Don't let it go to your head, darling. Because you'd be one of a long line, Ashley, and he's a bigger bastard than I am.'

'I find that hard to believe,' she said. 'But as it happens I wouldn't have the gallant Mr Hollings on toast.' In spite of her wretchedness, a golden memory warmed her, and a reluctant smile curved her mouth. 'Or served up with hollandaise sauce.' She glanced at her watch. 'How time does fly! Unless you have any other letters you'd like me to answer, I think I'll go back to the house. Please don't forget we're having dinner with the Bretts this evening.'

Jago came round the big desk and caught at her arm, halting her. 'You're not leaving yet. There are things we need to have a serious talk about.'

She felt the warm pressure of his fingers through her clothes as though she'd been naked, and pulled herself free, her face furious, her eyes gleaming cat-like. 'Take your hands off me!'

'That has a familiar ring,' he said insolently. 'Only it doesn't work any more, remember?' He took her hand, his thumb smoothing the gold of her wedding ring. He said quietly, 'You can't get away from me so easily this time, Ashley. You can't send this back by messenger, and call it a day.'

'I'm aware of that.' Her senses were jumping, her nerve-endings going mad as they always did even at his lightest touch. 'But I'll do whatever I need to do to be free again.' With a flood of relief, she heard Sue's voice in the corridor outside, and snatched her hand away.

As the door opened, she turned and smiled at the secretary. 'I'm just leaving,' she said brightly. 'Don't let him work late tonight, Sue. We have a dinner engagement.'

There was an angry flush staining Jago's cheek-bones as he turned away. He said, 'Then I'd better not waste any more time. Get your notebook, Sue.'

Ashley managed to keep her step jaunty as she left the room, but she slowed when she reached the corridor, almost stumbling into the wall, as she fought for control. Tears she dared not shed were stinging her eyes, and every breath she drew seemed torn from her lungs. The few yards to her own office seemed endless, a punishing marathon performance.

As she went in, Katie was just putting down the telephone. Her eyes widened as she looked at Ashley. 'Are you all right, Mrs Marrick? You look terribly pale.'

'I have a slight headache,' Ashley managed. 'I don't think I'll drive myself home tonight, Katie. Perhaps you'd get me a taxi.'

'Right away,' the girl said, buzzing Reception, but her expression was still puzzled.

Ashley's head was aching in real earnest by the time the taxi deposited her at the Manor. She paid off the driver and walked quickly inside and straight up to her room. She wanted some tea, but if she rang for any, or even went to the kitchen, she would be bound to encounter Mrs Bolton, and she wasn't up to dealing with any of the older woman's little pinpricks tonight.

She took some paracetamol and lay down on the bed, deliberately relaxing every muscle. She would get through the evening ahead, somehow, and then she would go away for the weekend somewhere where she could think, make herself face what she had to do next. She supposed she would have to see a solicitor, although inwardly she cringed from the idea of having to tell old Mr Whincliffe who had always looked after Silas' affairs that her marriage was over almost before it had begun.

She'd heard there were law firms which specialised in divorce. She would try and find out more, consult such a firm, perhaps. They would know how to make things easy for her. She made a little harsh noise in her throat. Easy? she asked herself bitterly. What was simple about cutting the heart out of her body?

She sighed helplessly, closing her eyes as a great

wave of weariness swept over her, and almost before she knew it, she had fallen asleep.

When she awoke, it was getting dark, and she sat up abruptly, peering at her watch, an exclamation escaping her lips as she saw what the time was.

She swung herself off the bed and went to the wardrobe, giving the rail of dresses a hurried scan. The last thing she wanted was to go to a dinner party, but after tomorrow at least she would be able to stop pretending, she thought, pulling one of the dresses off its hanger. Although not new, it was a favourite of hers, black lace, low-necked and long-sleeved over a sleek taffeta underskirt, with a sophistication she needed tonight to boost her confidence.

She looked at her watch again. Where was Jago? she wondered. If he didn't hurry, they were going to be late, or was that what he intended? Or did he mean to come back at all? The possibility that he might have decided to end their marriage there and then hit her with the force of a blow. She laid the dress across the bed and went into the bathroom, turning on the shower. She wouldn't think about that. She would behave as if this was a conventional evening in a normal marriage, and get ready for her party.

The warm rush of the water felt like soothing balm on her skin. With a little sigh she reached for the soap, then cried out as the cubicle door opened abruptly.

Jago said pleasantly, 'Sorry I'm late, darling. Had you given me up? Let's save time and water and shower together.'

He took the soap from her slackened grasp, and began to lather her shoulders and breasts, shocking her back to life and speech.

'Get out of here!'

'Nonsense,' Jago said mockingly. 'Do you realise we've been married just over a week, and you've not washed my back for me yet?'

'Nor will I.' Ashley set her teeth, pushing away his caressing tantalising hand which was straying down over her stomach. 'If you won't get out of here, then I will!'

'Your wish is my command.' Jago reached up and switched off the spray, then lifted her out of the cubicle, scooping up the towel she'd left waiting as he did so, and muffling her in its folds. She was pinioned against him, her arms shrouded in the clinging towel, or she would have hit him. Her feet kicked wildly at his wet shins as he carried her.

'Put me down, damn you!'

'When I'm good and ready.' He dropped her on to the bed, kneeling over her while he pulled the wet towel away. Ashley read the purpose in his face, and began to struggle more violently.

'Let me go!'

Jago shook his head slowly. 'That isn't what either of us wants.' He framed her furious face in his hands, and bent and kissed her mouth, not gently, almost forcing her lips apart.

When she could speak again, she said huskily, 'You disgust me. Wasn't this afternoon's episode enough for you? How many women do you need at a time?'

'For now, I want you,' he said. 'And I thought you didn't want to discuss this afternoon.'

He kissed her again, his hands ridding her of the towel completely, his fingers trailing the length of her naked body, stroking and inciting. She was aware of his mastery, alive and responsive to the dark magic he was weaving round her, and against which she had no defence. With a sob she put her face against his shoulder, tasting the cool dampness of his skin.

He said her name, and entered her, their fusion explosive, with a hint of savagery. Her taking was as deep and urgent as his own, her need as compelling. There was no mercy in him, and she wanted none.

Nothing existed in the world but this man, hers in the act of love if in no other way. The damp, silken brush of his skin against hers, each heated male thrust into her satin warmth were driving her beyond reason, beyond coherent thought to some deep and dreamless void. She was his mate, his counterpart, offering total completion, as her body arched and twisted beneath his, her shallow, frantic breathing echoing the harsh rasp of his own. Her flesh was wrenched, torn apart by sensation. Clinging to each other, mouths and bodies locked together, they fell headlong through time and space into the void.

Normality returned slowly. Ashley was floating somewhere, her whole body languid and luxuriant, after the ferocity of culmination. She felt Jago leave her, lift himself away from her, and her eyes flew open, enormous, brilliant in her flushed face as she looked up at him.

His voice was cool, ironic. 'I'm afraid we're going to be late for Henry's dinner party.'

He swung himself off the bed and went into the bathroom, and presently she heard water running. Ashley stayed where she was. She doubted if she was capable of movement. She'd wanted him to stay in her arms. Perhaps then they could have talked, reached some kind of understanding.

As he came back into the bedroom and walked

over to the long line of panelled wardrobes, she lifted herself on to one elbow.

She said softly, 'Must we go?'

He didn't even look at her. He said crisply, 'Unfortunately, it can't be avoided.'

He was dressing, pulling on his clothes with swift economical movements.

She felt humiliated, raging at herself because she had offered and been rejected. She collected her own things together and dressed in the bathroom, the door between them closed, as if the dark, sensual madness of the last few minutes had never happened. She made sure that her make-up was immaculate, but there was nothing she could do to hide the heady glow in her eyes, or tone down her love-warmed skin.

Jago was waiting, with obvious impatience, when she finally emerged. It was the first time she had worn this dress since their marriage, and she waited for him to say something, give some sign of approval.

He said brusquely, 'Shall we be going? I've brought the car round.'

There was a tension about him, she thought as they drove in silence to the Bretts'. There was a grimness about the set of his mouth which she could not explain—unless he was regretting have made love to her. Perhaps he was feeling guilty at having betrayed Erica, she thought painfully.

Almost before the car had stopped, the door was open and Shelagh was waiting to welcome them, her face wreathed in smiles.

'Of course you're not late,' she dismissed. 'And you both look marvellous. I think marriage agrees with you, Ashley.'

Ashley made herself smile in response, aware of

Jago's swift, sardonic glance.

'Where's Colin this evening?' she asked, glancing round the pleasant living room.

'He's gone to spend the weekend with a friend.' Shelagh cast her eyes to heaven. 'They're supposed to be studying together, but if I know them they'll be listening to heavy metal records, rather than getting to grips with Chaucer.'

'Oh, Colin will pass,' Ashley said with a shrug. 'He has Jeanne's example to follow, after all. He can't let a girl best him.'

'His thinking does run along those lines,' Shelagh agreed, grinning. 'One way he could improve on her performance is by writing a few more letters home when he gets to university. Jeanne sometimes lets weeks go by without a word, and then we get a few scrawled lines.'

'She's snowed under with work,' Henry broke in, as he poured sherry. 'You mustn't fuss so. She's all right.'

'It's natural to worry,' Jago said quietly. 'Do you never go to visit her, Mrs Brett?'

'Oh, please call me Shelagh.' She took the glass her husband handed to her. 'I went to see her in her first year, to make sure she was all right. But each time I've planned to go this year, something seems to have happened to prevent it. But Henry's been a couple of times, haven't you, darling?' Her face clouded. 'It was an awful blow when she didn't come home for Christmas, but she'd got this vacation job in a hotel, and they couldn't spare her.'

'I think we'll change the subject,' Henry said brusquely. 'There's nothing more boring for guests than hearing long stories about other people's offspring.'

Ashley saw Jago give him a long considering look. Talk turned to the economic situation, and after a while Shelagh excused herself to go to the kitchen. Ashley followed.

'I hope this evening isn't going to be a strain for you,' she said with a slight sigh. 'Jago isn't exactly Henry's favourite person at the moment.'

Shelagh tasted the soup simmering on the stove and added a pinch of salt. She gave Ashley a wry look. 'I don't think anyone's Henry's favourite at the moment! I don't know what's the matter with him these days. According to Betty next door it's the male menopause.' She frowned. 'But I thought that meant having affairs with girls half his age.'

Ashley laughed. 'I don't think you need to worry about that,' she said affectionately. 'I'm sure Henry's never looked at another woman.'

'No, he's always been a family man,' Shelagh agreed. 'But part of being that was his temperament. He always used to be so cheerful and even-tempered, even during the children's squabbles and adolescence. Now, he seems like a stranger much of the time.'

'Perhaps he's still worried about how things are going at work,' Ashley suggested. 'We're not out of the wood yet, by any means.'

'But he always used to talk about the office,' Shelagh pointed out. 'Now it seems to be a taboo subject—and not the only one.' She squared her shoulders determinedly. 'Let's think about food instead. If you've come out here to help, you could keep an eye on those croutons for me.'

The meal was excellent. Shelagh, Ashley thought, was a heavenly cook of the stockpot, substantial helping variety, and tonight she had excelled herself with a dish of small spring chickens braised in wine, and other delights. Ashley usually amused herself by trying to distinguish the various herbs and flavourings that went into each dish, but then previous dinner parties at Shelagh and Henry's had always been relaxed affairs. But tonight's gathering could in no way be described as that, she realised unhappily. There was tension in the air, almost tangibly. Jago and Henry were being civil to each other, she thought vexedly, but little more. They were more like antagonists weighing each other up before some duel than working colleagues or a host with an important guest. Shelagh was clearly making a determined effort to make the evening go well and Ashley made herself rally round in support. But their efforts only seemed to underline the basic lack of rapport between their husbands.

'Some brandy with your coffee?' asked Henry when they returned to the big sitting room, and the log fire crackling on the hearth.

'Thank you,' Jago nodded. He turned to Shelagh. 'That was the most delicious meal,' he told her. 'I shall never doubt my wife's eulogies again. I would hate to have missed it, although at one time it seemed possible—it's been one of those days, I'm afraid.' He paused. 'Has Henry told you anything about the Craigmore project?'

Shelagh's brow wrinkled. 'Not that I recall.'

'It's a contract we're tendering for,' Jago told her. 'A big one, and vital to our future. It had to go off today. And I'm afraid it kept me late at the office.'

Ashley put down her coffee cup. 'But it was ready this morning,' she protested.

'Not quite,' Jago said quietly. 'You see, I wasn't altogether happy with the final figure we'd arrived at, so I changed it, quite drastically, before it went off.'

There was a crash, as the brandy decanter slipped from Henry's hand and landed on the parquet floor, its contents spilling towards the thick Chinese carpet.

Ashley's mouth was suddenly dry, her heart thumping. She was looking at Henry. They were all looking at Henry, and seeing, as she did, the fear, the wretchedness, and the overwhelming guilt in his pale face.

Shelagh began uncertainly, 'Darling ...' but Jago cut in smoothly.

'Ash, take Shelagh to the kitchen and find something to clear up this mess. Henry and I have to talk.'

CHAPTER ELEVEN

'It was heroin,' Henry said. It was a long time later, and they were all together in the sitting room. He was on the sofa, Shelagh beside him, pale but dry-eyed, twisting a handkerchief in restless fingers. 'I was as worried as Shelagh when Jeanne stopped writing, so I went up to see her without telling anyone.

'To be honest, I thought she might have got herself pregnant. I'd met this fellow she was involved with on a previous visit, and I didn't like him or any of his friends. I could see at once that she was different, but at first I didn't know why.' He paused. 'I should have known, of course. They spell it out for you these days—the signs, the danger signals, but somehow you always think in terms of other people's children—never your own ...' He broke off, his voice cracking slightly.

Then he resumed, more quietly, 'When I realised what was happening, I went a bit mad, I think. She'd run up this massive overdraft at the bank to pay for drugs, and they were pressuring her about it. She'd been stealing from shops too—it was only a miracle she hadn't been caught—prosecuted ...' He swallowed. 'She wanted to stop—she promised she did, and I wanted her to have a chance. After all, she was brilliant. Everyone said so. I couldn't let all that go to waste.' He lifted his head, almost defiantly, 'I couldn't!'

Jago nodded. 'I can accept that. But how did

Marshalls come into it?'

Henry stared at the carpet. 'I needed money,' he said with difficulty. 'Oh, I had a good income, but we lived up to it. I suppose everyone does nowadays. I had to settle the overdraft, and then I was told about this private clinic where they were getting wonderful results, not just curing the addiction, but rehabilitating the users afterwards. Only it wasn't cheap. And the most important thing was for Shelagh not to know. She was so proud of the children—we've never had any real problems with either of them before—and so happy too. I couldn't bear to see that end. I could have got a bank loan to pay the clinic fees, but I knew she'd see it on our statements. I didn't know where to turn. And then, one evening, I got a phone call.'

'From Paul Hollings?' Jago asked.

Henry nodded jerkily. 'I'd never met him before, but he seemed to know a lot about me—as if he'd been having me watched. He said he understood I was having some family troubles, and that he'd like to help. I told him to go to hell, but he called again, and eventually I arranged to meet him.' He laughed, the sound bitter. 'Oh, he made it sound so easy at first. All he wanted, he said, was "a friend at court"—someone to plead Marshalls' case for a takeover with the board. For that, he said, he'd be willing to pay a retainer. And that's all it was, at first. It was only later that he started asking about tenders, getting me to pass on the figures we were submitting so that they could underbid us.'

'As you did today?' said Jago.

He nodded. 'He was really putting the pressure on about Craigmore. He said it was make or break time. I told him you'd installed the safe, but he wouldn't listen. Then, when I saw Ashley had got hold of the file somehow, I phoned Hollings and he invited her out to lunch, to make sure she'd be out of the office for a while.'

'There was no need to go to those lengths,' Jago said harshly. 'I'd left the bloody file on my desk, waiting for you. I'd even given you an excuse to come to the office. You see, I too did not wish my wife to be involved. You'd already used her, and her friendship for you, too often as it was.'

'Or not enough,' Ashley put in softly. 'Henry, if you needed money, why didn't you come to me? I'd have been glad to help.'

His face was wretched. 'Because I couldn't guarantee that Shelagh wouldn't find out somehow through you. Ashley, the last thing I wanted was to hurt you, believe me. But the Marshalls takeover was beginning to seem so inevitable ...'

'In that case, why did you warn me about it—bring me back from abroad?'

'He had to,' Jago told her. 'Because people were beginning to notice his lack of action, and comment on it. As it was, he left it as long as possible, thinking it would be impossible for you to reverse the way things were going. When you came back, the takeover was as near a *fait accompli* as he could manage. The fact that I was back in town was inconvenient, but he counted on the rift between us being permanent. The news that we were getting married must have been like a thunderbolt.'

Henry winced. 'It was. And Hollings was wild with fury, I can tell you! But he said if you'd split up once, there was a chance it could happen again, and he'd work on that angle. And then he started talking about Craigmore. I told him things were different, that I thought you suspected something, but he wouldn't listen.'

'How very unwise,' Jago drawled silkily. 'Yes, I guessed there had to be a rotten apple in the barrel from that first board meeting. Clive Farnsworth had come to the same conclusion, and we had a very interesting private chat when the meeting was over. We decided the best thing was to supply you with the rope and let you hang yourself. At the same time, knowing how fond Ashley was of you, I wanted to keep her out of it. She'd have had to know eventually, of course, so I tried to prepare her a little—drop a few hints, to cushion the blow when it came.' He shook his head. 'But you had me worried, Henry. I thought you'd seen the trap I'd set for you and sidestepped it. But then when Katie told me you'd been in Ashley's office while she was at lunch, I breathed again.' He shrugged. 'I don't know what figure Marshalls are putting on the Craigmore tender, but this time we'll give them a run for their money.'

Shelagh's voice shook. 'And all to protect me. Oh God, Henry, how could you?'

He turned on her almost fiercely. 'Because I thought you'd blame yourself, think you'd been deficient in some way. And you haven't. You've been a wonderful mother—the best wife a man could want. I wanted to preserve everything we had together, keep it intact for you. I'd have done anything—anything …'

She took his hand and held it.

Jago got to his feet. 'I don't think there's anything more to be said. It's time we were going.'

Henry looked up at him. 'What's going to happen?'

Jago's brows rose. 'I think—discreet early retirement on full pension, don't you? Don't come in to clear your desk. I'll have your things sent to you.'

He paused. 'Of course, any future arrangements you come to with Marshalls will be your own business, naturally.'

Henry said heavily, 'There won't be any. You've been—generous. I don't deserve that.'

'No.' Jago's mouth twisted. 'But I presume that's what my wife would want me to do—for the sake of past friendship.'

Henry looked at her. 'Ashley, my dear, I'm sorry.'

'So am I,' she said quietly. 'More sorry than you'll ever know.'

In the car, silence enfolded them both like a web. Ashley said at last, 'That was—awful.'

'Yes, it was,' Jago agreed. 'I'd planned to handle the whole thing at the office, after I'd altered our tender, and then break the news to you at home. But when I sent for Henry, his secretary said he'd already left.'

'Couldn't it have waited—until Monday?'

'Perhaps,' Jago said abruptly. 'But I don't want him back in the building. He's done enough damage.'

'I suppose so.' She moistened her lips with the tip of her tongue. 'And I never saw it coming—not even when you made me take another look at those other tenders. I never thought of him.'

'Why should you?' he asked flatly. 'Henry was someone you trusted implicitly, and anyway I couldn't prove a thing. I had to make him give himself away—rely on the fact that he was getting jumpier by the day.'

She said, 'Poor Shelagh ...'

'She's a tough lady,' said Jago. 'She'll pull something together out of this mess. Henry should have recognised this, and shared his problems with her, instead of assuming that because he'd gone to pieces, she would too.'

'You're hard on him …'

'He was hard on us.' His face was set, implacable. 'For God's sake, you little fool, he almost lost you Landons. Don't you realise that?'

'Yes,' she admitted in a subdued voice.

He shot her an edged look. He said, 'About Hollings. I hope it hasn't hurt you to realise his attentions had an ulterior motive?'

'He never fooled me for a moment,' Ashley said quietly.

'I'm pleased to hear it,' he said. 'Poor Ash, you haven't had a great deal of luck with the men in your life. A fiancé who couldn't remain faithful for the duration of your engagement, a father who wanted to sacrifice you to his own commercial ambitions, and an old friend who sold you out.' He paused. 'I thought you found Paul Hollings attractive.'

Ashley shrugged. 'In an obvious way, I suppose he is. But I'm not as naïve as I once was.'

He turned the car into the drive. 'I suppose I should be glad to hear you say so, but oddly I'm not. Although I suppose it will make it easier to leave you to your own devices.'

'What do you mean?' She followed him into the house, the sudden thudding of her heart sounding an alarm call.

'I've had an offer to go back to the States,' he said curtly. He walked into the drawing room, clicking on the light, and busied himself pouring two brandies from the decanter on a side table.

Ashley dropped her wrap on the sofa. Dry-mouthed, she asked, 'Are you going to take—this offer?'

'I have no reason not to, although I wouldn't leave until Landons has turned the corner, if that's what you're worried about.' Jago lifted his glass in a mock toast. 'I won't renege on my business obligations to you, Ashley. As for the personal ones—don't pretend you wouldn't find it a relief to rid of me. You've learned to accept my presence in your bed, but you don't welcome it.'

'I see,' she said numbly. 'So what will happen— about this house, for instance?'

'You can stay here. And if the thought of having to share it with Erica concerns you, then forget it. She won't be coming back here.'

'She'll be going to the States with you?' Ashley took a gulp of brandy.

'Good God, no,' Jago said flatly. 'I'd as soon take a black mamba.'

'But she said ...'

He put his glass down and came over to her. His mouth was set. 'Listen,' he said. 'I am not responsible for Erica's fantasies. I never have been, nor do I plan to be. In fact one of my priorities, apart from dealing with Henry Brett, has been to get her out of my hair once and for all. And today I did it. I got her to sell me her life interest in the estate. The negotiations have been a nightmare. She's been blowing hot and cold, wringing every ounce of drama out of the situation, looking for any excuse to give me hassle, and jack the price up— yet again,' he added grimly. He sent her a wry look. 'That's why I couldn't let you summarily dismiss that ghoul of a housekeeper. If Erica had found out, she'd probably have thrown a tantrum and backed out of the deal. But now you can fire the woman with my blessing.'

'But you were always with her. You were drinking champagne, and you didn't come back to the office ...' Ashley's voice was trembling.

'I felt the situation deserved champagne, but that's as far as the celebration went. The rest of the afternoon we spent at the lawyers, signing the necessary papers.'

She said, 'Why didn't you tell me?'

Jago sighed. 'Because I didn't want to build up your hopes too soon. She was threatening to change her mind right up to the last moment, but fortunately she's even more mercenary than she is spiteful, and I was able to make her an offer, finally, that she couldn't refuse.'

'I thought you were in love with her,' Ashley whispered.

'You must be confusing me with my cousin Giles,' he said courteously. 'Now he, poor devil, was crazy about her, so much so that he never even thought of giving her the hiding she so richly deserves.'

'But she told me,' Ashley said blankly. 'She let me think ...'

'I'm sure she did, and revelled in every minute of it,' he said unsmilingly. 'But I'm telling you here and now that I have never for even a fleeting moment cherished any warm thoughts for Erica. I was sorry for her, initially, when Giles died, because I thought it had hit her harder than she expected.' His mouth curled. 'But I soon changed my mind. Her plan is now to be a merry widow in St Tropez, or Marbella, and bloody good luck to her.'

He paused, his hazel eyes ironic as they rested on her. 'No, my sweet wife, I, for my sins, have always been in love with you, almost from the first damnable moment I set eyes on you. And I wanted to marry you more than I've ever wanted anything in my life, although I admit I suffered a slight check when I discovered you were only marrying me from a sense of duty, to provide Silas with the successor he wanted for Landons.'

She said hoarsely, 'But that's what you wanted—not me, but Landons....'

'Don't be insane,' he said coldly. 'I hadn't the slightest interest in Landons, nor did I want to be groomed for future stardom on the board, as Silas suggested. I'd already made up my mind to take that American job, but when I told him so he let me know, regretfully but very plainly, that I couldn't expect you to go with me. Why would you go to America, he asked me, when you were only marrying me to ensure the future wellbeing of the company?' He gave a bitter laugh. 'A lot of things became clear at that moment. I realised, for instance, why you froze me off every time I tried to get near you. When I mentioned this to Silas, he got very embarrassed, and said he'd talk to you—make sure you knew your duty when the time came. His very words,' he added flatly.

'Silas—said that?' Ashley's head was spinning crazily. 'But he wouldn't—he couldn't ...'

'Oh, but he did,' Jago corrected. He shook his head. 'I didn't want to believe it either. You see, I'd kept telling myself that somewhere underneath that almost hysterical frigidity there was a warm, loving girl, and that if I was patient enough, I'd find her. Silas' revelations gave me a whole new insight into our relationship—one that, frankly, made me sick to my stomach. I felt as if I'd been poleaxed! After I left Silas, I went into town, with the intention of getting roaring, stinking drunk.' He finished his brandy and set down the glass. 'The rest, of course, you remember, far more lucidly than I do.'

'That—girl …'

He nodded. 'Exactly. I have to confess that between leaving the bar and waking to find myself in bed with a complete stranger, and you battering the door down, there's nothing but a total blur.' He shrugged. 'Not that it excuses anything, of course, but I gather from my companion's hostile remarks before she left that I'd passed out before fulfilling any of her expectations. So I was technically faithful to you all along.' His smile was self-derisive.

Ashley swallowed. 'That—night, I'd seen Erica. She told me you were only marrying me for the company, and that I should allow you some freedom before tying you down. Finding you with that girl just seemed to—confirm everything she'd said.'

There was a silence. Then Jago said quietly, 'So that's what it was. I'd wondered, naturally, how you just happened to—turn up at the flat like that. Not that it matters now.'

'Why doesn't it matter?' she asked tensely.

He shrugged. 'Because it's time we cut our losses, Ashley. I should have never have pushed you into this marriage. It's been a disaster from first to last, and I have no right to keep you tied to me, no matter what I may have said. But when I walked back into your life, and saw you looking so anxious, so burdened, all I could think of was taking it all off your shoulders.' He sighed. 'I thought, in my arrogance, you see, that if I loved you enough, you'd be bound to care for me in return. How wrong I was!' His voice held a kind of weary finality. 'But you don't have to worry any more. I won't inflict my presence on you for much longer. I'll wait to make sure we have the Craigmore project in the bag before I leave for the States, but now that you haven't Henry to contend with, you should find things much easier. I could remain nominally chairman of the board, if they'd prefer, but you'll have your company back again, Ashley.' He smiled faintly. 'And, more importantly, your life.'

Ashley felt as if she'd been turned to stone. She fought for words, but none would come. Seeing him turn away and walk towards the door was the spur she needed. She flew after him.

'Jago.' It was barely more than a croak. He swung round, the brooding hazel eyes assessing her pallor, the sharp glitter of tears on her face. She flung herself at him, clinging frantically to his shoulders, pressing little heated kisses on his face and throat, her voice feverishly whispering, 'Don't leave me ...' over and over again.

His hands closed on her, not gently, pushing her backwards so that he could look into her eyes. His face was incredulous, but underneath there was a dawning hope.

He said hoarsely, 'You—want me?'

'I love you. You can't leave me! You have to take me with you!' She beat on her chest with clenched fists. 'Wherever you go, I want to be with you.'

He said, 'You will be,' and it was somehow more than a marriage vow.

He picked her up in his arms and carried her to the sofa. He sat cradling her on his lap, his arms wrapped round her, kissing the tears from her face, murmuring to her until she was calm again. Then they were very still together, Ashley's face buried in the curve of his throat, his lips against her hair, closer in some strange way than they had ever been, even at moments of greatest intimacy.

At last he sighed a little, and cupped her chin in his fingers, making her face him.

'Three wasted years,' he said huskily. 'Darling, why didn't you tell me—why didn't you let me know? You were always so cold ...'

'I was frightened,' she confessed.

Jago looked remorseful. 'Of something I did? God, sweetheart ...'

'No.' Ashley stroked his face with her fingertips. 'Of myself. I—I didn't know what was happening to me. Every time you touched me, I seemed to—go up in flames, and I was overwhelmed.' She flushed. 'You see, all Silas had ever said was that no matter what the permissive society had to say, men still valued purity in the women they were going to marry. He gave me the impression that sex was something a decent woman—just put up with. I couldn't tell him that when I was with you I felt neither pure nor decent. I was terrified in case I was unnatural in some way, and there was no one I could talk to about it.'

'You could have talked to me,' Jago told her gently. 'I was going to be your husband.'

Ashley sighed. 'I suppose I was a little in awe of you,' she said slowly. 'Marrying you was like having every dream come true at once. I kept telling myself that once we really were married, everything would be all right. That you'd make everything all right.'

He groaned. 'I wish I'd shared your certainty,' he said ruefully. 'At first, I told myself you were just shy, but that you'd relax when you came to trust me. Only you never did. The wedding was coming nearer and nearer, and you still shrank every time I tried to touch you.' He shook his head. 'My conversation with Silas was the last straw. Being saddled with a duty wife was a terrifying prospect.'

'How could he have said such a thing?' Ashley asked helplessly.

Jago shrugged. 'Because he believed it. He was a good business man, darling, but his knowledge of human nature left a lot to be desired. He should have seen that Henry was a potential weak link in his chain, long before you took over. Silas was obsessed by Landons, and he assumed everyone else had to be too, including you. Our marriage fitted his plans, and the fact that our own plans might be different would never have occured to him. He was genuinely shocked when I told him I was going to the States and taking you with me. I think he honestly thought that you'd share his viewpoint.'

'He'd never discussed why I was marrying you,' she said slowly. 'He was delighted about it. I thought it was for my sake, at first anyway. Then I began to wonder—odd things he said about you being "a chip off the old block", as if he was congratulating himself on having—engineered the whole thing. I—I began to ask myself questions. For instance, why had you talked about making me happy, but said nothing about being in love with me?'

There was a silence, then Jago said quietly, 'My God.' His arms gathered her closer still. 'I was trying hard not to frighten you, sweetheart. I thought if I started telling you even half the things I felt for you and about you, I might panic you into a complete retreat. You have a lot to forgive me for.'

'No,' she began to protest, but he laid a silencing, caressing finger on her lips.

'I should have taken longer over wooing,' he said softly. 'I should have made absolutely certain that you knew I loved you and wanted you for yourself.

I should have come to you that night and demanded an explanation, instead of heading for the nearest damned bar.'

'I don't blame you for that,' she told him, her mouth trembling into an unsteady smile. 'I was shattered too, after speaking to Erica. I wish I'd made for the same bar.'

'Erica and Silas.' He groaned. 'They couldn't have done a better number on us if they'd been in collusion! I should have realised that bitch would get at you if she could, and protected you better. That's the main reason I was so keen to buy her off this time round. In case she started sharpening her claws on you. It never occured to me that she might have already begun.'

She said, 'Jago, why didn't you come after me—that night?'

'I did. But by the time I'd dragged on some clothes, got rid of my visitor, and pulled myself together, you were nowhere to be found. And first thing in the morning, I got my ring back, and a message making it clear you didn't want to see me again. It seemed you couldn't wait to be rid of me. I decided Silas had been quite right, and you had only been marrying me for the company's sake, after all. That you were glad to have an excuse to call the whole thing off. So I told myself I was better off without you, and cleared out to the States.' He smiled crookedly. 'But try as I might—and I did try, darling—I couldn't forget you. Any fragment of news about you that came my way, I used to treasure obsessively. Giles used to tell me how you were getting on. He was always very fond of you. And then he died, and I had to come back, only to find the town and the newspapers full of rumours about Landons and its problems.' He grimaced. 'It seemed like a way to get back to you again, although I told myself I was simply curious to see if you were prepared to sell yourself a second time. But it made no difference. After seeing you at the Country Club that night, I was lost. I had to have you,' his voice grew almost sombre, 'by any means available. You looked so beautiful, so sure of yourself, I told myself you couldn't possibly still be the same innocent virgin I'd loved and lost. Witham was lucky I didn't kill him,' he added savagely.

Ashley choked back a giggle. 'Poor Martin!'

'To hell with him.' Jago tugged gently at the lobe of her ear with his teeth. 'Save your compassion for me.'

She smiled into his eyes. 'Oh, I had a different sort of comfort in mind.' She moved against him with a deliberate and delicate sensuality, hearing the breath catch in his throat.

He said unevenly, 'Tell me more—or even better still, show me.'

She kissed him slowly, running her tongue along the curve of his lower lip, feeling his muscles stir and clench under the first tentative exploration of her hands.

She was his love, and the realisation made the blood sing for joy in her veins, but tonight he wanted her to be his lover, and it would be her pleasure to please him, to return some of the delight he had taught her. To let him know beyond question that she belonged to him completely, to give him the reassurance he seemed to need.

Tonight, she thought, their marriage would begin. And her heart soared.

JASMINE CRESSWELL

Internationally-acclaimed Bestselling Author

SECRET SINS

The rich are different—they're deadly!

Judge Victor Rodier is a powerful and dangerous man. At the age of twenty-seven, Jessica Marie Pazmany is confronted with terrifying evidence that her real name is Liliana Rodier. A threat on her life prompts Jessica to seek an appointment with her father—a meeting she may live to regret.

MIRA®   **AVAILABLE NOW IN PAPERBACK**

ERICA SPINDLER

Bestselling Author of *Forbidden Fruit*

FORTUNE

BE CAREFUL WHAT YOU WISH FOR...
IT JUST MIGHT COME TRUE

Skye Dearborn's wishes seem to be coming true, but will Skye's new life prove to be all she's dreamed of—or a nightmare she can't escape?

"A high adventure of love's triumph over twisted obsession."

—*Publishers Weekly*

"Give yourself plenty of time, and enjoy!"

—*Romantic Times*

DEBBIE MACOMBER

THIS MATTER OF MARRIAGE

Hallie McCarthy gives herself a year to find
Mr Right. Meanwhile, her handsome neighbour
is busy trying to win his ex-wife back. As the two
compare notes on their disastrous campaigns, each
finds the perfect partner lives right next door!

*"In the vein of When Harry Met Sally,
Ms Macomber will delight."*

—Romantic Times

LINDA
HOWARD

ALMOST
FOREVER

THEY PLAYED BY THEIR OWN RULES...

She didn't let any man close enough.

He didn't lrt anything get in the way of his job. But Max Conroy needed information, so he set out to seduce Claire Westbrook.

BUT RULES WERE MEANT TO BE BROKEN...

Now it was a more than a game of winners and losers. Now they were playing for the highest stakes of all.

AVAILABLE IN PAPERBACK
FROM AUGUST 1997

MARGOT DALTON

first Impression

Be *very* careful who you trust.

A child is missing and the only witness tells a chilling story of what he's 'seen'. Jackie Kaminsky has three choices. Dismiss the man as a handsome nutcase. Arrest him as the only suspect. Or believe him.

"Detective Jackie Kaminsky leads a cast of finely drawn characters... An engrossing read."
—*Publishers Weekly*

"Jackie Kaminsky is a great addition to the growing list of fictional detectives."
—*Romantic Times*

EMMA DARCY

*at her most daring with an
unforgettable tale of ruthless sacrifice
and single-minded seduction*

THE SECRETS WITHIN

When Tamara Vandlier learns that her mother is dying
she is elated—and returns to the family estate to
destroy her mother's few remaining months, in
return for her own ruined childhood. Loyalty turns
to open rivalry in this novel that explores the dark,
hidden secrets of two branches of a powerful
Australian family.

MIRA®   **AVAILABLE NOW IN PAPERBACK**

DISCOVER
THE SECRETS WITHIN

*Riveting and unforgettable -
the Australian saga of the decade!*

*For Tamara Vandelier, the final reckoning with
her mother is long overdue. Now she has
returned to the family's vineyard estate and
embarked on a destructive course that, in a
final, fatal clash, will reveal the secrets within....*

Valid only in the UK & Eire against purchases made in retail outlets
and not in conjunction with any Reader Service or other offer.

50ᵖ OFF COUPON

VALID UNTIL 30/11/1997

EMMA DARCY'S *THE SECRETS WITHIN*

To the Customer: This coupon can be used in part payment for
a copy of Emma Darcy's THE SECRETS WITHIN. Only one coupon
can be used against each copy purchased. Valid only in the UK
& Eire against purchases made in retail outlets and not in
conjunction with any Reader Service or other offer. Please do
not attempt to redeem this coupon against any other product
as refusal to accept may cause embarrassment and delay at the
checkout.

To the Retailer: Harlequin Mills & Boon will redeem this coupon
at face value provided only that it has been taken in part
payment for a copy of Emma Darcy's THE SECRETS WITHIN.
The company reserves the right to refuse payment against
misredeemed coupons. Please submit coupons to: Harlequin
Mills & Boon Ltd. NCH Dept 730, Corby, Northants NN17 1NN.

9 904170 180504

0472 00166